THE MANIC SUN

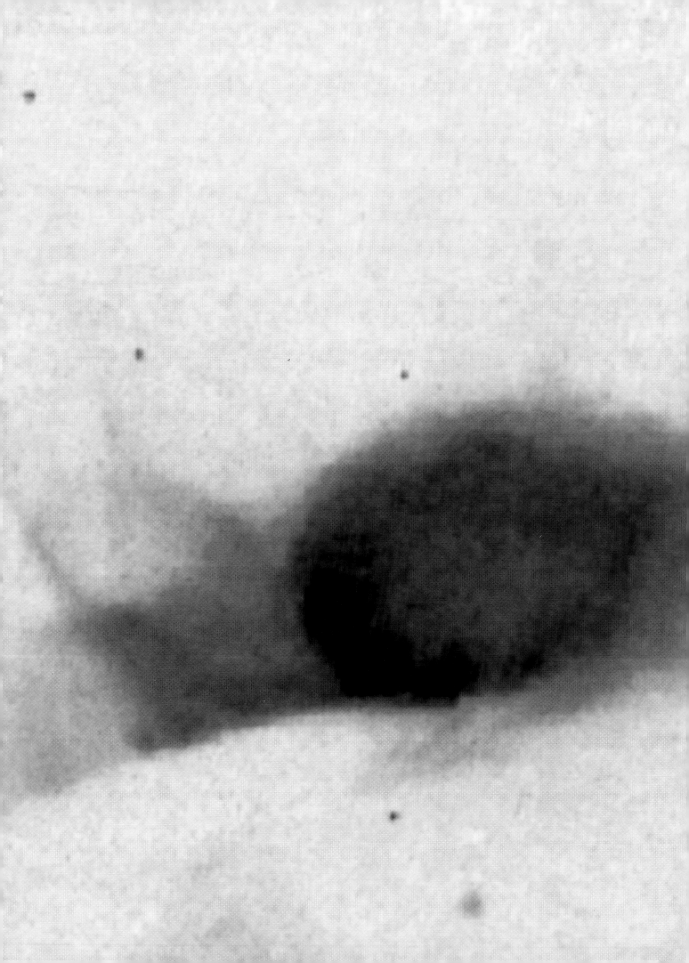

The Manic Sun

WEATHER THEORIES CONFOUNDED

Nigel Calder

PILKINGTON PRESS

LONDON

First published 1997
By Pilkington Press Ltd
Yelvertoft Manor
Northamptonshire NN6 6LF

ISBN 1 899044 11 6

Designed, Produced and Typeset by:
A.H. Jolly (Editorial) Ltd
Yelvertoft Manor
Northamptonshire NN6 6LF

Printed in Great Britain by:
Jarrold Book Printing
Thetford, Norfolk

CONTENTS

Ingen ville lade sig mærke med, at han intet så, for så havde han ikke duet til sit embede, eller været meget dum.

No one would admit that he couldn't see anything because then he would be unfit to hold his post, or very dumb.

Hans Christian Andersen
The Emperor's New Clothes

AUTHOR'S NOTE

THIS is a controversial subject. Normally I would name at least a selection of the many scientists in a dozen countries who, wittingly or unwittingly, helped me when I was gathering information over the past four years, for what evolved into this book. Doing so in this case might land some of them in trouble or give the impression that they subscribe to my views when they do not.

The Danes are in trouble anyway. At the maelstrom of the scientific currents, it was I who chose to join them there. Eigil Friis-Christensen, Henrik Svensmark and Knud Lassen of Copenhagen found time to tell me of the progress of their work, and helped to clarify personal and scientific aspects of the story. I am heavily in their debt, but they are not responsible for the outcome. No one is except me.

As an independent science writer I have deliberately avoided any contact with the environmentalist, political or industrial pressure groups on either side of the greenhouse warming debate. My only loyalty is to science and my only referee is Nature, delivering its verdicts through the results of observations and experiments.

Special thanks are due to Pilkington Press for backing my judgement at a critical stage and undertaking quick publication. At the time of the book's completion, the explosive reconnection of scientific opinion has yet to occur. Critics beware. Your reactions may provide material for a later edition including the aftermath of the Danish discovery.

Nigel Calder

Total eclipse, 11 July 1991. While the Moon masked the Sun at Mauna Kea, Hawaii, a graded filter revealed faint features in the hot gas streaming from the stormy Sun like enormous flames. The patterns are shaped by the contorted magnetic field. The Sun's poles are tilted slightly clockwise from the vertical.

Paris Institut d'Astrophysique/CNRS France. Courtesy of Serge Koutchmy

Chapter One

BLOWING BUBBLES

Hans Christian Ørsted won immortality by giving a public lecture. In 1820 physicists believed that electricity and magnetism were completely different things, but a strange thought occurred to Ørsted. Just as a fine wire radiated light and heat when an electric current passed through it, perhaps it might also emit magnetism. On a table in the lecture hall in Copenhagen, a compass needle pointed steadfastly towards Elsinore as usual.

In his hand Ørsted had a glowing electric filament. Following his hunch, he held it over the compass and the pivoted needle swung sharply, trying to align itself at right angles to the wire. In that unrehearsed moment Nature tore up the scientific script and unified the cosmic force of electromagnetism. Ørsted would be remembered in the name of a unit of magnetic field strength, a crater on the Moon, and a Danish satellite for measuring the Earth's magnetism from space.

Physics kept lurching forward by such reversals of previous ideas. Yet some physicists of every generation believed that their science had reached such a peak of excellence, they were now immune to upsets. As in the tale of the emperor's new clothes, which won immortality for the Danish story-teller Hans Christian Andersen, whatever was fashionable was true.

This stuffiness was surprising because mental life at the cutting-edge of discovery was not like that. Whenever the fragile two-legged creatures on a small planet tried to make sense of an endlessly astonishing universe, bright eyes popped at puzzling observations and hairy heads burst with crazy ideas to explain them.

Conflicts with received wisdom often involved the Sun. The lamp in the daytime sky was by far the grandest thing in sight. If human eyes, tuned to its brightest rays, ever peered directly at it, they were damaged beyond repair. Leaves of plants were tuned to the same waveband, but braved the fierce rays and used the energy to grow, thereby nourishing all animals, no matter how many legs they had.

The Sun played endless peekaboo. It popped up from one horizon and disappeared at another. Toying with the Earth's water it made clouds that hid its shining face. So intricate and various was the weather game, that in the rain-blessed regions where most plants and people lived, the question of whether the Sun would deign to show itself was an infallible topic of conversation.

Most shocking was the peekaboo with the Moon. During an eclipse of the

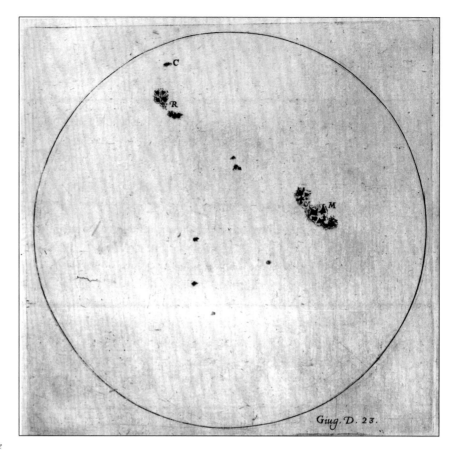

Galileo's sunspots. His drawings correctly depicted a grey penumbra around well-developed spots. Until telescopes were invented, Western astronomers had believed the Sun was immaculate.

From Galileo, Istoria e Dimostrazione delle Macchie Solari 1613, p. 79.
Courtesy of Royal Astronomical Society, London

Sun the birds stopped singing, bees returned to their hives, and human beings watched in dread. At totality the Sun's atmosphere came into view. With tufts and swords of brightness poking far into space, and the iris of the Moon in the middle, it looked like the eye of God. From folk memories of such rare apparitions, artists put halos on the heads of deities. And long before scientists knew of its existence, children surrounded their pictures of the Sun with the streak-marks of the solar wind.

The great lamp was supposed to scamper around the Earth once a day like a sheepdog. For saying that it didn't, and supporting the notion that a spinning Earth orbited around the Sun once a year, the founder of modern physics was forced to recant and spend the last eight years of his life under house arrest. Churchmen saw Galileo Galilei as a worse threat to established teaching than Luther and Calvin put together – and they were right of course.

Dark spots on the Sun's face triggered the row. With the astronomical telescope that he had perfected, Galileo observed recognizable groups of sunspots moving from one side of the visible disk to the other in the course of two weeks. They told him that the Sun revolved on an axis. He had already discovered the moons of Jupiter and the phases of Venus, which boosted the Copernican hypothesis, but it was in his accounts of sunspots in 1613 that Galileo was moved to declare that the Earth went around the Sun.

Sunspots kept people looking (warily) and arguing (heatedly) for four centuries. A curious lull in the Sun's activity in the latter part of the seventeenth century caused Giovanni Cassini of Paris to complain in 1671: 'It is now about 20 years since astronomers have seen any considerable spots on the Sun.' The lull continued till the early eighteenth century, but then both the sunspots and the speculations about them returned to normal.

Among those who joined the sport was William Herschel. He was in his eighties when Ørsted discovered electromagnetism, and he was the most celebrated astronomer of his time. As a refugee musician working in England, Herschel built giant telescopes as a hobby and discovered the planet Uranus, mistaking it for a comet. He turned professional and settled in Slough. The first chart of the Milky Way Galaxy came from his pen, and he had his own ideas about the Sun.

Herschel imagined that light was a luminous fluid. It gathered itself into comets which fell into the Sun, where the comet-stuff made glowing clouds around a solid surface. Sunspots were gaps in the clouds, through which you could glimpse the surface where the Sun's inhabitants lived. And the Sun's weather manifest in the sunspots affected the weather on the Earth. In Herschel's opinion, the growing season for wheat in England was longer whenever there were plenty of sunspots.

'From the price of wheat,' Herschel wrote in 1801, 'it seems probable that some temporary scarcity or defect of vegetation has generally taken place, when the Sun has been without those appearances which we surmise to be symptoms of a copious emission of light and heat.'

Successors of Herschel discarded his theory of the Sun's composition and habitability, but pursued the notion of sunspots affecting the weather and climate on the Earth. Others preferred to nibble at a different fruit of the musician's brain. Herschel was the first person to identify invisible rays.

In a spectrum of sunlight, a man-made rainbow, Herschel measured the heating power of different colours. His thermometer reacted even to black light beyond the red end of the spectrum. Thus he discovered the infrared rays. They started a fashion which, during the nineteenth century, revealed to physicists an invisible rainbow from radio waves to gamma-rays.

Infrared rays sparked speculations among Herschel's successors about the Earth's temperature. The rays could suck warmth from the planet and throw it away into cosmic space. Only five years after Herschel's death, people were talking about the greenhouse effect, whereby certain gases and vapours in the atmosphere might trap some of the escaping infrared rays and keep the Earth warmer.

With his remarks about sunspots affecting the weather and his discovery of infrared rays, Herschel set in motion two theories of climate. They were never mutually exclusive, but two centuries later influential experts chose to behave as if they were. An ill-tempered competition between the theories in the 1990s is the story in this book – the Sun versus the greenhouse.

Another cautionary tale for physicists remains to be told before the narrative begins. William Thomson of Glasgow was one of the ablest men in Victorian

Twentieth-century reverence for the Sun. People in their millions submit to its fierce rays during annual pilgrimages to sunny places like Gran Canaria. Many of their ancestors, more conscious of the Sun's perpetual role in human survival, regarded it as a deity.

Ecoscene

OPPOSITE ABOVE: Twentieth-century reverence in the scientific fashion. To receive the Sun's radio transmissions, the Nobeyama Radio Observatory in Japan constructed and operates the Nobeyama Radioheliograph. Its large assembly of small dishes achieves detailed images.

NRO, Japan

OPPOSITE BELOW: A solar outburst seen by radio. Energetic electrons broadcast radio waves as they whirl in the Sun's magnetic field. Here they follow the magnetic field lines for about 700,000 kilometres (complete view, right) while the pattern of radio emissions changes from minute to minute (close-ups, left). Weak signals are coloured red, and the strongest, yellow and white.

NRO, Japan

Britain. He knew physics inside out and was co-author of the standard textbook. So Thomson thought it his duty to let everyone know that Charles Darwin was grossly exaggerating the age of the Earth. Darwin and the geologists needed hundreds of million years for all the sedimentation and evolution they could see.

The Sun could not possibly have shone for so long, Thomson said. Forget about chemical energy. If it were a burning mass of coal and oxygen it would be good for less than 100 years. There was only one possible source for the heat of the Sun, the slow collapse of a mass of gas under gravity. By Thomson's reckoning the energy so released could keep the Sun hot for only 20 million years.

This was no passing quibble but a war that Thomson waged against Darwin for the last 20 years of the naturalist's life, and then continued unrelentingly into the 1890s. He felt a similar responsibility in respect of silly people trying to make flying machines, which he declared to be impossible. Thomson became Lord Kelvin in 1892 by the quaintly feudal honours system of his homeland. As president of the Royal Society of London, he was keen to keep science united. So why couldn't the stubborn biologists and geologists accept a top physicist's ruling about the Sun with good grace?

Oops. In 1896 Henri Becquerel in Paris found something not dreamt of in Lord Kelvin's philosophy. Wishing to make X-rays from sunbeams, he discovered nuclear energy instead. Revealed by nothing more dramatic than the fogging of photographic material by a uranium salt, nuclear energy transformed the physical universe. Studies of radioactive decay soon showed that Darwin had indeed erred about the age of the Earth. He had grossly underestimated it.

The impudent Sun had been burning when Kelvin said it couldn't, and nuclear energy liberated it and all the stars from his miserly audit. Within 40 years physicists had figured out how the Sun acquired its huge resources of energy by fusing hydrogen into helium. In a world interminably at war, men soon made nuclear bombs and then perfected fusion weapons, H-bombs, that could pour the fire of the Sun on to cities.

During the Cold War the bipeds came at least once within a hair's breadth of an all-out thermonuclear exchange. But one alliance collapsed from within, as signalled by the demolition of the Berlin Wall in 1989, when our story begins. Nations rejoiced and turned their minds to more wholesome matters like caring for the environment. That too was first and last a question of physics.

The Sun hummed to itself as it turned hydrogen into helium in its nuclear core. The gassy interior conveniently screened the gamma-rays but the turbulent outer layer flung out visible light with an abandon that gave free lunches galore to every creature except the economists. Spacecraft captured the energy in solar cells and saw the Sun bright against a black universe.

It was huge. You could fit a million Earths inside the Sun's visible surface, but its empire was far larger than that. Material from the Sun pervaded the wide spaces where its family of planets orbited. The solar wind of electric particles,

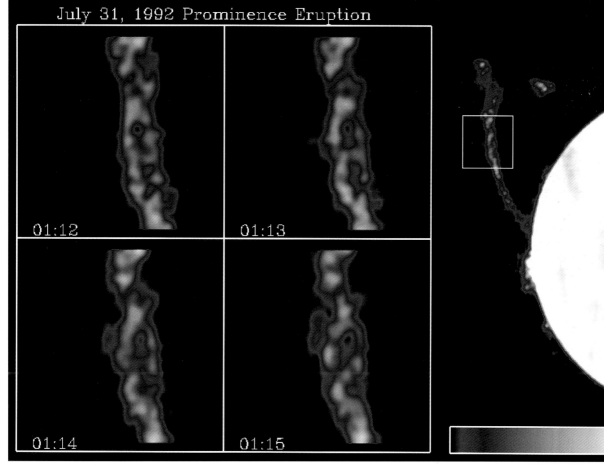

July 31, 1992 Prominence Eruption

01:12

01:13

01:14

01:15

freighted with magnetism, washed over the planets and made them tingle night and day like a Cole Porter lover. It was only the spin of the Earth that created the local theatricals of sunrise.

As the planet turned, the Sun woke the birds of each village in turn and outshone the street lights of cities, curing nightmares with thoughts of break-fast. Daylight painted afresh all the colours of the place. Plants silently opened their pores to take in carbon dioxide and busy themselves with the morning's growth, lapping up the energetic photons. The direction of sunrise told the farmers and priests what season they were in, and newborn children discovered sight.

It was a daily miracle, except that satellites visiting the night side saw light radiating from the richer cities of the Earth as if trying to rival the stars. Many millions of years of fossilized sunshine in the form of coal, oil and gas were being consumed in a few industrial generations. Converted into electric light they devalued the Sun, which for city dwellers became an absence of rain or a stress for the air conditioning. Seasonally the Sun teamed up with travel agents to supply ultraviolet rays for tans and melanomas, and commuters ran to the reckonings of an average Sun carried on their wrists.

In the land of the rising Sun the sacred cocks still crowed at the shrine of Amaterasu, the Sun goddess, as they had done for two millennia. Shinto priests still worshipped her as the giver of light and life, and the ruler of the world. The Sun glowed red on every Japanese flag. In 1989 Japanese physicists were preparing new solar temples, and prayer-sticks to fling into space.

In a deep mine at Kamioka they already did solar astronomy underground by detecting neutrinos from the Sun, ghostly particles from the nuclear reactions in the core. There weren't nearly enough neutrinos, as American physicists had discovered twenty years before. Something was wrong with the theories of the Sun's nuclear combustion, or perhaps with the particle physics. Wags asked, 'Is the Sun still burning?'

Radio microwaves told of upheavals spreading outwards through the Sun's atmosphere, and eighty-four radio dishes were to image them in a new radioheliograph at Nobeyama. The astronomers planned to feed their images of the radio Sun to colleagues operating the Solar-A satellite, also under construction, which would see the Sun by X-rays. Solar-A would carry instruments contributed from the United States and the United Kingdom. It was conceived to make sense of the Sun's most violent events – the solar flares – which were magnetic explosions with the force of millions of H-bombs.

The Japanese satellite Geotail would follow Solar-A into space but fly far out on the dark side of the Earth. There the planet left a wake in the solar wind, which dragged out the planet's magnetic field like a comet's tail. When the Sun was stormy, an invisible egg-like entity called a plasmoid could shoot off down the tail, removing part of the Earth's magnetic field. The field reconnected and sprang planetwards like a rubber catapult, flinging solar particles into the air of the polar regions and making auroras. Geotail would investigate the Earth's habit of laying magnetic eggs, as a contribution to a growing fleet of spacecraft from Russia, Europe and the United States that were under orders to make sense of the Sun.

Whilst the Cold War was still on, collaborative space programmes were a way of building confidence and averting the nuclear showdown. After a multinational flotilla had intercepted Halley's Comet in 1986, another swarm of spacecraft would be useful in tracing the effects of the Sun on the Earth, in the Interagency Solar-Terrestrial Physics Programme. With project delays, budget problems, and the Soviet Union falling apart, it was largely by good luck that a number of solar space missions would coincide with Geotail in the 1990s.

Solar physicists were concerned with the visible Sun and its atmosphere, and solar-terrestrial physicists with the solar wind and its effects on the Earth. They made a small world. Although the Sun was the nearest star, astronomers preferred to look for black holes and dark matter. Space scientists thought other planets more interesting to explore.

To Earth observers it seemed much more useful to look inwards at the rocks, water, ice, air and living things that comprised the obvious stuff of the Earth system, rather than outwards at invisible battles between the solar wind and the Earth's magnetism in the space environment. The discovery that the Sun engulfed the Earth in its solar wind had scarcely sunk in, except among the professionals.

In the 1940s astronomers had nursed a theory about a solar wind of interstellar gas blowing into the Sun. In 1951 Ludwig Biermann of Göttingen put them right and said the solar wind blew outwards. From the gassy tails of comets, which always pointed like wind-vanes directly away from the Sun, he deduced the existence of a wind of charged atoms and electrons filling interplanetary space.

Eugene Parker of Chicago developed the idea of a non-stop effusion from the Sun's atmosphere, which drew out the Sun's magnetism like bubble-gum and wound it into spirals as the Sun rotated. When spacecraft began leaving the Earth's vicinity in the 1960s, for voyages to other planets, they flew through an invisible windscreen in the sky made by the Earth's magnetism. On the sunward side, where the wind came from, the windscreen was usually about 70,000 kilometres over the earthlings' heads. The wind was a mass of electric particles laden with a magnetic field, as Parker had predicted.

NASA's later Pioneer and Voyager missions followed the solar wind and its storms into the outer solar system. From 1974 to 1984 two German-US Helios spacecraft operated closer to the Sun. The results raised more questions than answers. No one could say what drove the solar wind, or why its speed varied according to its region of origin on the Sun. But it became clear that the empire of the Sun extended far beyond the planets.

The Sun's hot breath maintained a huge bubble in space called the heliosphere. At some far-flung boundary the pressure of a thin gas pervading space between the stars must finally match and check the pressure of the solar wind travelling outward from the Sun. The distance to the boundary could be vaguely

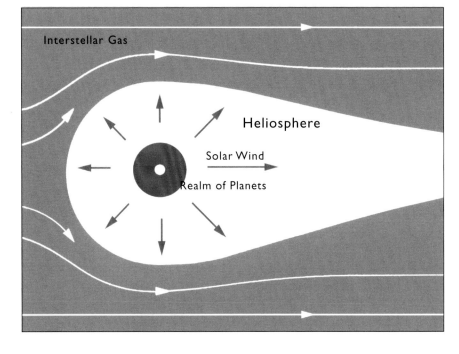

Interstellar Gas

Heliosphere

Solar Wind

Realm of Planets

The Sun's bubble in interstellar space. Called the heliosphere, it is created by the solar wind blowing outwards from the Sun. Eventually the pressure of a thin interstellar gas stops it, at a boundary much farther than the outlying planets. Disturbances in the heliosphere affect the Earth.

estimated at 15 billion kilometres or 100 times the distance of the Earth from the Sun. For comparison, the furthest major planet, Neptune, orbited only 4.5 billion kilometres out.

The American probe Voyager 2 encountered Neptune in August 1989. Along with its sister Voyager 1 and the earlier Pioneers still heading out beyond the planets, Voyager 2 would continue to observe the gusty solar wind until its power supply failed. None of these far-flung spacecraft detected any hint of the heliosphere coming to an end.

Much nearer home, other US and Soviet spacecraft examined the solar wind's interplay with the Earth. Its battle with the Earth's magnetism provided another remarkable but often baffling set of discoveries. A geiger counter flown in 1958, on the very first US satellite Explorer 1, was swamped by energetic particles in unexpected radiation belts girdling the Earth. The source of the particles was obscure.

While the windscreen of the Earth's magnetism forced the solar wind aside, the wind confined the magnetic field in a magnetosphere, rounded on the sunny side and stretching away downwind. Early European satellites exploring the magnetosphere revealed that solar particles could sneak into the Earth's atmosphere by the back door, via the tail of the magnetosphere, lighting auroras in the polar skies. Other streams of solar particles crowded around dents in the magnetosphere over the Earth's magnetic poles.

Suspicions grew that the solar particles could also punch holes in the front of the windscreen. By the 1970s the non-stop succession of magnetospheric satellites were investigating fields and waves that accelerated particles. Scientists wanted to know why particles breaking into the magnetosphere were more energetic than the ordinary particles of the solar wind. But Nature teased the

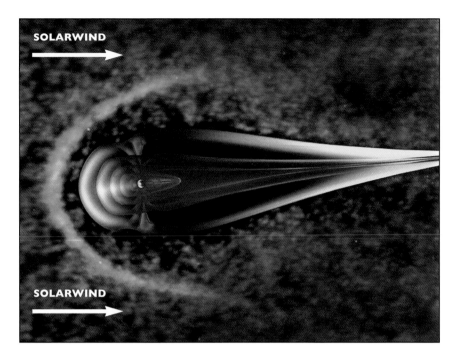

SOLARWIND

SOLARWIND

The Earth's bubble in the heliosphere. Called the magnetosphere, it is created by the Earth's magnetic field. While it screens the planet from most of the solar wind, the wind compresses the magnetic field and stretches it downwind like a comet's tail. Dents in the magnetosphere occur over the Earth's magnetic poles.

ESA and 4:2:2 Videographic Design

world's solar-terrestrial physicists and progress was excruciatingly slow.

Changes in direction in the magnetic field, carried by the solar wind, complicated the picture. The wind of the moment might come from the northern or southern hemisphere of the Sun. Slants in the solar magnetism had long-range effects too. As a result, the field lines in the solar wind sometimes ran in much the same direction as the lines of the Earth's magnetic field, and sometimes in an opposite direction. Effects on the Earth seemed to be most severe when the magnetic lines quarrelled.

The Earth's magnetosphere remained a very small bubble of comparative tranquillity inside an immense and storm-racked heliosphere that surrounded it on every side. Yet to most people, even environmental scientists, the Sun was still just a poker-faced ball in the sky, no wider than a pea held at arm's length. And there was scarcely enough information from the spacecraft to say how much it flickered.

The space age was 20 years old before NASA began installing monitors of solar brightness on spacecraft; first Nimbus-7 in 1978 and then Solar Max of 1980. The US National Oceanic and Atmospheric Administration added solar instruments to its routine weather satellites. Sensitive detectors gauged the Sun's output of visible light, which could never be measured reliably from the ground. Other sensors in the satellites watched for X-ray pulses and particles from the Sun, telling of eruptions.

By 1989 the light meters in space had confirmed that the Sun was a variable star. It was not like the unstable stars that waxed and waned quite obviously in brightness once a month or thereabouts. The Sun varied over an 11-year cycle as sunspots multiplied and diminished. It changed its average output of light by one thousandth, and flickered by a few thousandths in the course of a

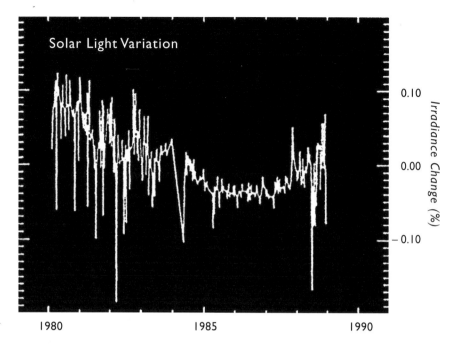

Solar Light Variation

0.10

0.00

− 0.10

Irradiance Change (%)

1980   1985   1990

The Sun as a variable star. The average brightness measured by the Solar Max (SMM) satellite over a period of nine years changed by only about 0.1 per cent. The average output was least when sunspot counts were fewest, in 1986.

After R.C. Willson and H.S. Hudson, 1991

week, when sunspots moved across the visible disk. Strangely the Sun was brightest when most spattered with dark spots. A network of less obvious activity at the visible surface, vaguely called faculas, more than compensated for the darkening of the spots themselves.

Official climatologists seized on the figure of 0.1 per cent variation in the Sun's output. They liked it. They were engaged in an intergovernmental exercise to show how carbon dioxide added to the air might warm the Earth's climate by trapping heat escaping from the planet, in an enhanced greenhouse effect. Solar physicists begged them not to forget about the variable Sun, in assessing the climate and the causes of its changes. But now that the Sun's variability had been measured, it was trifling compared with what a little carbon dioxide could do, according to the official hypothesis.

Official was a term that deserved more careful definition, but public servants were involved and the work was masterminded at the Meteorological Office at Bracknell, England. The hypothesis was that carbon dioxide released by burning fossil fuels, and by deforestation, was going to warm the world by several degrees C. Other greenhouse gases such as methane and the refrigerant CFCs (chlorofluorocarbons) would speed the warming. The event would be unprecedented and catastrophic, so mankind would have to mend its ways.

The solar physicists cared just as much as the official climatologists, about keeping the world safe for their grandchildren. They said it was rash to suppose that every possible variation in the Sun's output of light had been seen by the satellites in the course of a single solar cycle. The solar-terrestrial physicists, for their part, pleaded for consideration of other ways in which the Sun might affect the Earth via the the solar wind – auroras, that sort of thing. They were awfully vague, though, about how it could happen.

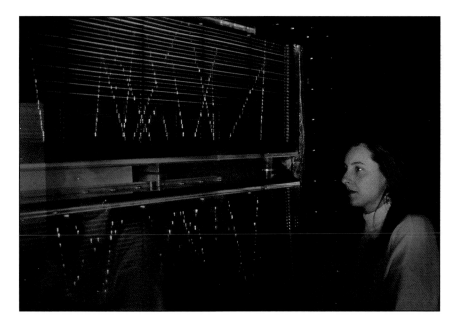

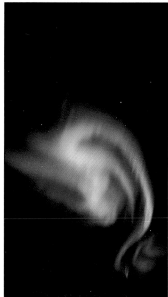

Solar-terrestrial physicists had a peculiar science that only they bothered to try to understand. They wrote ever-changing numbers all over the sky to describe invisible particle streams and magnetic fields that wriggled like snakes. Auroras gave them a rough impression, by projecting a TV image of activity in space on to the upper air. The solar-terrestrial events defied tidy theories because they were actually untidy, with cause and effect all mixed up.

Important clues came from cosmic rays. Originating in exploded stars of the Milky Way Galaxy, a never-ending spray of atomic bullets arrived at the Earth with enormous energy. The discovery of cosmic rays was another quirky tale from early in the twentieth century. Physicists knew that if you charged an instrument with static electricity, the charge would inevitably leak away. After the discovery of radioactivity, they blamed its radiation for creating charged particles in the air, which gradually abolished the experimental charge. But starting in 1910 physicists began taking their electroscopes up on towers, mountains and even balloons, in an attempt to escape the Earth's radioactivity. To their amazement, they found that their instruments discharged faster the higher they went. The Nobel prize for discovering cosmic rays went to Victor Hess of Austria, who made the pioneering balloon flights.

Half a century of research went into describing the cosmic rays correctly, and it involved the discovery of antimatter. Primary cosmic rays arrived at the top of the Earth's atmosphere as heavy particles, the nuclei of atoms stripped of all their electrons and therefore positively charged. They possessed very high energy, acquired in stellar explosions. Hydrogen nuclei, or protons, were the commonest cosmic rays, but the other chemical elements were represented too. The Earth's magnetic field deflected the primary cosmic rays, and their intensity was greater towards the poles than near the equator, where only the most energetic particles could reach the atmosphere.

Wherever they hit the air, the particles caused nuclear mayhem in their

ABOVE LEFT: Cosmic rays made visible. Atomic particles from exploded stars rain from the sky, riddling everyone continuously. No one notices them until special equipment reveals cosmic ray tracks, as in this demonstration spark chamber at the European Laboratory of Particle Physics.

CERN, Geneva

ABOVE: A natural TV image. Electrons hitting the polar air make auroras, much as man-made electron beams light the screen of a television picture tube. The auroral shapes reveal invisible events far out in space, where disturbances in the solar wind accelerate the electrons.

Norbert Rosing and Silvestris/FLPA

encounters with nitrogen and oxygen atoms. A single primary particle could give rise to a million or more secondary particles whizzing through the atmosphere. Heavy cosmic-ray nuclei broke up into their component parts, charged protons and uncharged neutrons. So did the atoms of the air, when hit by the cosmic rays, and some of their protons and neutrons released acquired very high energy from the encounters. The interactions continued, in a nuclear cascade.

Other kinds of subatomic particles, called pions and muons, appeared as by-products of the nuclear encounters. Neutral pions started another kind of cascade by turning into gamma-rays, which then make pairs of electrons and anti-electrons, or positrons. When a positron next encountered an electron in the atmosphere, they annihilated each other, disappearing in a puff of gamma-rays, which could in turn make more electrons and positrons. And so the process went on.

Human beings were continually riddled by cosmic rays, but they could be grateful that as the particles multiplied they lost energy. The air was a screen protecting living things from the violence of exploding stars. By the time they reached the ground, at normal altitudes in the temperate zone, cosmic rays were somewhat less harmful than natural radioactivity. People could also thank the Sun, because the solar wind acted as a shield, weakening the cosmic rays before they reached the Earth.

Scott Forbush of Washington DC, starting in 1936, discovered an effect of the Sun's variations on the cosmic rays, after he set up a network of recording instruments around the world. In 1937 he reported a sudden drop in the count of cosmic rays, occurring shortly after an eruption on the Sun. Such single events came to be known as Forbush decreases. By 1957, he had seen the cosmic rays increase and decrease through two sunspot cycles, but going in the opposite sense to the sunspot count. Many spots, fewer cosmic rays; fewer spots, more cosmic rays.

The discovery of the solar wind offered an explanation of these variations. A vigorous solar wind could hamper the cosmic rays trying to reach the Earth. In 1960, the spacecraft Pioneer 5 was first to detect a shock wave in the solar wind associated with a reduction of the cosmic rays on the Earth.

Such shocks became standard fare in space physics, while the trace of variations in cosmic ray counters on the ground could thenceforward be read as a daily indicator of the state of the heliosphere. Almost no one imagined that the cosmic rays had any significant effect on the Earth's physical environment. Nevertheless, their variations told of unceasing changes in the Sun and the solar wind which, the solar-terrestrial physicists said, might have other, very striking effects on the Earth.

In March 1989 the Sun looked like Humpty Dumpty with a spotted cummerbund. It was approaching the peak of its sunspot count for cycle 22, by a numbering of cycles that went back to 1755. Still humming to itself, the Sun twiddled with intense magnetic fields on its far side, and fashioned a large rosette of sunspots.

Experts would complain that this sunspot group was too far north according to their theories, but so much the worse for their theories.

Pirouetting ponderously, the Sun brought the sunspot group into view on 6 March, as a dark region on the left-hand side. Then it detonated major flares as if they were mere firecrackers at Chinese New Year. They went off at a rate of about one a day for twelve days while the sunspot group moved across the Sun's visible face. There were dozens of lesser flares in between.

Apart from the watching scientists and satellites, the first to notice were people using radios, as X-rays from the Sun doused their radio mirror in the sky, the ionosphere. Short-wave radio failed in many places, while local VHF calls were heard across continents. All radio navigation systems became untrustworthy.

The biggest flare was on 9 March. The space environment services of the National Aeronautics and Space Administration at Boulder, Colorado, issued a magnetic storm warning. The heliosphere was in turmoil, with puffs and shocks in the solar wind racing outwards among the planets. Into the big bubble of the heliosphere the Sun blew smaller but expanding bubbles of ejected mass. On 13 March such a mass, released at the same time as the big flare exploded, reached the Earth's magnetosphere and crushed it like a squeeze-bottle.

The torment of the Earth's magnetic field, that day and the next, made the biggest magnetic storm ever seen in 120 years of continuous observation. Compasses wandered and magnetometers went off scale. The changing magnetic field stirred up electric currents in any long bits of metal it could find, like telephone cables, pipelines and electric power lines.

In Sweden several distribution lines lost power simultaneously. A current surge in lines serving a Canadian power station tripped a circuit breaker, which triggered other automatic shut-downs. Most of Quebec province, including Montreal and Quebec City, was without electricity for 9 hours on 13 March. And while engineers were being summoned from their beds to get Quebec back to work again, the cosmic rays dwindled.

That day the count of the cosmic rays at ground level slumped by more than 10 per cent, in a major Forbush decrease. The Sun's big atomic puff batted many of the cosmic rays away, and stopped them reaching the Earth. The screening action continued as the puff hurried on its way towards the orbit of Mars. The count of cosmic rays remained low for a week after the magnetic storm had subsided.

The squeeze on the magnetosphere reached its peak before 13 March was out. The height of the Earth's windscreen on the sunward side fell from the normal 70,000 kilometres to 30,000, for several hours. As that was below the height of communications satellites, in the orbits that let them hover over chosen spots while the Earth turned, they were exposed to the full blast of the solar wind and energetic particles from the Sun. Weather satellites in similar geostationary orbits reported their discomfiture in detail.

The satellites fussed and dithered like duchesses in a cloudburst. Never had their controllers been so busy. The communications birds needed more manual attention in the course of two days than they would normally have in a year. There was worse to come a few days later. Even after the windscreen was restored, hits by energetic particles killed a Japanese communications satellite and seriously damaged several others.

Satellites in lower orbits had a different problem. The Earth's outer atmosphere swelled with the heat of incoming particles, and threatened to bring the satellites to an untimely demise. Solar Max dropped in altitude 'as if it had hit a brick wall,' a spokesman said. It would burn up in the atmosphere like a man-made meteorite before the year was out.

You didn't have to be a satellite controller or a French Canadian deprived of your morning coffee to know that the Sun was up to its tricks. Solar particles punched holes in the windscreen and slammed into the Earth's outer atmosphere. They made spectacular auroras. The Sun's disco lights were normally confined to ovals around the magnetic poles, but now the auroras hung their multicoloured drapery over the United States and Western Europe, far to the south of the usual showground. Antarctic auroras were spotted in tropical Australia.

The inhabitants of Denmark saw the auroras of a lifetime. Weather forecasts from the Danish Meteorological Institute in Copenhagen alerted the public to look out for them, on the initiative of the institute's own solar-terrestrial physicists. The head of a research division was Knud Lassen, himself an expert on auroras. Magnetic observations were the responsibility of a colleague, Eigil Friis-Christensen, and early in the morning of 13 March the magnetometers at the observatory at Brorfelde went mad.

Friis-Christensen was frustrated by having at that time no telemetry from his many recording magnetometers in Greenland. But reports coming in of remarkable sunspot activity convinced him that he was seeing an exceptional magnetic storm. Friis-Christensen suggested to the forecasting services department that there might be splendid auroras the following night.

He was also able to advise a schoolteacher in Sønderborg who wanted to photograph the auroras. The resulting pictures showed the flames of the Sun licking the Danish air. Broad red streaks turned white towards the horizon, in the colours of the Danish flag, as solar particles agitated the oxygen atoms. They were not just pretty, but welcome publicity at a time when people were asking whether solar-terrestrial physics served any purpose in a meteorological establishment.

'Here I am, all around you,' the Sun said. 'You don't know the half of the mischief I can do.'

The most dramatic effects of carbon dioxide were in the Arctic, according to the computations of the official climatologists. Rises of 8 to 20 degrees C, depending on whose reckonings you believed, were anticipated over parts of the Arctic Ocean in winter with a doubling of carbon dioxide in the air. The effects in summer were muted, the climate forecasters said, by effects of melting sea ice and a cold ocean. But Greenland, for example, would experience temperature rises between 2 and 6 degrees.

Aurora in Denmark. Uproar on the Sun in March 1989 caused intense magnetic storms and widespread auroras. Students obtained this picture late at night on 24 March with an ordinary family camera. Comparisons with German photos fixed the aurora's distance at 350 kilometres. The base of the red colour, typical of low-latitude auroras, was at 300 kilometres altitude.

EUC Syd and Amtsgymnasiet in Sønderborg. Courtesy of Mogens Winther

You would have been tactless to mention global warming if visiting Greenland, the mountainous heap of ice that stuck out like a rude tongue into the North Atlantic. Politically joined to Denmark, like Jutland or Lolland, Greenland's few thousand inhabitants perched like the seals on fringes of land around the vast ice sheet. A warm current, a branch of the Gulf Stream, penetrated the Davis Strait and licked the western shore. Mighty glaciers oozed unceasingly into the sea, and the icebergs that they calved never stopped hunting for another Titanic, or threatening to smother the Gulf Stream.

Even in the nightless Arctic summer, temperatures in Greenland barely struggled above freezing and blizzards struck at any season. Mean temperatures by land and sea had not stopped falling for 60 years. The chill drove away the cod

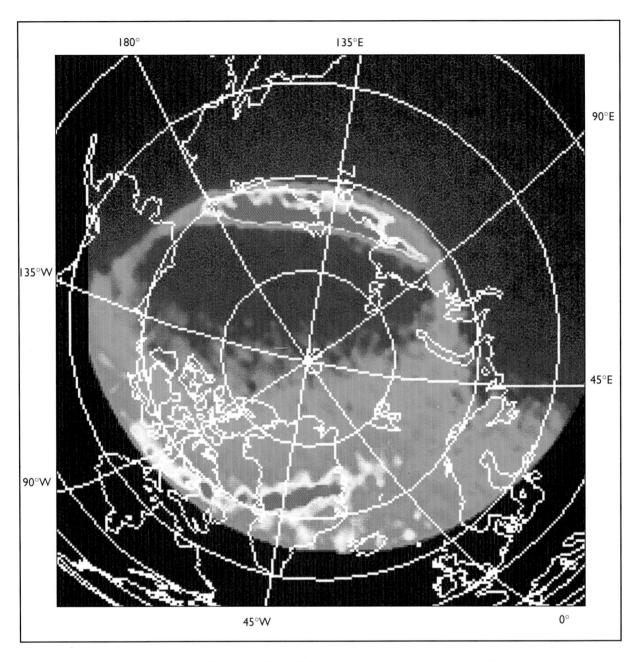

Auroral oval seen from space. Ultraviolet light coming from nitrogen molecules, hit by incoming particles, makes a near-circle around the north magnetic pole. NASA's Polar satellite made this observation from an altitude of more than 50,000 kilometres, on 9 April 1996. Red colouring denotes the strongest ultraviolet emissions. The dayside is towards the bottom, where the blue-green tinge signifies an effect of sunlight. Polar achieves the best-ever images of the dayside aurora, which in this case slants across Greenland. On the nightside, towards the top of the image, the auroral zone is expanding towards the pole, in an event called a substorm.

Polar/NASA and UVI Team

that had moved into the Davis Strait in warmer decades, briefly offering themselves in the warm mid-century as a substitute for the scarcer seals. When the coming ice age seemed to climatologists the greater danger, back in the 1970s, television producers used pictures of Greenland to show what Chicago or Berlin would look like in such an eventuality.

It seemed an unlikely place to go to study the Sun. Solar telescopes for looking directly at its shining face were better sited to do that in sunny places like the Canary Islands or the southwestern United States. Instead, observers in Greenland joined with others in the polar regions to watch the flames from the Sun in the Earth's upper air. Solar particles made the Merry Dancers of the auroras glow and curl in the long-lasting darkness of the Arctic midwinter.

When gusts in the solar wind shocked the Earth's environment, magnetic needles wandered, as the main magnetic field of the Earth tried, with mixed success, to sustain the windscreen that shielded the planet from the solar particles. Magnetometers in Greenland sensed variations in the field due to electric currents high in the atmosphere and in inner parts of the little bubble in space commanded by the Earth, the magnetosphere.

The Sun's influence on the Earth's magnetism became plain in one of the earliest global science programmes. In 1836 the German geographer Alexander von Humboldt, backed by the Royal Society of London, persuaded the British government to set up magnetic observatories in several of its far-flung colonies, and to equip an Antarctic expedition. By 1852, after sifting the results, Edward Sabine confirmed that the sudden fluctuations in the magnetic field called magnetic storms originated outside the Earth's crust. They occurred most frequently and violently when there were a lot of spots on the face of the Sun.

That the local cause of the magnetic changes was electric currents flowing high in the Earth's atmosphere, was an idea coming from Balfour Stewart in 1882. By coincidence, that was when Greenland first became a scene of systematic magnetic observations, for the International Polar Year of 1882–83. The icy island was a prime site because the auroral zone was an oval surrounding the Earth's north magnetic pole in Canada, and the oval slanted right across Greenland.

By 1989, chains of observatories, some manned, some automatic, fringed Greenland's ice sheet, equipped with modern auroral cameras and magnetometers. The physicists eagerly compared their results with those from scientific radars that probed the upper air in other polar regions, and with satellites that observed the solar wind and the magnetosphere directly. East–West collaboration in solar-terrestrial physics was nurtured by the International Geophysical Year of 1957–58. It persisted all through the Cold War, even though the Arctic was the shortest route for nuclear strikes between the superpowers and Greenland was a platform for NATO's radars and bombers.

The observatories in Greenland were run by the Danish Meteorological Institute. It occupied a stylish modern building in a much milder climate, beside the Elsinore motorway on the northern side of Copenhagen. And there the solar-terrestrial physicists, Knud Lassen and Eigil Friis-Christensen, pursued a hobby. While they often worked together on such questions as the link between auroras and electric currents in the atmosphere, in spare moments they discussed how the ever-variable Sun might vary the Earth's climate.

Lassen had the gruff authority and faraway eyes of an old Greenland hand. As a young auroral specialist he spent ten years in charge of the main observatory at Godhavn, where he became hardened to the bitter darkness of the Arctic winter. He was due to retire in June 1991 when he reached the age of 70. His former student Friis-Christensen was then expected to take over a sector of Lassen's responsibilities, as head of a newly-created solar-terrestrial physics division. Aged 44 in 1989, Friis-Christensen had a Viking's fresh face and brown hair. He was a specialist on magnetism, with experience in the exploration of the Earth's magnetic environment by sounding rockets and satellites. He knew Greenland too.

In 1972, the young Friis-Christensen had helped to set up a unique chain of magnetometers there, conceived to make images of the electric currents high overhead. Sea ice hampered the shipping that year. Deputed to establish the northern observing stations far up the Davis Strait, he finished up hitch-hiking in a medical ship. While establishing one of his stations he needed to receive a time signal to set the clock of an automatic recorder, but a disturbance of the ionosphere caused by the Sun blocked his radio. When he carefully aligned a magnetometer to the Earth's magnetic field, he found half an hour later that it was crooked by several degrees, because a magnetic storm was in progress.

Both Lassen and Friis-Christensen therefore shared with sailors a more-or-less hostile intimacy with weather and climate not known to city folk of the temperate zones. To that they added professional knowledge of the Sun's actions. Lassen was being pressed by his director to justify the continuation of solar-terrestrial physics research. So began a long, intermittent conversation with Friis-Christensen about how much of the climate change of the twentieth century might be due to variations in the Sun.

Friis-Christensen had organized a series of seminars on the subject in the 1970s. On a visit to the United States in 1987 he had learned about more recent studies which gave him fresh inspiration. Two meteorologists not afraid to say that the Sun affected the weather were Karin Labitzke of Berlin and Harry van Loon of Boulder, Colorado. They examined patterns of weather over the North Atlantic and found them changing with the sunspots. Measurements from weather balloons showed temperatures varying high in the air during the sunspot cycle. The biggest changes seemed to occur just below the stratosphere.

'As for Lassen, he had long been tantalized by a sketchy link that he saw between auroral activity due to the Sun and the extent of the sea ice in the Davis Strait. Life in Greenland was largely governed by the ice drifting each year from the Arctic Ocean, down Greenland's east coast, and around the southernmost tip. From there it rode into the Davis Strait on the warm current heading north from the Atlantic.

In the mildest years the ice failed to turn the corner at Cape Farewell. In cold winters it spread northwards to Godthaab and beyond, making life miserable

Sea ice in the Arctic. Influenced by solar activity, the extent of sea ice at high northern latitudes can vary by a million square kilometres from one year to the next, with profound effects on human life and work.

John Noble / Wilderness

ashore and balking seafarers until it melted at midsummer or later. In the Middle Ages pioneering Viking settlers were trapped behind an impenetrable barrier of ice. The hardier Greenlanders survived, but every Viking family perished.

Enormous variations from year to year and decade to decade encouraged Lassen and Friis-Christensen to use the reach of the ice as the gauge of a changing climate. Ships' logs and harbour histories recorded the extent and duration of the Davis Strait sea ice, and reliable compilations existed for the period since 1821. Since the 1970s, satellite observations of the ice were available.

The count of sunspots was the primary source of historical data on the Sun. The measles-like rash on the Sun's face rose to its peak every 11 years or so, and then abated. Like generations of sunspot chasers before them, the two physicists stumbled through a bumpy landscape of wiggles in graphs. The game was to match the wiggles of the sunspot cycle and the wiggles representing the Davis Strait sea ice. But they went up and down like the stock market and could drive a man mad. Nice cases of a simultaneous upturn in the two graphs could be confounded by a badly mismatched downturn.

In the years that followed, Lassen and Friis-Christensen would find themselves unexpectedly cast as the world's chief advocates of the proposition that the global warming of the twentieth century was due, in part or in whole, to a change in the Sun's mood. They would endure a professionally risky battle with the powerful supporters of the greenhouse warming hypothesis. Against all the odds, both scientific and political, they would be vindicated, with an unbidden intervention by a third scientist at the Danish Meteorological Institute. But at the end of the 1980s, the hobby of the solar-terrestrial physicists seemed as uncertain of success as all other efforts since Herschel's time to find a convincing link between the Sun's behaviour and the Earth's climate.

Sea surface temperatures. Grey-red tinted patches in the tropical Indian Ocean (centre right) and in the narrow Red Sea denote 29 degrees C, the highest annual averages found in infrared measurements from space by the ERS-1 satellite. A natural thermostat seems to prevent sea temperatures from rising higher. The coldest water, coloured purple, averages minus 2 degrees C.

ERS-1/ESA and ATSM/Rutherford Appleton Laboratory, Didcot, UK

Chapter Two

CHANGING THE CLIMATE

THE SOLAR FIREWORKS failed to move the official climatologists. Under the leadership of John Houghton, of the UK Meteorological Office, they were busy proving that the enhanced greenhouse effect of man-made carbon dioxide changed the climate. They had little time to watch auroras, when they were making models of the Earth's climate by complex calculations in the most powerful computers available.

Solar experts were not the only scientists dubious about this intergovernmental exercise, but the greenhouse warming theory had escaped from the normal give-and-take of scientific debate in the previous summer, which was unusually warm in the United States. James Hansen from NASA's Goddard Institute in New York City gave testimony to to a Senate committee.

'The Earth is warmer in 1988 than at any time in the history of instrumental measurements,' Hansen declared. 'The global warming is now sufficiently large that we can ascribe with a high degree of confidence a cause and effect relationship.'

As perceived by Richard Lindzen, a sceptical meteorologist of Cambridge, Massachusetts, the hysteria as he called it began with Hansen's testimony. It created headlines in the newspapers. The Senate committee's chairman, Al Gore, later dubbed the summer of 1988 the 'Kristallnacht before the warming holocaust'.

In 1989 a colleague of Lindzen's at the Massachusetts Institute of Technology lost a federal research grant because his data showed no obvious warming over the past century. Reviewers said that such a result was dangerous to humanity. Lindzen wrote a critique of global warming theories. The distinguished journal *Science* rejected it on the grounds that it was of no interest to the readership, but then attacked the article before its later publication by the American Meteorological Society.

A panel of the US National Research Council reported that there was no scientific basis for costly action against greenhouse gases. Its subcommittee argued that the United States would have little difficulty in adapting to even a severe global warming. Lindzen noted that these reports were not discussed in the popular media, except in incorrect claims that they supported the catastrophic vision.

Among American climatologists, Lindzen affirmed, a healthy debate continued, with only a small minority arguing that any identifiable man-made warming had occurred. But the greenhouse warming passed out of the specialists' hands. Only three or four climatologists were listed among 700 scientists who signed a petition in 1989. It urged recognition of global warming as potentially the great danger to mankind and it called for renewed consideration of nuclear power, which released no carbon dioxide.

When the petition was published in the *New York Times*, the passage about nuclear power was omitted. The president of the US National Academy of Sciences felt obliged to warn his distinguished members against lending their credibility to issues about which they had no special knowledge. But the greenhouse warming passed out of the hands of science.

'Scientists may disagree,' Congresswoman Claudine Schneider declared, 'but we can hear Mother Earth and she is crying.' Movie stars including Barbra Streisand, Meryl Streep and Robert Redford joined the greenhouse crusade. At a grand heat-in at his ranch in Sundance, Utah, Redford said that it was time to stop research and begin acting.

American utterances were the shriller because many other experts in the United States besides Lindzen still doubted the greenhouse warming. The oil companies and other powerful interests had commercial reasons for questioning it. In the United Kingdom, by contrast, the matter was already firmly in the hands of the government. It had written the greenhouse warming into the national programme of scientific research and was taking the lead on the international stage. In the 1980s all significant political action was by the say-so of the Prime Minister, Margaret Thatcher.

In her memoirs *The Downing Street Years*, Baroness Thatcher related how Sir Crispin Tickell, a former ambassador to the United Nations, had persuaded her to make a major speech on the subject of global warming. Choosing to deliver it to an august scientific body, the Royal Society, in September 1988, she spoke of enormous and rapid changes in population, agriculture and the use of fossil fuels, which might amount to a massive experiment with the system of the planet itself.

Thatcher affirmed that she wanted consideration of the implications for policy to be founded on good science to establish cause and effect. The assembled scientists appreciated that. But she was disappointed in the lack of attention from the media to what she regarded as a seminal pronouncement.

'I had been relying on the television lights to enable me to read my speech in the gloom of the Fishmongers' Hall, where it was to be delivered,' Baroness Thatcher recalled; 'in the event, candelabra had to be passed up along the table to allow me to do so.'

Never mind, the real business was already going on behind the scenes. After an international gathering of scientists and others concerned about the greenhouse warming, in 1985 in Villach, Austria, two big initatives followed. The International Council of Scientific Unions initiated at Bern in 1986 an International Geosphere-Biosphere Programme to co-ordinate multidisciplinary research on global change. For many of those taking part, global change was a code for the greenhouse warming. Nevertheless the mandate was for fundamental scientific research.

Politically more weighty was the creation by the United Nations of an Intergovernmental Panel on Climate Change, managed by the UN Environment Programme and the World Meteorological Organization. Starting work in 1988, this panel was to report by 1990. The task was divided into teams, of which by far the most important was Working Group I, responsible for the scientific assessment.

The British Prime Minister ensured that the UK Meteorological Office should receive from the environmental and energy ministries the increased funding it needed to capture the science working group of the climate change panel. By international consent, the Meteorological Office provided the secretariat and technical support. Its core team ran the workshops and did the editing for a large team of scientists around the world who contributed to the report.

John Houghton, chief executive of the Meteorological Office, became chairman of the science working group, as one of those genial urbane Englishmen who often crop up when science has important international business to do. As head of atmospheric physics at Oxford University, Houghton had devised cunning instruments for NASA's series of Nimbus satellites of the 1970s. He pioneered the art of sounding the temperatures of the Earth's air from space, and checking its composition. He also wrote standard textbooks on infrared physics, the physics of atmospheres, and remote sounding of atmospheres.

Entering government service, Houghton first helped to reorganize the Rutherford Appleton Laboratory as the prime centre of British space research. He became head of the Meteorological Office in 1983. Under his leadership, the skills it had acquired in using large computers, to forecast the weather day by day, progressed into calculating climates. So it came about that, just when the Intergovernmental Panel on Climate Change was being created, the Meteorological Office had the only large computer model of climate outside the United States.

Houghton did more than any other person on the Earth to nurture the scientific case for believing in the greenhouse warming and in the need for urgent action to curb emissions of carbon dioxide and other greenhouse gases. As chairman of the official science working group, his job was to collate and sift the research results, and spell out their implications for policymakers.

A sense of mission sustained him through ceaseless globetrotting, arduous analysis, and arguments with the scientific and political sceptics he encountered everywhere. Houghton wrote later: 'A clear understanding of the responsibilities and abilities we have been given coupled with trust in God's presence and trustworthiness is the mixture that makes stewardship of the Earth an exciting and challenging activity.'

Houghton was not quite chief scientist of the planet. That role fell to an amiable and respected climatologist from Stockholm, Bert Bolin. As chairman of the Intergovernmental Panel on Climate Change he oversaw the progress of Houghton's team and of the other working groups, concerned with the impacts of climate change and the implications for policy.

When promoted to be the world's Mr Greenhouse, Bolin was aware of the irony. Twenty years earlier he could hardly persuade anyone to take his warm-

The cruelty of climate change. Southern Africa experienced frequent years of low rainfall from 1980 onwards, like those already afflicting the sub-Saharan Sahel. As the deadliest of natural disasters, drought has killed more than a million people since 1967.

W. Wisniewski/FLPA

OPPOSITE ABOVE: A lost pasture. Rock paintings at Tassili, deep in the Sahara Desert, show that herdsmen grazed their cattle there before 2500 BC, when the regional climate was much moister.

Walter Grunwald/AKG London

OPPOSITE BELOW: Heyday of the Vikings. A carved stone from Gotland in the Baltic Sea commemorates the seafarers who took advantage of a global warming for raids, conquests and settlements. They started in the late eighth century AD, at a time when the Sun was in a manic mood.

AKG London

ing hypothesis seriously. Carbon dioxide in the air was increasing ever more rapidly, because of human action. Elementary physics said that the increasing carbon dioxide would reduce the escape of infrared rays from the Earth, by an enhanced greenhouse effect, and so warm it. With ever-rising carbon dioxide from increasing use of fossil fuels, the consequences might be grave. Bolin faced scorn and neglect from the official meteorologists, and makers of national research policies, whose successors sat reverently at his feet.

'Not only does knowledge have to evolve,' Bolin remarked, 'but also the way people react to knowledge.'

To understand the change in Bert Bolin's fortunes required a little background knowledge about past changes of climate, and about evolving ideas as to their causes. When he was trying to win support for the greenhouse warming, climatologists were preoccupied with a cooling of the world that was in progress in the 1960s and early 1970s. It was associated with terrible droughts in Africa and with widening areas of snowfall and sea ice.

Fears that human beings were affecting the climate focused at that time on man-made dust, created by industrial pollution and the farming of marginal land. The dust would tend to reduce the intensity of sunshine and promote the formation of clouds. But there was a new awareness, too, of Nature's ability to change the climate. The study of climate history was both fashionable and alarming.

Noah's Flood, for example, was a sea-level rise traceable in many parts of the world, at a time of global warming around 2900 BC. That was during a period when the climate was at its hottest, after the last ice age ended about 8000 BC. Around 2500 BC the Sahara Desert became much drier than it had been. It drove out nomads who left behind them rock paintings of their cattle in what became a desiccated wasteland. In about 2100 BC, in a cooling of the world, the monsoon broke its promise in the Indus valley and the Harappan culture collapsed.

In the sea off Greece, in an event later dated to 1628 BC, the island of Thera blew up. It covered nearby Crete in 5 centimetres of ash, and its dust also darkened the Sun, creating a volcanic winter which brought frost to the trees of North America and reduced the annual growth rate of trees in Ireland to one-half for a period of years. Other major eruptions that appeared in the climatic record had similar effects on trees world-wide. The associated human suffering and upheavals were debated by the historians.

Paradoxical names given to Iceland and Greenland by Viking explorers reflected the ever-changing climate. Iceland was by far the greener of the two places, but in AD 865 when a Norseman tried to settle there, his cattle died and sea ice beset him, so he went home grumbling about 'Iceland'. By AD 985 Iceland was long settled and colonists went on to the much icier 'Greenland'. The name was propaganda of course, to lure other settlers, yet the climate there was warmer then than at any time since. More generally, the warm period around AD 1000 was not just the heyday of the Vikings but a prosperous time world-

Ice skating on the Thames at Henley 1895

Before the global warming. In the 1890s the world was, on average, about 0.5 degree cooler than the 1990s. The Sun was in a lazy mood, as shown by the low sunspot counts (OPPOSITE).

Royal Meteorological Society, Bracknell

wide, marked by large growths of population in Europe and China.

From medieval to modern times the climate was on a roller coaster. A period variously defined between 1300 and 1850 was known to historians of climate as the Little Ice Age, because conditions appeared to have been chilly over much of the world. The human misery it caused was apparent in countless records of famine and revolt. Marked fluctuations occurred throughout the period.

Regional differences complicated the attempts to reconstruct an overall picture, but in the northern hemisphere cold conditions were probably common around 1500, 1620, 1700, and 1810. Warmer interludes peaked around 1470, 1550, 1650, 1770, and 1870. In England the winter of 1683–84 appeared in retrospect to have been the coldest there since the last real ice age ended 10,000 years before.

After a cold spell around 1890, the land climate in the northern hemisphere improved sharply in the first half of the twentieth century, reaching a peak of warmth in about 1940. It then turned down in the 1950s. The reasons for these variations were debated, but the candidate attracting widest interest among climatologists of the 1970s was the Sun.

For Jack Eddy of Boulder, Colorado, the most striking feature of climate in the past few centuries was that the coldest phase of the Little Ice Age – around 1700 – coincided with a time when sunspots were exceedingly scarce. The period 1645–1715 was the Maunder Minimum, named after the British scientist

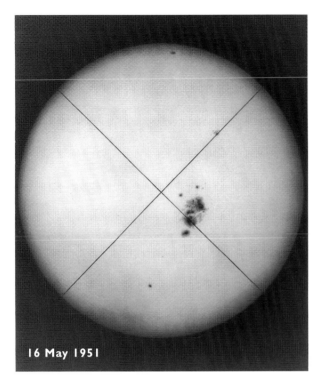

16 May 1951

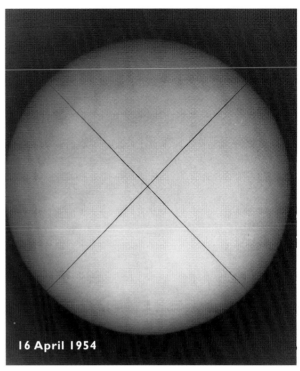

16 April 1954

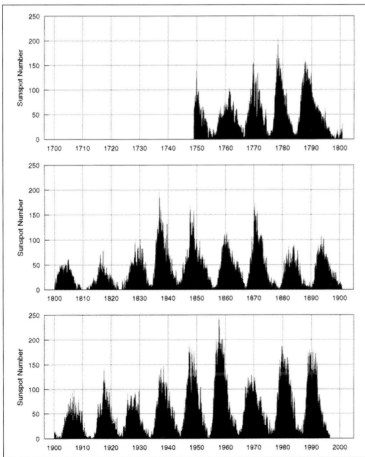

ABOVE: A cryptic message. What is the Sun saying, when it lays out a stall of sunspots, or clears them entirely? For more than a century the Royal Greenwich Observatory photographed sunspots routinely, while generations of scientists wondered why they came and went, and whether they affected the weather.

Royal Greenwich Observatory, London

LEFT: The sunspot cycle. The Sun alternates between visible activity and a deceptive appearance of calm, as the number of dark spots on its face rises and falls every 11 years or so. Heinrich Schwabe, an amateur astronomer of Dassau, Germany, discovered the cycle in 1843. Sunspot numbering was formalized at Zurich a few years later and now involves two dozen observatories worldwide.

National Geophysical Data Center / NOAA, Boulder, Colorado

Walter Maunder who, at the end of the nineteenth century, had retrospectively identified that phase of very feeble solar activity. In 1976 Eddy suggested that the radiant energy emitted from the Sun was temporarily reduced around 1700, and the shortfall could explain the severe climatic conditions.

The notion that the Sun behaved oddly in the Little Ice Age had independent support in abnormally high levels of radiocarbon in wood dating from that period. Cosmic rays created radioactive atoms of carbon in the air. A very high production rate during the Maunder Minimum confirmed that the Sun was dozing, and neglecting its task of batting the cosmic rays away.

Other commentaries continued to appear, on the sunspots and their possible links with climate, and on regular fluctuations in climate that experts wanted to ascribe to slow rhythms in the Sun. A particularly tantalizing 88-year rhythm was apparent in the vigour of solar activity, as reckoned by the number of spots attained at each sunspot maximum. For the next two decades Eddy's link between the Little Ice Age and the Maunder Minimum remained the chief talking point for those who favoured a solar explanation for climate change from century to century.

Conceivably not every fluctuation in climate needed an external cause. The prime candidate for a spontaneous fluctuation was El Niño, named for the Christ Child because it usually happened at Christmas. This was a poorly understood spread of warm water into the eastern Pacific Ocean every few years, which in 1973 for example wiped out an immense anchovy fishery off Peru. El Niño seemed to have widespread effects on weather in other parts of the world.

For climatologists in the 1970s, a gnawing anxiety provoked by the mid-century cooling concerned the next ice age, of the kind that could bury Canada and Scandinavia under ice sheets a kilometre thick. Discoveries from variations in heavy oxygen atoms in fossils of the seabed, and from multiple layers of wind-blown dust recognized in Czechoslovakia, showed that many more ice ages had occurred in the past two million years than the four or five that the textbooks said. The warm intervals between ice ages were typically about 10,000 years, and the present warm interval was 10,000 years old.

Scientific climatology took a stride forward with confirmation in the mid-1970s that the large-scale comings and goings of the ice were strictly related to the Earth's vagaries as a planet orbiting the Sun. This theory traced back a hundred years to a Scottish janitor, James Croll, but it was usually credited in its modern form to a Yugoslav civil engineer, Milutin Milankovitch, who advocated it in the 1920s.

The gravity of the Sun, the Moon and the other planets caused the Earth to change the shape of its orbit over periods of about 100,000 years. The changes were trivial, astronomically speaking, yet huge in relation to climate because they altered the Sun's distance at different seasons. Even in the prevailing near-circular orbit the Sun's intensity dropped by 7 per cent from January to July. A swivelling of the planet's axis, over periods of 19,000–23,000 years, determined when the seasons occurred, at variable positions on the orbit. Finally, the Earth was known to roll like a ship, modifying the tilt of its axis in relation to

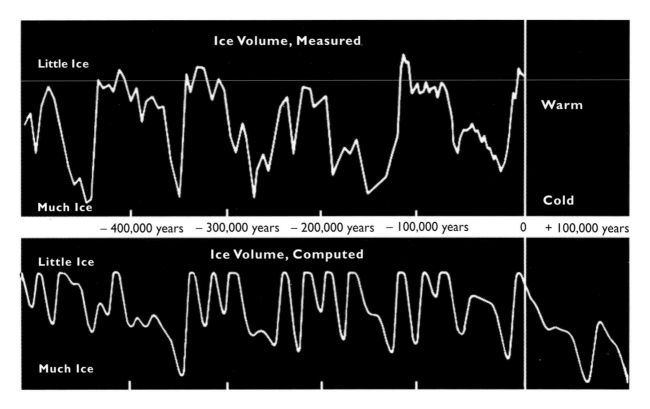

the Sun by almost 3 degrees, and returning, in a period of 41,000 years.

These actions altered the relationship of Sun and Earth, without any need for the Sun itself to change. All the Earth's wobbles put together on a graph made wiggles that fitted the record of ice in the world very well. They described, for example, relatively warm spells in the middle of ice ages, which occurred in reality. The ice ages were governed especially by the height of the Sun in the sky over the northern lands in summer. If the Sun was too low in the sky, or too far away in the northern summer, the snows of winter would fail to melt entirely. As a result the snowfalls of each year would build an ever-thickening ice sheet.

A disconcerting discovery was that heavy ice cover was normal. Sometimes a propitious arrangement of the Earth in orbit would allow the Sun, relatively close and relatively high in the sky, to blast the northern ice sheets with strong summer sunshine and melt most of them. That happened at the end of the last ice age. Since then, the July sunshine in the northern hemisphere had weakened and the Earth was also rolling into a more upright stance, reducing the height of the Sun in the northern summer sky.

At the crucial latitudes around 60 degrees north, taking in the Baltic Sea and Hudson Bay near the cores of the ice age ice sheets, the summer sunlight had diminished by 7 per cent since the end of the last ice age, and was still falling slowly. The next ice age appeared to be due, overdue some said. But within a timetable of thousands of years the odds were long against the downturn in temperature in the mid-twentieth century signalling the onset of the big freeze.

Ice ages, real and computed. The upper graph shows changing volumes of ice in the world over the past half-million years, measured by variations of heavy oxygen in fossils from the Pacific Ocean floor. Below are ice fluctuations calculated from the Earth's orbital variations. An extension into the future depicts another ice age pending.

Adapted from N.J. Shackleton and N.D. Opdyke, 1973, and N. Calder, 1974

37

Much more likely, because such events occurred in a timetable of centuries, was another Little Ice Age due to a lazy Sun. Since the previous event of the kind, the human population had soared and food supplies were precarious at the best of times. The famines that followed a failure of the rains in the Sahel region south of the Sahara in the early 1970s, demonstrated how climate change could bring suffering and death even to the modern world. There was talk about averting a severe cooling by spreading soot on the Arctic ice to melt it, or putting large mirrors in orbit to increase the supply of sunshine.

The climate then mocked all these thoughts by taking a sharp upturn at the end of the 1970s. In the early 1980s, the global mean temperature was back at its peak of 1940. By the end of the decade it was slightly higher. These were the climatic circumstances in which the assertion of Bert Bolin and others, that man-made carbon dioxide would warm the world drastically, came to be taken seriously at last.

An intellectual shift helped too, occasioned by the evidence that the Milankovitch wobbles explained the rhythms of the ice ages. The climate was sensitive to special causes of change. This was in distinction to a persistent opinion that the climate varied of its own accord, with many possibilities besides El Niño latent in the complex Earth system, which might concoct home-made trends or oscillations.

That human beings were changing the climate by mistake was an idea sharing a common ancestry with proposals to change the weather and climate on purpose. In the 1950s the oceanographer Roger Revelle of La Jolla, California, was an enthusiast for the idea of busting hurricanes by whitening the ocean surface with aluminium oxide dust to reduce its intake of sunlight. The same Revelle was the first to describe the rise in carbon dioxide as an inadvertent geophysical experiment with the planet, which became something of a catch-phrase for greenhouse scientists and politicians.

The theory of climatic warming due to an enhanced greenhouse effect was ready and waiting. A quarter of a century after William Herschel's discovery of infrared rays, the polymathic secretary of the Académie des Sciences in Paris pondered their implications. Jean-Baptiste-Joseph Fourier realized that certain gases in the air could absorb infrared rays from the Earth, which would otherwise escape into space. Fourier likened the gases' role to the action of a greenhouse window, which let sunlight in but trapped heat on the way out – hence the name of the greenhouse effect.

Astronomers and meteorologists came to appreciate that life depended utterly on the greenhouse effect. Without the warming influence of water vapour and carbon dioxide the Earth would be a frozen iceball. Depending on various assumptions, the average surface temperature would be somewhere between minus 34 and minus 6 degrees C compared with about plus 15 degrees for the actual average temperature.

Yet there might be too much of a good thing, if this benign greenhouse effect were boosted by a greenhouse warming. In the 1890s, after enormously elaborate calculations, the Swedish scientist Svante Arrhenius estimated that if

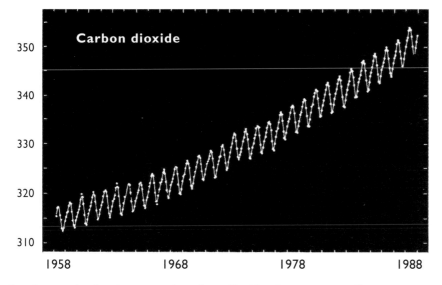

Carbon dioxide

350
340
330
320
310

1958   1968   1978   1988

the air contained twice as much carbon dioxide, the average surface temperature would go up by 5 or 6 degrees. As another Stockholmer and Arrhenius's successor, Bolin not only kept the greenhouse thesis alive but pondered the continual trade in carbon dioxide between air, sea, living things and sediments, as well as the new man made additions from fossil fuels and deforestation.

In 1958, in response to urgings from Revelle and others, the US government's weather service begin monitoring carbon dioxide at the South Pole and on the lava-strewn summit of Mauna Loa in Hawaii. The graphs wiggled up and down each year as the planet breathed and exhaled carbon dioxide in response to the seasonal growth of vegetation, primarily in the northern lands. But an upward trend sounded the alarm for the greenhouse warming. Bolin used measurements from aircraft to confirm an inexorable rise in carbon dioxide in the air, by 2.5 per cent in a decade.

The calculations that had troubled Arrhenius became easier with large computers. These had fulfilled a dream of farsighted meteorologists who wanted to predict the weather, not by expert intuition, but by using the laws of physics to calculate tomorrow's weather from today's weather. The enterprise became practicable only when supercomputers could do the sums faster than the weather itself evolved, and when a high-speed system of telecommunications for worldwide weather data gave the computers the numbers they needed.

A revolution in meteorology ensued, with the advent of global models which calculated the whole world's weather as a basis for regional and local forecasts. The revolution was assisted by the weather satellites that gave unprecedented impressions of the whole world and its evolving cloud patterns. The satellites also helped local forecasters with thunderstorms and the like, which were too small for the grids on which the computers did their sums. The weaknesses of the computer models in respect of clouds would be a persistent concern in the developments that followed.

For the daily weather, the computers did better on the whole than the intuitions of human meteorologists, and comedians gave up making jokes about

ABOVE LEFT: Carbon dioxide, 1958–88. Measured in millionths of the air volume, on Mauna Loa, Hawaii, the gas increased by 12 percent in three decades. Annual dips occurred as the preponderant plants of the northern hemisphere absorbed carbon dioxide for their summer's growth.

Adapted from Intergovernmental Panel on Climate Change, 1990 and C.D. Keeling et al.

ABOVE: Breathalysing the planet. High on a Hawaiian mountain, samples of clean Pacific air come down the tube for measurement of the carbon dioxide they contain. Rising levels of carbon dioxide, monitored at Mauna Loa since 1958 by the US National Oceanic and Atmospheric Administration, provoked fears of a greenhouse warming.

Alec Nisbett

weather forecasts. There were still blunders, such as the failure to forecast a major windstorm in England in October 1987, but these were now matters for inquiries into what went wrong, rather than the traditional shrug of the weatherman's shoulders.

After calculating the weather for about a week, the computer models deviated too far from reality to provide sensible forecasts. They drew the isobars of storms and heatwaves that never existed. But the theory was that this fictional weather was typical of the real thing, so that if you went on running the models for long enough, the variations would average out correctly and you could build up a picture of real climate.

Then you could study climate change. For example you could double the carbon dioxide in the atmosphere and see what happened to the climate. The results, so the argument went, could then become the basis of international policy to check the ever-rising levels of carbon dioxide.

Many experts were deeply sceptical about the computer models, which were oversimplified both in their arithmetical powers and in the assumptions about the workings of the Earth system. Critics said that science had a long way to go before sensible climate forecasts could be made. Clouds, for example, were a major uncertainty. A warmer, moister world might make more clouds and keep the warming in check.

From the outset it was obvious that clouds would be a great nuisance for the greenhouse warming theory. Pioneer computer modellers were the first to admit that a small increase in cloud cover could mostly cancel any warming, although they also pointed out that a decrease in clouds could intensify it. Until clouds were tamed by adequate meteorological knowledge and computing power, would it not be better just to keep an eye on the climate and take international action if and when it seemed necessary?

Against any wait-and-see policy, the contention was that power stations being built in the 1990s would still be emitting greenhouse gases far into the twenty-first century. As for the possibility that control of emissions might turn out to be unnecessary, a moral argument was introduced. People were too profligate with fossil fuels and forests anyway. If the threat of global warming prompted more rational use of the world's resources and a curbing of pollution, it could only be beneficial. For many people, including some doubters of the greenhouse warming, that last argument was persuasive, but it had nothing to do with the science of climate change.

To make sure the projections were taken seriously, the aim was to involve the world scientific community on a large scale. For the first spurt of work, 1988–90, 170 scientists from 25 countries were engaged. The core team at Bracknell, England, from John Houghton's Meteorological Office, co-ordinated the scientific work for the Intergovernmental Panel on Climate Change. The aim was to produce a definitive report on which politicians could act.

Bolin, Houghton and their collaborators took the view that increases in carbon dioxide and other greenhouse gases had already forced the climate of the twentieth century to become warmer, and the forcing could intensify disastrously in the twenty-first century. Miscellaneous wiggles in the temperature graphs were still assigned vaguely to 'natural' variations, and the possibility of 'surprises' was not ruled out. But the official group was engaged in a single-minded estimation of the greenhouse warming.

The idea of an enhanced greenhouse effect was quite persuasive to scientists. Allowing for the lack of evidence in 1989, one way or the other, it might even have been correct. But a decade earlier climate change had been a subject abuzz with many different possible causes. Now even man-made dust, which could cool the world, got short shrift. The Sun, which had recently loomed so large in climatology, had but three pages in a report of some 365 pages.

The team could not ignore the light in the sky entirely, because Frederick Seitz, a former president of the US National Academy of Sciences, was suggesting that the Sun was preparing a Little Ice Age that would offset any greenhouse warming. Not so, said the report's authors. The greatest possible change in the intensity of sunlight would be quickly swamped by the increase in carbon dioxide expected by Houghton's group.

Calculations of climate change relied on estimates of the energy rates available at the Earth's surface, averaged at so many watts per square metre. The strength of sunlight out in space was about 1370 watts per square metre, but to allow for the Earth's curvature and the fact that half of it was in darkness at any one time, you divided that number by four to arrive at the average solar energy at the top of the atmosphere. Almost a third was scattered back into space from clouds, dust and air molecules, which left 235 watts per square metre to warm the Earth.

Climate change involved much smaller numbers. An increase of 25 per cent in carbon dioxide in the air, since the Industrial Revolution, was supposedly equivalent to increasing the heating by 1.5 watts per square metre. The maximum estimate of the change in the intensity of the Sun since the Little Ice Age was similar, at 1.3 watts per square metre, and much of that change would have occurred before the twentieth century. Moreover, solar variability measured from satellites suggested a much lower figure for changes in the Sun's output, of about 0.2 watt. A doubling of carbon dioxide, or the equivalent realised with the addition of other man-made greenhouse gases, would mean an extra 4.5 watts per square metre, or 6 watts altogether.

In the years that followed, there would be two issues about these figures. One was the extent to which the enhanced greenhouse effect explained the warming of the twentieth century. The other was whether the projections of future temperatures due to an expected doubling of carbon dioxide were right. The issues were closely linked. For expectations of a large effect in the future to be correct, there had to be a moderate but non-negligible greenhouse warming already.

To achieve its remarkable projection of future temperatures, the report had to argue that the global warming of the twentieth century was largely due to carbon dioxide and other greenhouse gases. The role of the Sun had to be minimized. The commentary concentrated entirely on changes in the output

Watching over the planet. Every half hour, the Meteosat spacecraft transmits images of clouds and other weather data for a huge segment of the Earth, including Africa and Europe. Dispassionate robot eyes in space help to distinguish fact from fancy, about global changes.

Eumetsat

of radiant energy from the visible disk. As for the invisible heliosphere that embraced the Earth in the solar wind, and might contain other possible ways of changing the climate, for Houghton's group it did not exist.

Satellites buzzing around the Earth like gnats measured many things besides sunlight. The physicists who conceived them and interpreted their results had created a new global geography. In contrast to the parochial start-points of traditional geography, satellites saw the whole planet. And in contrast with the theory-dependent propositions of the greenhouse warming, the satellites told objectively by observation what was really going on in the world.

Early weather satellites of the 1960s had discovered, over the tropical oceans, the giant cloud clusters that served as the main boiler houses powering the Earth's weather machine. Their existence had never properly penetrated the meteorological consciousness before. Also in those pioneering days, the satellites corrected a basic number in climatology. Meteorologists thought that the Earth absorbed 63 per cent or so of the sunlight falling on to it. The real figure was about 70 per cent, because there were fewer clouds than expected, sending the sunlight back into space from the tropical and sub-tropical zones.

The objectivity of the satellites gave environmentalists a hard time, by correcting their tendency to jump to conclusions about global issues. This was by no means the intention of the funding agencies and the scientists preparing the satellites, who dedicated their work to a better understanding of the environment and the human impact.

One creative group, at NASA Goddard in Maryland, used infrared data from the NOAA weather satellites to chart the growth of the world's vegetation. NASA's vegetation experts helped the UN Food and Agriculture Organization in Rome to develop operational systems for Africa. They reported the occurrence of vegetation in the desert, where locusts could breed, and predicted famines due to drought when vegetation was weak in the afflicted lands. Europe's Meteosat weather satellite contributed information on clouds over Africa to the operation. When an early warning of a famine came, no one did anything about it – but that was not the fault of the satellites or the interpretation system.

As a by-product of this work, the satellite results corrected a much-repeated saying of the environmentalists, that the Sahara Desert was advancing inexorably southwards as a result of overgrazing at its edge by the cattle of the nomadic pastoralists. This was not the case. The desert edge simply moved back and forth according to the quality of each year's rain. The real damage, as other satellites revealed, was being done in nodes of overgrazing in comparatively well-watered regions, where the nomads had been persuaded to settle down.

The satellites also gave vivid pictures of the destruction of the rain forests. They showed ugly gashes in the tree cover made by roads, mines, logging and new farms, in Asia, Africa and Central and South America. Brazil was the chief target of wrath, because calculations by an American expert, much quoted by environmentalists, predicted that 44 per cent of the Amazon forest would be gone by 1988.

The Brazilians had experts too, in remote sensing by satellite. Using early Landsat images they had established a baseline of 0.6 per cent of the Amazon forest destroyed up to 1975, not counting some very old colonial clearances. In 1989 they repeated the operation with the latest Landsat images. Their scrutiny, image by image, showed the additional loss of Amazon rain forest up to 1988 to be not 40-something per cent but 5 per cent.

Never mind, there was always the ozone hole. A surprising environmental discovery in the mid-1980s led to surprisingly swift intergovernmental action. The depletion of high-level ozone detected over Antarctica, first by British scientists at Halley Bay and then by NASA's Nimbus 7 satellite, was blamed on chloroflurocarbons used in refrigerators and aerosol sprays. The ozone layer intercepted the Sun's most harmful ultraviolet rays, so any thinning might cause harmful sunburn to living things. Within a very few years of the discovery, governments were agreeing to halt the manufacture of the chemicals in question.

The ozone hole had nothing to do with the greenhouse warming. If anything, it would tend to cool the Earth, because ozone itself was a greenhouse gas. Contrary to a widespread misapprehension, the only real link between the ozone hole and the greenhouse warming was at the political level, because similar intergovernmental action was envisaged in both cases to protect the atmosphere. Carbon dioxide entered the chambers of diplomacy on the coattails of ozone.

While the ozone hole was plain for all to see, in the satellite images, the same could not be said for the greenhouse warming. A series of satellite results, if they had been taken seriously enough, might have saved the official climatologists from sticking their necks out.

From 1979 onwards, the American NOAA weather satellites carried microwave sounding units that could measure the temperatures in the lower atmosphere objectively. The results showed the mean temperature at moderate altitudes wobbling up and down by about 0.2 degree C from year to year. In 1989 it was just about the same as in 1979. So where was the greenhouse warming? Ah, said the official climatologists, no one should try to discern a long-term trend in 10 years' data.

The Sun itself was indifferent to the earthlings' low opinions of its powers. It was still busy making magnetic explosions. After the big bout in March 1989, in August the Sun forced the Toronto Stock Exchange to close, by faulting its fault-proof computer disk drives in a magnetic storm. At the end of September, an American researcher into cold fusion thought he had struck gold with a huge count of neutrons, only to discover that energetic particles direct from the Sun, solar protons, were bombarding the Earth more intensively than in any such event since 1956. Concorde passengers were mildly irradiated, and for several hours cosmic ray counters at ground level found the solar particles outnumbering the normal influx from the Galaxy by a factor of four.

In October 1989 the crew of NASA's space shuttle Atlantis saw solar protons with their own eyes. They had just launched the Galileo probe to Jupiter, and took shelter in the innermost part of their vehicle as the particles from the Sun doused them. Even there they were disconcerted by flashes of light caused by the particles hitting their optic nerves. Later reckonings showed that such a burst of energetic radiation was potentially fatal for an astronaut fully exposed to it, if walking on the Moon for example.

Our story about the Sun versus the greenhouse has hardly begun, but already there are several hares running off in different directions. An attentive reader is in danger of being almost as confused as were the scientists involved at the time. The fog of war is relatively transparent compared with the mists of scientific discovery. To help in understanding why various events and results in different fields of research crop up in the tale, a questionnaire that poses the issues may be useful, together with the answers that unprejudiced scientists might have given at the end of 1989.

About the Sun

Does the Sun control changes in the Earth's climate, over decades and centuries?
Possibly. The best evidence (in 1989) comes from variations in cosmic rays as registered by radiocarbon counts in old wood, which seem to be highest when the world is cool.

Is the physics of the solar warming persuasive?
No. At this time there is no clear link between solar action and the decade-to-decade changes in temperature in the twentieth century.

Are variations in solar brightness sufficient to explain the global warming of the twentieth century?
Probably not.

Is there another solar mechanism that is sufficient?
Who knows?

Can the new solar spacecraft discover this mechanism?
Possibly. They will certainly give information about the Sun and the solar wind not previously available.

What is the solar prognosis for climate in the twenty-first century?
A solar cooling is quite probable, but there is no clear evidence that the Sun's effects can be large enough to counteract the anticipated greenhouse warming.

About the greenhouse warming

Are man-made greenhouse gases warming the Earth?
Yes, in principle they should be doing so, though the intensity of the warming and its contribution to climate change in the twentieth century are hard to assess.

Is the physics of the greenhouse warming persuasive?
In 1989, it makes a neat story.

Is the meteorology of clouds understood well enough for assessing human impacts on climate?
Who knows? Small increases in cloud cover could largely cancel a greenhouse warming, and the ability of computer models of climate to handle clouds properly is at least questionable.

Are the predictions of the computer models of climate credible?
Possibly. In the absence of any other coherent account of current climate change, they are taken at face value for caution's sake.

Can the Earth-observing spacecraft prove the greenhouse warming?
This is their most important task.

What is the greenhouse prognosis for climate in the twenty-first century?
In material being prepared for publication in 1990, the officially projected global warming is 3 degrees C, before 2100.

Flood or drought? A billion people rely on the summer Sun to draw rainclouds to the Indian subcontinent. The monsoon's arrival brings joy but every few years excessive rains cause serious flooding (India, BELOW). Alternatively, shortfalls in the annual supply of water from the sky can leave fields and waterways desperately dry (Bangladesh, ABOVE). Climatologists ponder the effects of climate change on the monsoon's fickle behaviour.

Popperfoto / Reuter

Chapter Three

MANIC-DEPRESSIVE MOODS

WHEN HE EMERGED from 10 Downing Street in London, on a May morning in 1990, John Houghton could be pleased with his work. He had given the British cabinet a preview of his global assessment of climate change, warning them that emissions of carbon dioxide and other gases resulting from human activities would surely raise temperatures at the Earth's surface. Taking their cue from Margaret Thatcher, the politicians and attendant officials heard him out in silence.

'I had been led to expect many interruptions and questions during my presentation,' Houghton wrote later. 'The questions and discussions afterwards demonstrated a large degree of concern for the world's environmental problems.'

It would have been more surprising if they had heckled him. He had delivered what Margaret Thatcher had hoped for, a projected 3 degree C rise in temperature in the twenty-first century, as the basis for a major diplomatic drive for a global climate treaty. She rewarded Houghton by giving the report a ringing endorsement, when she formally opened the new Hadley Centre for Climate Research and Prediction at the Meteorological Office.

'We have a full repairing lease on the Earth,' she said. 'With the work of the Intergovernmental Panel on Climate Change, we can now say we have the surveyor's report; and it shows there are faults and that the repair work needs to start without delay.'

The very name of a centre for climate research and prediction implied that its creator believed that he knew how to predict climate. That was certainly part of Houghton's thesis. His working group aimed to present as clearly as possible the state of knowledge about climate change and a best estimate of climate change in the next century. No official climate forecast had ever been issued before. Scientists who thought the idea rash were overruled. The reasoning was that people found a forecast of tomorrow's weather useful, even though it might be uncertain. Similarly climate projections could provide useful guidance for policymakers.

The 'likely' increase in global mean temperature by 3 degrees C by the year 2100, if emissions of greenhouse gases were not controlled, was the headline result of the Houghton group's scientific assessment in *Climate Change*, published by Bert Bolin's intergovernmental panel. Anyone who read the report carefully would find many caveats and margins of uncertainty. These applied also to an estimated rise in global sea level by 65 centimetres by 2100.

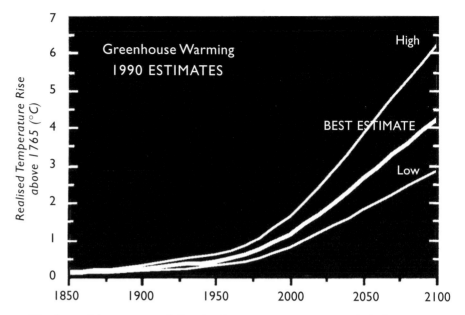

An alarming prediction. In 1990, official climatologists foresaw a very large rise in the global mean temperature in the twenty-first century, if nothing were done to curb the human output of carbon dioxide and other greenhouse gases.

After Intergovernmental Panel on Climate Change, Bracknell

The loss of huge areas of farmland to a rising sea in Bangladesh, and increased loss of life in cyclones, were among the specific consequences most often cited by scientific commentators. The swamping of low-lying islands like the Maldives and the Marshalls was another, together with a spread of malaria as the mosquito vector found ever-wider territories congenial to it. But as the regional projections were admitted to be thoroughly unreliable, the descriptions were often tautological: 'If there is less rain there will be droughts, if there is more rain there will be floods'.

What the models used in *Climate Change* could do really well was to convert their crude estimates of global warming into pictures using advanced computer graphics. Regrettably for human judgement, the resulting illustrations were not cartoons of camels in New York or beach huts in Antarctica, but were maps of the world.

Drawn and coloured superbly by the computers, the maps looked as authoritative as a city street-plan. So if the computer covered the Great Lakes with a splodge of red to signify a 10 degree rise in winter temperatures, many people, even scientists, took the picture literally. When the silicon-brained artist saw fit to coat the American grainlands with orange to denote a 2-centimetre loss of soil moisture in summer, experts started doing sums about the cost of irrigation.

If you took the trouble to compare the maps from different computer modellers, any sense of awe was quickly dispelled. Although produced by similar programs, and with similar assumptions about the physical factors in climate, the painted maps looked very different. One promised drought in India, and another, floods. You could go around the world picking the regional forecast of your choice.

Houghton wrote in the foreword to *Climate Change: the IPCC Scientific Assessment* (1990): 'The Assessment is an authoritative statement of the views of the international scientific community at this time.'

He justified the assertion by saying that 170 scientists from 25 countries had contributed to the Assessment. In fact the writing of the report was mainly in the hands of 34 lead authors from 12 countries. Of this diminished band, two-thirds (23) came from two countries, the United States and the United Kingdom.

To bolster the authority of the report, Houghton explained that a further 200 scientists were involved in the peer review of the draft report. Many of these reviewers were government employees rather than academic climatologists. Geographically the list was very patchy, with 72 from the United States, 56 from Australia, and one each from India and Brazil.

The impression was given that the reviewers agreed with the report, although a caveat near the back acknowledged that the opinions of a 'minority' had not been accommodated. Among those listed as giving the document authority was the scientific director of the Royal Netherlands Meteorological Institute, Henk Tennekes. He gave his personal view in vehement language during the report's preparation.

'I worry,' Tennekes declared, 'about the eagerness with which we tend to prostitute ourselves in order to please politicians who might be seduced into financing our craving for expansion. I worry that our claims will backfire on us.'

No scientific or political analysis, however penetrating, could jolt the consensus itself. Regardless of how they were arrived at, the prognostications were the most coherent propositions about climate change available. If Nature so wished it, they were correct. But they were also shielded by bureaucratic procedures from the ordinary day-to-day research which interrogated Nature and compared its answers with theory. As Houghton's group remained in existence to produce further reports, it would be judge and jury on any new results.

A battle line was drawn, reminiscent of a great divide at the origin of modern science. In the seventeenth century, René Descartes deduced how Nature worked by mathematics and imagination. Voltaire described his philosophy as 'nothing more than an ingenious novel'. Voltaire preferred Isaac Newton's use of mathematics and observation. To their critics, John Houghton and his followers were Cartesians writing science fiction about imaginary weather in the supercomputers, not heeding what Nature did. Others put more trust in the all-seeing eyes of satellites, observing what really happened in the atmosphere from hour to hour, year to year, and decade to decade.

There was no pressing need for scientists to prove the greenhouse story wrong, comparable with the need to prove it right. Any critique would come from scattered individuals and small groups of researchers who conducted their enquiries as if climatology were still a natural science, and who patiently pursued their observations and ideas wherever they might lead.

One line of contradictory enquiry led nowhere. It concerned the possibility that the climate in the twentieth century had not really changed. Acting like climatic thermometers, the snouts of glaciers had retreated in many parts of the world, compared with their extent in the nineteenth century. There was though a case for saying that most of the warming occurred in the first half of

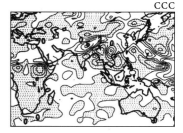

CCC

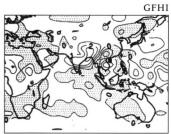

GFHI

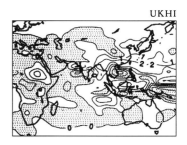

UKHI

Disagreements about the monsoon. Very different expectations for changes in the Asian summer rainfall, with doubled carbon dioxide, came from computer models running on greenhouse assumptions. Tinted areas denote reduced rain, and numbers are in millimetres per day. CCC was a Canadian computation, GFHI American, and UKHI British.

Intergovernmental Panel on Climate Change, Bracknell, 1990

the twentieth century, and that any changes since then had been quite small. If so, that was at odds with the notion that increasing inputs of carbon dioxide and other greenhouse gases into the air should produce an ever-faster rise in temperature.

All the historical, archaeological and geological evidence said that the climate never remained the same for very long. But that same palaeoclimatology exposed the weakness of any proposition that the warming in the twentieth century was due to the greenhouse. If Nature varied the climate in previous millennia and centuries, why not now? Houghton's group was more cautious than the most enthusiastic greenhouse prophets in saying that the twentieth century warming was due to carbon dioxide etc. While the warming was broadly in line with the predictions of climate models, it was also of the same magnitude as natural climate variability.

'The unequivocal detection of the enhanced greenhouse effect from observations is not likely for a decade or more,' the Policymakers' Summary declared, in the 1990 report.

Regardless of individual opinions, the exercise that produced *Climate Change* was scientifically and technically flawed. You needed no argument about a role for the Sun to say that. For computing the greenhouse warming, neither the understanding of meteorology nor the capacity of the computers was up to the job.

All of the experts knew that their computer models were inadequate, but said so loudly only when asking for more powerful supercomputers. The models had to assume that the oceans were 50 or 100 metres deep instead of 4000 metres. They could not reproduce the present climate of the world without tweaking, and they computed the greenhouse warming by doubling the carbon dioxide in the air instantly. In real life, the carbon dioxide increased gradually, and the ocean water delayed and redistributed any warming effect. Proper attention to the ocean was only just beginning.

Even the events in the atmosphere were over-simplified. As a teacher of meteorology at the Massachusetts Institute of Technology, Richard Lindzen gave the computer modellers low grades. Most heat went aloft, not in infrared rays from the ground, but in the form of rising moist air. Most of the tussles between infrared rays and greenhouse gases took place at high altitudes. Computing the outcome, the global mean temperature at the surface, depended critically on calculating correctly the motions of the atmosphere and the distribution of water vapour at different altitudes.

Water vapour was a far more important greenhouse gas than carbon dioxide, and accounted for more than 98 per cent of the entire natural greenhouse effect. Compared with water vapour, the effect of enhanced carbon dioxide by itself was bound to be small. A straight calculation of warming by a doubling of carbon dioxide gave a not uncomfortable temperature rise of 0.5 to 1.2 degree C. Higher temperature rises, of the kind visualized by the Intergovernmental Panel on Climate Change, required feedbacks that increased the water vapour in the atmosphere.

The enhanced water vapour was achieved in models so poor that they predicted a physical impossibility – negative quantities of water vapour in some parts of the atmosphere. Again the modellers had to correct these errors arbitrarily. And in Lindzen's opinion there was compelling evidence that all of the known feedbacks used in the models to augment the warming could work in the negative sense to reduce the temperature rise from carbon dioxide alone.

The computer models of climate could not handle clouds in detail and had to make broad assumptions about them. Expensive meteorological experiments were in progress to study cloud formation and behaviour, and the funding of these experiments confirmed the scientific uncertainty about how clouds worked. Although they were extremely difficult to compute, the average effects of clouds were observable by satellites.

In the 1980s academic researchers in the United States joined with NASA in using satellites to find out how clouds affected the climate. In the Earth Radiation Budget Experiment a special satellite launched in 1984, and similar instruments in NOAA satellites, provided the measurements. They showed clouds exerting, overall, a natural cooling action ten times greater than the warming predicted for a doubling of carbon dioxide. Relatively small changes in cloud cover could therefore intensify or weaken the supposed human impact on the climate. Scientists involved in this pioneering project included Edward Harrison, Bruce Barkstrom and Robert Cess.

A rainbow of hope. Cooling by clouds might partly counteract a global warming, some meteorologists reasoned, so moderating the expected climatic catastrophe. This scene is from the southern Pacific Ocean, a key region for interactions between the sea and the air.

C. Carvalho / FLPA

Another leading participant was V. Ramanathan, then at Chicago, and he also proposed and confirmed a mechanism by which increased clouds could help to keep a warming in check, by controlling ocean temperatures. It explained a remarkable feature of the oceans, observed by the satellites. Measuring the temperatures of the whole world's sea surface they rarely saw any water hotter than 29.5 degrees C.

If a patch of the ocean became very warm, Ramanathan said, it was less steamy than expectations might suggest. The local evaporation rate was rather low. Instead, the warm patch sucked in moist air from surrounding regions. As a result the warm ocean made a lot of high, bright-topped clouds, which cooled the underlying water by reflecting back into space much sunlight that would otherwise have warmed the water.

Lest anyone should miss the point of the reasoning, Ramanathan called it the Thermostat Hypothesis. The eastern Pacific became very warm in El Niño of 1987, and Ramanathan was able to observe the thermostat in action. It operated just as he had proposed. But Houghton's group was not ready to accept any misbehaviour by the clouds that might spoil the projections for the dreadful greenhouse warming.

'Although clouds produce net cooling of the climate,' the 1990 report *Climate Change* said, 'this must not be construed as a possible means of offsetting global warming due to increasing greenhouse gases.'

The ice sheet of Greenland stored the heaped-up snowfalls of more than 100,000 years. Among the Danish geophysicists who went with the migrating birds to the chilly wilderness in the summer of 1990, some ventured on to the ice sheet and drilled into it. In 1966 American and Danish scientists had first obtained a core that revealed the entire history of the most recent ice age and the warm interval that followed it. So fruitful was the use of the ice as an archive of climate, and so tricky the detailed interpretations, the drilling sites on the inhospitable ice sheets multiplied, in Antarctica as well as Greenland.

Variable proportions of heavy oxygen atoms in the recovered ice samples told of the fluctuating climate over years, centuries and millennia. Acidity in the ice recorded volcanic eruptions of the past. You could also recover traces of air trapped in the ancient ice, and confirm, for example, that carbon dioxide was in short supply in the ice age. In 1990 a multinational team at the ice summit of Greenland began a three-season programme to drill to the bedrock, 3 kilometres below. The project, called GRIP, was co-ordinated by the European Science Foundation and funded by Belgium, Denmark, France, Germany, Iceland, Italy, Switzerland and the United Kingdom, and by the European Commission.

Hanging from a thin cable, the ice drill penetrated 2.5 metres at every thrust into the ice sheet, returning to the surface with a core 10 centimetres wide. After processing in a subsurface laboratory at the summit drilling site, the ice would go via Søndre Strømfjord, the operation centre 800 kilometres away across the barefaced ice sheet, to a coldhouse at the University of Copenhagen.

In the 1990 season the drill reached to a depth of 770 metres, where the snows that formed the ice fell some 3800 years ago, when Indo-European charioteers were invading India, and solar experts of the time were laying out the first circles of Stonehenge.

More recent climate changes in Greenland were evidenced by the variations in the sea ice in the Davis Strait. These were still the subject of debate between Knud Lassen and Eigil Friis-Christensen in Copenhagen, in their spare moments between running a research division and planning new magnetic observations. They still looked for the elusive match between the wiggling graph of the sunspot counts, and the wiggles in climate recorded by the sea ice.

The chief climatic signal from the Davis Strait was not a wiggle but a trend. Conditions were very much milder in the mid-twentieth century than in the mid-nineteenth century. So the story was nothing so simple as an alternation of warmth and cold following the rise and fall in the sunspot count. If the sunspots offered any guide at all to solar effects on the climate, it had to be more subtle.

Lassen and Friis-Christensen knew the physical meaning of the sunspots. Solar physicists had established that they were scenes of intense magnetic activity on the Sun, near which occurred the magnetic explosions sending shocks through the solar system. But the sunspots were not just local events. They took part in an elaborate ritual in which the Sun reversed its entire magnetic field at the maximum sunspot count, swapping its north and south magnetic

A solar observatory. Starting 3800 years ago, successive arrangements of circles at Stonehenge in England let experts check that spring would return and end the hunger of winter. In temple-observatories all around the world, our ancestors acknowledged that life depended on the Sun's good behaviour.

Antony Miles Ltd / The Bridgeman Art Library

poles around. That had last happened in 1980, and it was happening again in 1990, after a relatively short sunspot cycle.

Although everyone talked of the 11-year sunspot cycle, that was only an average. Big differences occurred from cycle to cycle, with some peaks rising to very high counts and others remaining weak. As some peaks were broad, some narrow, the total counts of sunspots in a cycle varied greatly. So did the length of the sunspot cycles which, since records began, varied from 7 to 17 years. *That* caught the Danish scientists' attention. In the nineteenth century the cycles were longer than in the twentieth century. The increasing pace of the sunspot cycles meant that the Sun's magnetic motor speeded up. Perhaps slow cycles caused a chilly climate on the Earth, while fast cycles brought warmer conditions.

Lassen and Friis-Christensen were not the first to tread this path. Predecessors had experimented with different ways of averaging a number of sunspot cycles to obtain a picture of a changing climate on the Sun. Climate on the Earth itself was a poorly defined matter of average weather and extremes of weather, with no clear dividing line between seasonal oddities on the one hand and climatic trends on the other. Taking your averages over years, decades or centuries meant guessing what might be important in Nature's scheme.

The Danish physicists chose an average of five sunspot cycles, spanning half a century, but gave less weight to the first and last cycle in the series. They took an important step forward when they found that the intervals between the minimum counts of sunspots produced less erratic results than intervals between the maximum counts. The result was a graph with a distinctive shape.

Until 1890 the Sun's magnetic motor ran slowly. Then it accelerated steadily, except for a hesitation after 1900, to reach a peak rate around 1940. By then the sunspot cycles were averaging only 10 years. In the 1950s and 1960s the Sun slowed down, bottoming at 10.7 years in the running averages. In the 1970s it began to speed up again. It was if the Sun was given to manic-depressive moods, and was latterly in a manic phase.

Could this trend explain the changes in sea ice in the Davis Strait? Up to a point. The speeding of the Sun's magnetic motor was accompanied by the retreat of the ice in the first half of the twentieth century, and when it slowed the ice came back. But the study raised more questions than it answered. That was the opinion of the editors and referees of the journal *Nature*, who declined a paper offered by Lassen and Friis-Christensen. With hindsight, the Davis Strait was too hypersensitive a corner of the world for general climatic studies. The authors were not downcast, because their part-time research on the Sun and the climate took a dramatic turn.

The discovery began with a shock of pattern-recognition. The scientific and public furore about the global warming won wide publicity for a graph of the temperature rise. It was one of the prime exhibits of the Intergovernmental Panel on Climate Change. Prepared in 1988 by Philip Jones of Norwich, England, the graph showed running averages of mean land air temperatures in the Earth's northern hemisphere since 1860, with an overall rise of 0.6 degree C.

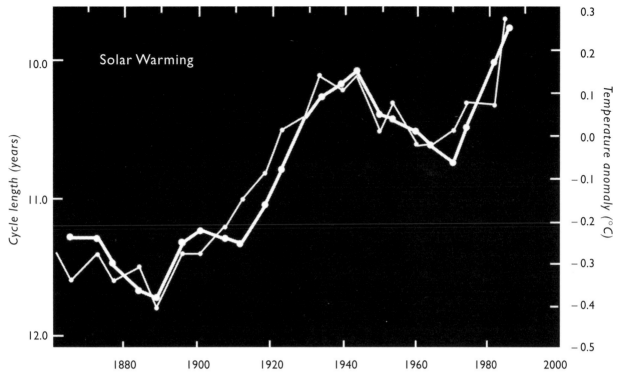

Solar Warming

Temperatures were low until 1890. Then they rose steadily, except for a hesitation after 1900, to reach a peak around 1940. In the 1950s and 1960s the temperatures fell, and in the 1970s they began to rise again.

Lassen was looking casually at Jones's graph and noticed that it was almost the same shape as the Copenhagen graph of the changing length of the sunspot cycle. At that moment, ideas about the Sun's effects on human life began an irrevocable change. Several years were to pass before the meaning of the solar graph became clearer, but the similarity to the northern-hemisphere temperature graph was provocative at once. It portrayed a *solar* warming of the Earth.

Friis-Christensen thought so, when Lassen showed him a hand-drawn sketch of the two graphs. He had been struck by a recent scientific paper by George Reid of Boulder, Colorado, which showed similarities between sea-surface temperatures and the intensity of sunspot cycles as indicated by 11-year averages of sunspot counts. Reid's graph also showed a drop at mid-century, but both the rise and fall of Reid's sunspot averages lagged behind the rise and fall in temperatures. A better index of the Sun's activity was needed, if it was to be a driver of climate on the Earth.

The close match between the graphs of cycle length and northern land temperatures suggested that the necessary index had been found. By a curious division of labour, which came about because Lassen had never computerized himself, it fell to Friis-Christensen to re-create the graphs on the computer, with proper averaging. The two physicists wondered whether to add the discovery to the Davis Strait paper, but decided that the global temperature was now the main issue.

Evidence of a solar warming. The first clear sign that the Sun was responsible for recent changes in climate came from the close match, discovered in Copenhagen, between changes in the length of the sunspot cycle (━) and mean temperatures on land in the northern hemisphere (—).

After E. Friis-Christensen and K. Lassen, 1991

55

The feature that should instantly impress an expert, in the graph of sunspot cycle length, was the dip in the 1950s and 1960s, matching the cold snap that had caused consternation among the previous generation of climatologists. The cooling made no sense with a greenhouse warming. The carbon dioxide and other greenhouse gases were increasing rapidly then, so why the pause in the rise of temperatures after the mid-century? To an objective observer, there had to be another climate-changing factor at work.

If a chorus of violent volcanic eruptions had shot dust into the air to blot out part of the Sun's rays, that might have explained the cooling. In reality the volcano count was lower than usual at mid-century. One climate theory popular at the time blamed 'the human volcano', meaning a dust pall created by industry and by the farming of drought-prone land. Friis-Christensen and Lassen associated the cooling with a temporary slowdown in the Sun's magnetic cycle between 1950 and 1970.

Scientifically the correspondences between the wiggles of the sunspot cycle length and the wiggles in temperature were best not judged by eye. A statistical test of correlation, applied to the differences between the wiggles, would give answers on a scale from 0, signifying no similarity between the variations in the two graphs, to 1, meaning a perfect association. When Friis-Christensen and Lassen carried out the test the correlation was 0.95. The merit of a correlation depended also on the number of pairs of points compared, and the effects of averaging which reduced the number of independent points. Nevertheless it seemed like heavy-duty climatology, by the norms of a science where much poorer correlations accompanied the most commonplace notions. For example the well-known fact that warmer weather caused snow to melt checked out statistically with a correlation of 0.77.

The economist John Maynard Keynes thought that any competent economist should by definition be rich, and he managed his own financial speculations very successfully while breakfasting in bed. An unorthodox meteorologist with a similar outlook was Piers Corbyn. He started his career as an astrophysicist at Queen Mary College, London, with interests ranging from galaxy formation and cosmology to the study of sunspots and other activity on the Sun. In 1988 he discovered what he thought was a link between solar activity and the weather. He did not publish his theory in the scientific literature but gambled on his weather forecasts with a bookmaker.

Using what he called vaguely the Solar Weather Technique, Corbyn won with remarkable regularity. He created, in 1990, a small company called Weather Action to compete with the official forecasters in long-range predictions. During the years that followed he built up an appreciative clientele among energy suppliers, clothes manufacturers, insurance companies, supermarkets and other weather-dependent industries.

Corbyn continued gambling too. Official weathermen were involved whether they liked it or not because the bookmaker paid the UK Met Office for help in calculating the odds. As they were sure that the weather was unpredictable months in advance, they just went by the records of past years to say, for example, how likely snow at Christmas might be in a particular city.

Oops. The crazy fellow went on winning. Corbyn's success as gambler and entrepreneur was arguably the most persuasive evidence of a link between solar action and the weather available at that time. But he kept the Solar Weather Technique secret for commercial reasons and so excluded it from normal scientific debate.

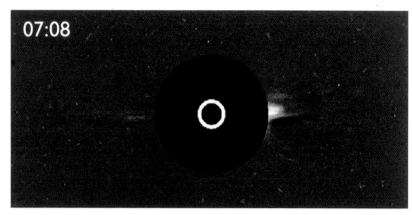

07:08

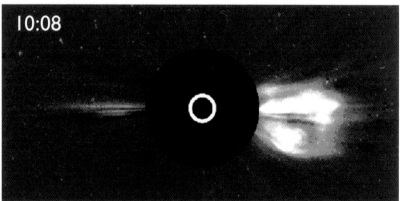

10:08

13:14

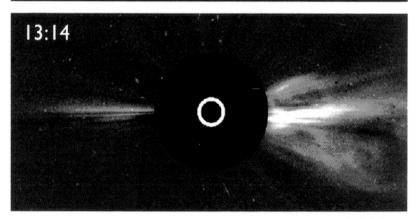

15:10

A mass ejection. Images from the SOHO spacecraft, spanning ten hours, show billions of tonnes of matter being flung from the Sun at 550 kilometres per second. The scale is evident from the size of the visible Sun, marked by the white ring in the mask that screens the instrument from its direct rays. Mass ejections into the heliosphere help to screen the Earth from some of the cosmic rays coming from the Galaxy.

SOHO/ESA & NASA and LASCO
Consortium

Chapter Four

TENNIS WITH COSMIC RAYS

T HE SPACECRAFT ULYSSES, built in Europe and fitted with instruments from European and American laboratories, set off to explore the polar regions of the Sun for the very first time. By a fifty-fifty agreement between the European Space Agency and NASA, the space shuttle Discovery sent it on its way on 6 October 1990. In Homeric myth, Ulysses the sailor was famous for his roundabout itinerary and devious ways. The spacecraft Ulysses departed for the Sun by heading away from it, towards Jupiter, in order to steal from the giant planet the energy needed for a solar-polar orbit.

After four centuries of telescopic observation and three decades of spaceflight, scientists still had a restricted view of the solar drama, like a theatregoer seated behind a pillar. Sunspots came and went on the visible part of the stage, and sensors in space felt the solar wind, but only within the narrow confines of the flatland where all the main planets orbited in the disk around the Sun. Most of the huge theatre-in-the-round of the heliosphere was unknown space.

'How could you expect to understand the Earth's weather if you lived at the Equator and were never quite sure about the climate in other latitudes?' asked Richard Marsden, ESA's project scientist, in explaining the originality and purpose of the mission. 'It's the same with the Sun. Yet astronomers and space scientists always had to make do with an equatorial view of the Sun, until Ulysses.'

Existing rockets were too feeble to send a probe out of the planetary flatland and over the Sun's poles. They could only subtract or add a little to the Earth's own speed in orbit around the Sun. Rocket motors gave Ulysses a speed of 41 kilometres per second, relative to the Sun, making it the fastest interplanetary spacecraft ever despatched. But it still needed to cancel the Earth's motion and build up speed in a new direction. That it would do by passing close to the north of Jupiter. The planet's strong gravity would deflect it southward on the novel orbit that would eventually carry it over the polar regions of the Sun in 1994–95.

Ulysses revolved like a windmill five times a minute around the axis of its radio dish, which remained locked on the distant dot of Mother Earth. Booms carried magnetometers to feel the magnetism of the solar wind, and an X-ray detector for solar flares. Completing the cross of the windmill were long wires for registering radio waves from the heliosphere. Most of the instruments were packed in the main box of the spacecraft, and the gold colour of its thermal blanket made it look like a gift-wrapped parcel.

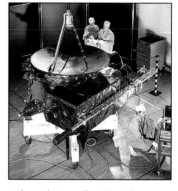

Solar-polar traveller. The Ulysses spacecraft was assembled at Friedrichshafen in Germany. Equipped with nine sets of instruments from European and American physicists, it made an unprecedented odyssey over the Sun's poles.

ESA

The particles of the solar wind, mostly electrons and charged atoms of hydrogen and helium, wormed their way into sorters which counted them according to their speed. Other instruments examined particles in low and high energy bands, or savoured the rarer elements such as carbon, nitrogen, oxygen and iron coming either from the Sun or in a breeze from other stars blowing into the heliosphere. Interstellar dust and grains from comets registered in a dust counter.

Ulysses' chief probe for the outer heliosphere was provided by Nature in the form of cosmic rays, and the biggest set of instruments in the spacecraft was designed to study them. For the atomic bullets arriving from the Galaxy, the Sun was both a lure and a repellent. Its magnetic field lines supposedly guided the cosmic rays towards the Sun's poles or in through the equatorial zone where the planets orbited. At the same time, the solar wind tried to push the cosmic rays away and scatter them by batting them with shock waves.

John Simpson of Chicago commanded the cosmic ray experiment in Ulysses. He was a highly experienced investigator of cosmic rays both on the Earth and in space. He first proposed a solar-polar mission as early as 1959. NASA and ESA adopted the plan in 1977, but there were severe delays, partly because of the disaster with the space shuttle Challenger shortly before it was due to launch Ulysses in 1986. To illustrate the variations of cosmic ray intensity at the Earth, Simpson liked to use the analogy that cosmic ray particles were tennis balls coming from the Galaxy.

'Imagine you are sitting at the top of an upward moving staircase escalator,' Simpson said, 'trying to roll tennis balls down the irregular stairs to the bottom, to reach the ball counter. When the escalator is moving slowly, a lot of the tennis balls will reach the bottom. Now speed up the escalator to simulate the increased solar activity and the solar wind carrying outward stronger, irregular magnetic fields. Now many more of the tennis balls will come back to you and fewer will reach the counter at the bottom of the escalator.'

Ulysses was an ambassador to the heliosphere on behalf of the trees. Its scrutiny of cosmic rays, and how they waxed and waned according to the Sun's behaviour, would help to explain why different portions of the wood in the same ancient tree could vary in radioactivity. And that in turn might help to explain changes of climate experienced by the trees.

Cosmic rays hitting the Earth's air made neutrons that could change nitrogen atoms into radioactive carbon atoms. Small traces of radiocarbon became absorbed in living things. When they died the uptake ceased, and the radiocarbon gradually decayed over thousands of years. An archaeologist could take any piece of wood or charcoal or bone, have its radiocarbon content measured, and so discover how old it was.

From 1950 onwards, radiocarbon dating worked a revolution in archaeology, but not before the scientists had overcome a severe difficulty for which, eventually, the Sun took the blame. At first the inventor of radiocarbon dating, the physicist Willard Libby of Chicago, said it was the fault of the archaeolo-

Archives of the changing Sun. By living for thousands of years, the bristlecone pines preserve in their rings of annual growth a unique record of climate in the mountains of California. By the variations in the amounts of radiocarbon in the wood, the trees also remember many alternations in the Sun's mood.

A.D.R. Brown / Ecoscene

gists if they didn't like the dates he gave them. But he was brought up short by a contradiction that he could not deny.

King Zoser ordered the building of Egypt's first rough-cast stone pyramid, about 4600 years ago. But the counts of radiocarbon in samples from that period indicated that Zoser lived after one of his successors, Snefru, who built the first smooth-faced pyramids. It made no sense, until Methuselah-like trees came to the rescue.

Bristlecone pines growing near the treeline on California's White Mountains lived for thousands of years, as counted by the rings of annual growth. The thickness of each ring depended on how favourable the growing season was that year. Patterns of variable weather from year to year, recorded in living trees, turned up also in remains of trees that experienced the same fluctuations. The University of Arizona at Tucson built up a sequence of living and dead bristlecone tree-rings going back 8000 years.

When scientists in other labs measured the radiocarbon in samples from dated tree-rings, they found many discrepancies. In some periods, typically lasting a century, the wood was slightly more radioactive than expected from its chronological age, fixed by the count of tree-rings. The wood appeared younger than it really was. In other rings, the radiocarbon was relatively feeble, exaggerating the age.

In 1967, more than a decade after the Zoser-Snefru contretemps, Hans Suess of La Jolla, California, published a chart of fluctuations in the bristlecone radiocarbon. All the tree-ring samples more than 3000 years old had more surviving radiocarbon than expected. The air of 6000 years ago was about 10 per

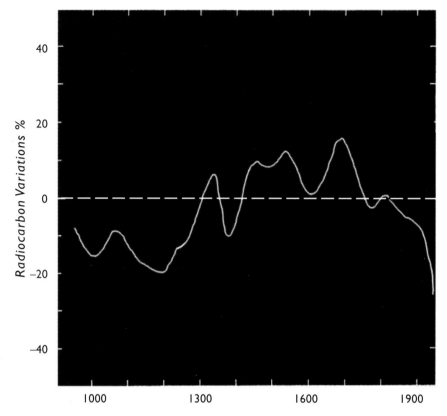

Radiocarbon wiggles. Changes up and down by 40 per cent in the radiocarbon in tree rings tell of drastic changes in solar behaviour. The Sun governs the supply of cosmic rays from the Galaxy, which make the radiocarbon in the air. Radiocarbon peaks, which imply a lazy Sun, coincided with cold periods in the climate record.

After J. Klein et al., 1980

cent richer in radiocarbon than in recent centuries. The radiocarbon declined steadily until Roman times, when it was 2 per cent lower than now, and then rose. Those changes were the result of a gradual strengthening of the Earth's magnetic field, which helped to ward off the cosmic rays, followed by a decline.

Simple inferences from radiocarbon understated the antiquity of the older objects, but Suess's chart enabled archaeologists to correct their dates. One of the most startling conclusions from the calibrations was that the archaeologists' cherished picture of civilization radiating from Egypt and Sumeria to the rest of the world was false. People in Brittany were building large stone monuments 1500 years before King Zoser had the idea.

Non-stop wiggles were another feature of Suess's chart. The abundance of surviving radiocarbon in the tree-ring samples fluctuated from one century to the next, and these could shift the apparent dates too. Applied to Libby's Egyptian problem, one of the Suess wiggles suggested that King Zoser seemed younger than his successor because he and all living things around him were more radioactive. Like the Californian bristlecones, Zoser breathed air more heavily dosed with radiocarbon than Snefru did, less than a century later. And that was probably because the Sun in Zoser's sky was feebler than Snefru's.

Suess soon convinced himself that his century-to-century wiggles told of solar variations that allowed more cosmic rays to reach the Earth when the Sun was especially inert. But other laboratories, perhaps less thorough in their methods, failed to reproduce the details by their own measurements. The wiggles were not real, many people said – just experimental errors. Archaeologists were

advised to ignore the Suess wiggles. Suess stuck to his guns, but the US National Science Foundation cut off its grant to the La Jolla laboratory in 1981. Suess went out of business just when his research was about to soar in importance, among scientists trying to understand the role of the Sun in variations in the Earth's climate.

In Northern Ireland, a tree-ring effort involving oak was set to match the Tucson efforts with bristlecone pine. While the Irish oaks did not share the unusual longevity of the Californian trees, there was an unlimited supply of old trees preserved in bogs going back thousands of years. By 1986 Queen's University, Belfast, had a 7000-year sequence of tree-rings, and Gordon Pearson charted the fluctuations of radiocarbon in the wood. He found wiggles just like Suess's. The correspondences, wiggle for wiggle, were not perfect, yet far too close to be due to random errors.

With two very different kinds of trees, in quite different environments, independent scientific teams used different techniques for their radiocarbon measurements, but in the end they told essentially the same story. At Tucson, Charles Sonett analysed the wiggles, looking for persistent rhythms. He found the same dominant cycles, of about 2300 years and 200 years, in both the bristlecone and oak data. Similar signals turned up in variations in radioberyllium, another product of cosmic rays, recovered in successive layers of the Greenland ice.

The proposal was on the table, that past changes in climate might be linked to changes in solar activity, as indicated by changes in radiocarbon and radioberyllium. The clearest evidence came from the high levels of radioactivity around AD 1700, at the worst of the Little Ice Age. A weak Sun supposedly

LEFT: Unearthing solar history. Although a nuisance for farmers in Northern Ireland, remains of ancient bog oaks preserved in the soil enabled Belfast scientists to make a dated sequence of tree rings going back 7000 years.
John Pilcher, Queen's University, Belfast

RIGHT: Example of overlapping matching ring patterns in timbers from three post-medieval Irish buildings. The arrowed ring is dated 1580. The indications of climate and radiocarbon variations confirmed the results from trees in other parts of the world.
Ulster Museum

chilled the Earth and at the same time neglected its duty of keeping cosmic rays at bay.

The cosmic rays were both a proxy indicator of the vigour of the Sun, and the manufacturer of the radioactive materials. So any solution to the puzzle of the Sun's effects on past climates would require a better understanding of the processes in the solar wind and the heliosphere that influenced the cosmic ray supply to the Earth, as recorded by the radiocarbon in the ancient trees. Ulysses would investigate exactly those processes, observing the heliospheric tennis from unprecedented vantage points.

Invited to speak at a meeting of the European Geophysical Society at Frankfurt in April 1991, Eigil Friis-Christensen briefly included in his talk the matching graphs of solar cycle speeds and the global temperature. Reactions ranged from scepticism to curiosity but Harry van Loon, over from Boulder, said that the result ought to be published as soon as possible. Friis-Christensen drafted a scientific paper while on magnetic business in Tromsø, Norway, early in May. After he had discussed it extensively with Knud Lassen, and revisions had been agreed, the paper went off to the American weekly journal *Science* in their joint names.

'This is very dangerous,' Lassen told Friis-Christensen. They were both aware of the momentum already achieved by the greenhouse idea, among scientists and politicians. Even within their own institute, many experts were committed to the greenhouse warming. A colleague had contributed to two of the key chapters for John Houghton's scientific working group of the Intergovernmental Panel on Climate Change, and others were involved in the peer review. It was against this background, and as two non-meteorologists, that Friis-Christensen and Lassen were proposing instead a solar warming.

Although quite persuasive to anyone with an open mind, the excellent correlation between the sunspot cycle length and global warming did not enforce the connection. You might plot passenger-miles in air travel and sales of recorded music, and find similar rising trends, but that did not prove that flying made people more musical: both were symptoms of other causes, economic growth or technological change. There was no obvious way in which the Earth was measuring the speed of the sunspot cycles. The search for a physical connection remained the challenge.

The environmental movement was hammering away about the greenhouse warming, making the most of the authority that the Intergovernmental Panel on Climate Change gave to their utterances. Children were an obvious target for the bad news. After all, they would inherit the misdeeds of their parents' generation and should be taught to live less wickedly. As subjunctive grammar and the language of probabilities would only confuse the kids, writers gave them the warming warning straight and scary. A typical book appeared in the children's reference list of a famous educational publisher.

'The problem today,' wrote Jeremy Leggett in *Air Scare*, 'is that we are putting huge amounts of artificial greenhouse gases into the atmosphere. They will cause the world to overheat.' This author used the future tense unrelentingly. Storms and droughts 'will' increase. The sea 'will' flood Bangladesh, Egypt, Holland and eastern England. Many plants and animals 'will' become extinct. There was no hint to teachers, parents or children that the author was an environmental activist.

The curious habit that the Sun had of humming to itself seemed to many solar physicists the best hope for making sense of its other strange ways. Four centuries after Galileo their profound ignorance made it hard for them to comment forcefully on the climatic question of how variable the Sun might really be. They knew that the Sun was a ball of plasma, made of gas so hot that all of its atoms were electrified. That knowledge was illuminating but daunting.

The plasma seethed with electric currents and magnetism, which gave them a liquid-like cohesion denied to ordinary gases but also made them very wriggly. Mobile particles stirred up and deformed magnetic fields, and magnetic fields constrained the particles, in a two-way interaction. Physicists found this to their cost, when they began imprisoning hot plasmas in magnetic bottles, to imitate the core of the Sun in their laboratories and so provide the human species with unlimited fusion energy. The squirming plasma kept escaping from magnetic bonds.

A similar war between plasma and magnetism raged non-stop at the solar surface. Throughout most of the Sun and the space around it, matter had more muscle than the magnetism it contained. But inside the Sun's turbulent layer, the magnetism seemed to become caught up in relative motions of different parts of the Sun, and intensified. Then it could bully the hot gas locally and assert itself in violent events near the visible surface.

If clouds on Earth were plasma and bounced off one another, and wrestled with the planet's magnetism, or if masses of electric air could take off into space, then terrestrial weather would be a little like the Sun's. Loops in the magnetic field built arcades of rising prominences that rose high above the visible surface of the Sun. Magnetic explosions ignited flares and blasted masses of gas into the solar system. Some other unknown mechanism, probably magnetic too, heated the Sun's atmosphere.

Half a century after a Swedish astronomer discovered wavelengths in the coronal light that could be created only by atoms at a temperature of more than a million degrees, there was no explanation. How the atmosphere came to be so hot, when the visible surface was at less than 6000 degrees, still perplexed the solar physicists. The same was true of the solar wind, also known for several decades. What force drove those ceaseless exhalations from the Sun?

Most taunting of all was the sunspot cycle, which gave an emphatic rhythm to the Sun's antics. Theories on offer talked about the Sun's magnetism winding itself up like a rope on a winch, until the field strength became so high that the lines of force broke through the surface, making pairs of sunspots. But no one knew for sure how the Sun created the magnetic field. Douglas Gough of Cambridge, England, acknowledged the uncertainty facing theorists like himself.

ABOVE: Modern pyramid on Tenerife. The Solar Laboratory for Helioseismology on the Teide mountain houses many instruments for recording music-like oscillations of the whole Sun, caused by sound waves reverberating in it.

Angel Gómez / Instituto de Astrofísica de Canarias

RIGHT: The humming Sun. Dark-looking areas of its visible surface are rising towards the telescope, while light areas are falling away, at speeds of hundreds of metres per second. The MDI instrument in the SOHO spacecraft divides the Sun into a million elements and detects intricate oscillations due to sound waves.

SOHO / ESA & NASA and SOI-MDI Consortium

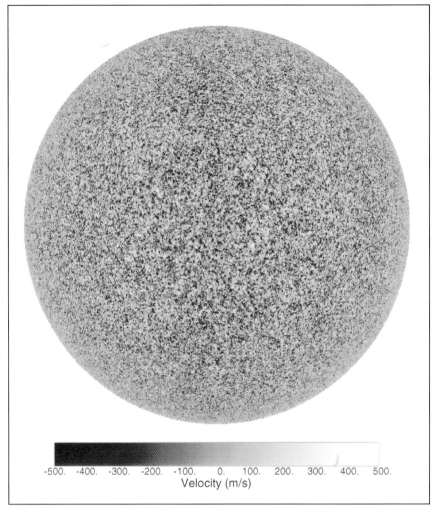

'We don't yet know whether the Sun is an oscillating dynamo,' Gough said, 'or whether the solar magnetic field is decaying from its primeval state.' Only if one could peer inside the Sun, behind its impassive face, was there much hope of answering the riddle. The discovery of the Sun's hum opened up just that possibility, of looking into the interior. The search for a dynamo would be an important objective.

The hum consisted of regular oscillations of the Sun's surface, which at each place rose and fell rhythmically, like the cone of a loudspeaker. American astronomers first detected the oscillations in 1960. About 15 years elapsed before theorists had fully digested their meaning and observers had begun to make measurements accurate enough for important inferences to be drawn about the Sun's interior.

The Sun resonated like a musical instrument, with sound waves travelling through its interior and ricocheting off its surface, which heaved and fell with rhythms of about five minutes. That made the hum far too deep for hearing, even if it could have reached human ears across interplanetary space. But the waves were detectable by instruments that measured changes in the wavelength of light as the solar surface approached or receded, on the same principle as the doppler radar used in police speed traps.

When solar physicists analysed the acoustic rhythms of the Sun, they found they could pick out many with a sharply defined pitch, like the notes of a musical scale. The way was open to using the sound waves as probes of the solar interior. As there was a close parallel with the use of seismic waves from earthquakes and explosions to explore the inside of the Earth, the scientists concerned called themselves helioseismologists.

Tenerife in the Canary Islands became a prime spot for helioseismic instruments developed at Birmingham, England, and Nice in France. They observed the light of the whole Sun and therefore saw the effects of deep-ranging sound waves. The European instruments were the prototypes for two world-wide networks, BISON and IRIS, created to record the oscillations around the clock. Only then could the frequencies be accurately measured with the highest accuracy, over months and years of unbroken observation.

American solar physicists used a station at the South Pole for continuous recordings through the months of the Antarctic summer, when the Sun did not set. At Tucson, Arizona, they developed an imaging doppler instrument which gave far more detail than the whole-Sun observations could, and promised better impressions of the shallow interior where a magnetic dynamo might lurk. Again a global network was conceived, with the neat acronym GONG.

In 1988, the Soviet Mars probe Phobos had carried a helioseismic instrument developed under the leadership of Claus Fröhlich, of Davos, Switzerland. Instead of measuring motions in the Sun's surface, it recorded small variations in brightness occurring as the sound waves in the Sun compressed and relaxed the gas at the visible surface. The same rhythms, with the same pure musical notes, were detectable as a five-minute strobing of the light.

By 1991 Douglas Gough was claiming to see inside the Sun and to use it as a physics laboratory. Yet when reviewing the state of helioseismology for an audience at the US National Academy of Sciences, he admitted that interpreting the oscillations was like trying to recognize a musical instrument one had never seen, just from the tone it produced. But theories of the Sun's interior already existed, and it was possible to check and calibrate these by deducing, from the observed frequencies of the oscillations, the speed of the sound waves at various depths in the Sun.

An abrupt change in the speed of sound, at 29 per cent of the distance down from the surface towards the centre, marked the base of the convection zone – the outer, turbulent region of the Sun. This was the first helioseismic calibration ever carried out, and it made the convection zone deeper than theorists had supposed. And below that depth the sound speed was slightly higher than expected. When theorists investigated the discrepancy they found they had miscalculated the opacity of solar material.

By matching observed sound speeds to expectations, the helioseismologists were able to estimate the abundance of helium in the core. This was partly helium present in the gas from which the Sun formed itself 4.6 billion years

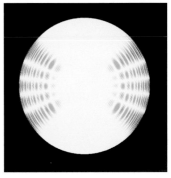

Oscillation pattern. One of the many acoustic notes of the Sun's hum is represented at an instant here, where some regions moving outwards (blue) and others inwards (red). The motions reverse twice in about 5 minutes. Analysis of such oscillations reveals the hidden interior of the Sun, seen in cross-section in the lower illustration.

D. Gough, Institute of Astronomy, Cambridge, UK

before, and partly material made in the subsequent nuclear reactions in the Sun. Although there were discrepancies in the measurements, they ruled out the idea of a low abundance of helium, which had been offered as a possible explanation of the shortage of neutrinos detected coming from the nuclear reactions in the Sun.

By 1991, helioseismologists were reliably detecting rotations inside the Sun down to about half way to the centre. In equatorial regions, the Sun's interior rotated more slowly than the surface layers, which nobody had predicted. Unlike the surface, where rotation rates varied markedly between the equator and the poles, the interior seemed to spin coherently, like a rigid ball.

The measurements of the Sun's internal rotation offered hope of understanding the mysteries of the sunspots and the rhythmic changes in their abundances and positions on the face of the Sun. There were hints that the rate of rotation in the interior changed during the solar cycle. Meanwhile, Gough was able to report that the observations already gave support to Einstein's general theory of relativity, the modern theory of gravity.

Europe was at that time taking the lead in space research devoted to the Sun. Besides its role in Ulysses, and in modest solar instruments to be flown from NASA's space shuttle in a recoverable carrier Eureca, the European Space Agency had decided that a pair of solar missions should be the first cornerstone of its Horizon 2000 space science programme. Five spacecraft were required.

One was SOHO, which stood for Solar and Heliospheric Observatory, and it would go far out into space to look directly and steadfastly at the Sun itself. The other four satellites would operate together in orbit around the Earth, to see the impact of the solar wind on the planet's space environment with unprecedented clarity. This mission was called Cluster.

To make this ambitious pair of projects affordable, the European Space Agency persuaded NASA to pick up 30 per cent of the tab. In exchange, American scientists had the chance to propose and lead some of the experiments, which was good for everyone. Europe was to build SOHO and NASA would launch it. The Cluster satellites, too, were to be built in Europe, and they would be launched together in one throw by Europe's beefy new Ariane 5 launcher, then under development. Cluster would get a free ride into space, as ballast for one of the test flights of Ariane 5.

SOHO was to be the most elaborate solar spacecraft ever assembled. Several instruments would examine the Sun by ultraviolet rays. The Earth's air blotted out X-rays and ultraviolet rays from the Sun's hot atmosphere. Space scientists had detected them, first in American and French rocket flights, and then with NASA's Orbiting Solar Observatories and the manned Skylab mission in the early 1970s. Short-wavelength ultraviolet rays looked best for finding out what heated the Sun's atmosphere and drove the solar wind. Better telescopes were needed though, and SOHO would have them.

The Sun's hum would be recorded with high fidelity by another set of instruments. Because of the success of ground-based stations in probing the Sun's

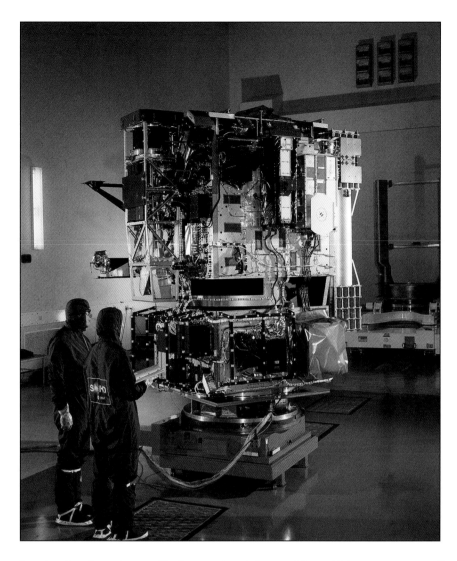

SOHO's scientific payload. Twelve sets of instruments, registering visible light, ultraviolet rays or atomic particles, make up the most elaborate package ever sent into space to scrutinize the Sun. The payload seen here was assembled in Portsmouth, England, and mated with the rest of the spacecraft in Toulouse, France.

ESA

interior, by detecting oscillations at its surface, critics said it was a waste of money to put equivalent instruments into space. In 1983, a proposal to the European Space Agency for a helioseismic mission was turned down in favour of an infrared space observatory for the wider universe. But ideas carried over into proposals for SOHO were adopted.

One of them, coming from Switzerland, offered explicit connections with the climate question. As with his trial in the Soviet Phobos spacecraft, Claus Fröhlich's VIRGO experiment would measure the rapid changes in the Sun's brightness associated with the oscillations. It would give new insight into how and why the average brightness of the Sun changed over longer periods.

'We can link changes in the Sun's output to visible activity,' said Fröhlich. 'The oscillations will tell us about mechanisms hidden below the surface. When SOHO has helped us to grasp the details of solar variability, we'll be better able to judge the long-term climatic issues.'

Particles in interplanetary space were targets for a third group of instruments. Like Ulysses, SOHO would detect cosmic rays, atoms from the interstellar gas, elements in the solar wind, and energetic particles coming from the Sun. Because it would be stabilized by flywheels, rather than by spin, its observations would not be interrupted by the spacecraft's rotation, as in Ulysses. Imagers in SOHO would observe outbursts on the Sun, and then the particle detectors would register the arrival of material accelerated in the events.

The wide range of observing facilities on SOHO, and the challenging tasks set for them, were further signs of how many basic questions about the Sun itself remained unanswered. The same was true of questions about the effects on the Earth of the Sun's effusions, as illustrated by the complexity of the Cluster mission. This was apparent both in the elaborate suites of instruments each satellite would carry, and in the need for four of them.

Cluster was invented after three decades of frustration for scientists trying to make sense of electrical and magnetic activity in space, and hunting the particles in the Earth's environment. The limited impressions from any individual spacecraft hampered the scientists. A car driver on the Earth noticing the rain stop might wonder whether it had really ceased, or if the rain had moved somewhere else, or if he himself had driven out of the affected area. Similarly, if a satellite reported a burst of particles that came and went, that could be because of changes either through time or through space.

Could two satellites cure the ambiguities? Between 1977 and 1988 NASA's ISEE-1 and the European Space Agency's ISEE-2, equipped with similar instruments, operated together. But the answer was No. An adequate analysis of the battle around the Earth, and of the holes in the windscreen that let the solar particles in, required four satellites in company.

Cluster was to provide that minimum number, needed to achieve a fully interpretable picture of events in the space between the four satellites. Identical sets of instruments would record particles, waves and magnetic and electric fields, as the satellites examined the events in different parts of the magnetosphere.

'Cluster will eliminate the ambiguities of previous missions,' said Rudolf Schmidt, ESA's project scientist for Cluster. 'With the data from four satellites our computers will build up a 3-D action picture of the physical processes at work in the Earth's space environment.'

European and American scientists contributing to Cluster expected definitive answers to fundamental questions that had teased everyone since 1958. Motives for the complex Cluster mission ranged from fundamental science to highly practical concerns. The space environment was a natural laboratory for plasma physics. The effects of solar storms on satellites and power supplies had recently been dramatized. And never absent from the ruminations of scientists was the thought that the interactions between the Earth and the solar wind might have something to do with the changing climate.

Roger Bonnet, director of science at the European Space Agency, was himself a solar physicist and a participant in helioseismic space experiments. For him the climate connection was always the best justification for the use of European taxpayers' money on the Ulysses, SOHO and Cluster missions devoted to the Sun. In a book giving his personal perspective on the culture of

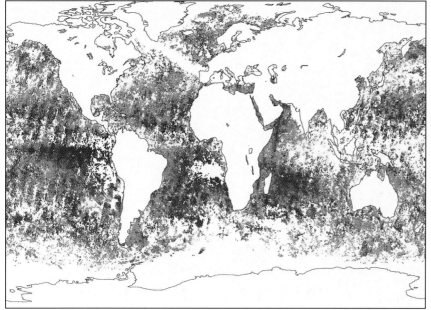

Volcanoes complicate the climate. Following the explosion of Mount Pinatubo in the Philippines in June 1991 (Above) the ERS-1 satellite charted the spread of airborne dust. The data for October 1992 (Below) show the dust at its most wide-spread.

Photo: Popperfoto
Chart: ERS-1/ESA, ATSM/Rutherford
Appleton Laboratory, Didcot, UK, and
University of Leicester

space research, Bonnet was eloquent about the responsibility of science for the care of 'the small blue planet' at a time of severe human pressures upon it, but he questioned the greenhouse predictions.

'One of the difficulties of the problem,' Bonnet wrote, 'is that the climate is naturally fluctuating. To separate the role of the greenhouse effect from that of these fluctuations is not an easy task, so that today one cannot yet say whether the man-made greenhouse is truly the cause of the century-long warming, or whether this results from natural causes – astronomical factors, for example.'

In June 1991 the count of sunspots was almost back to its 1989 peak, and the Sun went berserk again. It started the month by letting fly with seven large

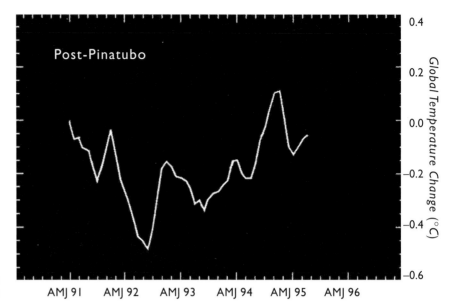

Post-Pinatubo

Global Temperature Change (°C)

AMJ 91   AMJ 92   AMJ 93   AMJ 94   AMJ 95   AMJ 96

Lost sunshine. Dust from Mount Pinatubo in 1991 reduced the solar rays reaching the Earth's surface. It probably contributed to a sharp cooling that briefly revoked 60 years of global warming. The graph shows 3-month averages and AMJ means April–May–June.

After Intergovernmental Panel on Climate Change

flares in 11 days. The watchers of the Sun's weather braced themselves for the usual crop of electric power failures on the Earth and mayhem among satellites in space. Less than three months earlier, a big flare had killed the communications satellite MARECS-1 and degraded others.

Nothing of the sort happened. The Sun watchers could only assume that a benign arrangement of the magnetic field in the solar wind had lessened the impact of the flares on the Earth's immediate space environment. But there was no doubt about the magnitude of the events in the Sun and the solar system. Ulysses on its way to Jupiter registered severe shock waves. And the count of cosmic rays arriving at the Earth was nudged downwards for a week, before dropping precipitately on 13 June to its lowest level since routine recordings began about 40 years before. This event, considered retrospectively four years later, would help to clinch a new proposition about the Sun's role in climate change.

The solid Earth demonstrated its lesser but still awe-inspiring physical powers by blowing up Mount Pinatubo in the Philippines. The largest volcanic eruption for many years occurred in June 1991, and put a veil of dust into the stratosphere. Satellites tracked the dust spreading around the world. The intensity of sunshine reaching the surface decreased, on average, by 3 per cent for several months, and then gradually improved during the next two years as the dust slowly fell from the sky.

Between June 1991 and December 1992, the global mean temperature fell by 0.5 degree C, with enough local episodes of cold and dismal weather to make many ordinary people wonder if a warming wouldn't be nicer. The mean temperature did not return to its pre-eruption level until the end of 1994. The possibility of occasional volcanic coolings had been anticipated by the greenhouse warming experts, and they happily modelled the Pinatubo event in their computers.

What shook them was a slow-down in the rate of increase of carbon dioxide in the air, which followed the Pinatubo eruption. According to the basic greenhouse scenario, fossil-fuel burning was increasing rapidly, making carbon dioxide levels rise faster and faster, and causing temperatures to rise in consequence. After Pinatubo, the carbon dioxide did not fall, but its annual rate of increase slowed to 0.6 parts per million in 1991–92, compared with 2.5 parts per million in 1987–88. That took it back to the rate of the 1960s, when fossil-fuel emissions were less than half those of the 1990s. Temperatures were almost half a degree cooler then, as in the aftermath of Pinatubo.

Was carbon dioxide following the temperature, instead of the temperature following the carbon dioxide? That would stand the greenhouse warming proposition on its head. Although temperatures and carbon dioxide growth-rates returned to pre-Pinatubo levels in 1994, the issue of cause and effect would remain, to puzzle the greenhouse experts.

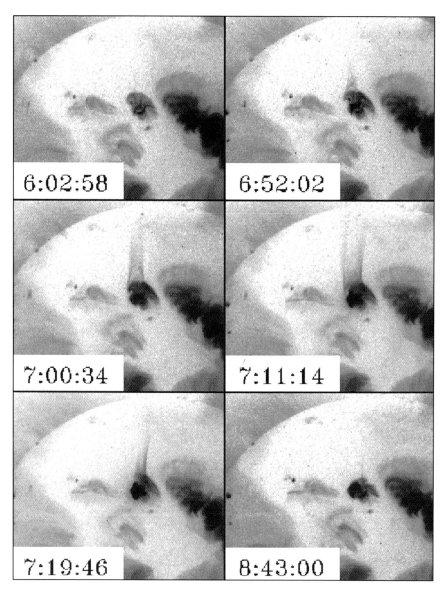

A jet from the Sun. A sequence of X-ray images from the Yohkoh satellite, spanning nearly three hours, shows a gigantic column of hot gas shooting upwards. The jet originates from a region of intense magnetism in an otherwise cool 'hole' in the atmosphere near the Sun's north pole. At its peak, at the time of 7:11:14, the jet is about 70,000 kilometres wide and 450,000 kilometres high. For comparison, the Earth is about 13,000 kilometres wide.

Yohkoh Team

Chapter Five

MAGNETIC BLOCKBUSTERS

O N 30 AUGUST 1991 the new satellite called Solar-A soared into space from Kagoshima in Japan and went into an orbit that took it around the Earth every 97 minutes at 600 kilometres altitude. At its launch it acquired a new name, 'sunbeam' – Yohkoh in Japanese. Observing X-rays from the Sun, Yohkoh began its task of making sense of the solar flares.

So the smart place for a solar physicist to be during the last phase of intense sunspot activity in the early 1990s was Sagamihara, west of Tokyo. There, in a room full of computer workstations at the Institute of Space and Astronautical Science, Japanese experts analysed the data radioed from Yohkoh, alongside visitors from the American and British participating teams.

The satellite quickly became celebrated for its movies of the Sun. At Sagamihara you could sample the rushes, so to speak, fresh from the satellite. Active patches of the Sun's atmosphere were not red hot, nor white hot, but X-ray hot. At temperatures of millions of degrees, these regions emitted most of their radiant energy in the form of X-rays. Besides being invisible to the human eye, the solar X-rays failed to penetrate the Earth's atmosphere. The only way to see the activity in the Sun's atmosphere clearly was to send X-ray telescopes out into space.

Astronauts in the US space station Skylab had made the first systematic observations of the Sun by X-rays, in 1973. The images were beautiful and informative, but they were like snapshots of dancers frozen in mid-ballet, because Skylab carried only a limited supply of photographic film for its X-ray telescope. Details in the images were smeared by stray X-rays scattered in the telescope.

With better mirrors, two decades later, Yohkoh could see features as small as 2000 kilometres, or roughly one 700th of the Sun's visible diameter. And as it used electronic detectors instead of photographic film, the Japanese satellite was lavish with its images. It could generate an X-ray image of the whole Sun in two minutes, or spot a change in a sector in a couple of seconds. A lens on the axis of one of the X-ray telescopes produced images by ordinary light, when required, which revealed the whereabouts of sunspots and visible flares.

One of its telescopes registered X-rays of relatively long wavelength coming from broad, hot areas. These showed the build-up of stormy weather in the solar atmosphere. Another telescope was tuned to X-rays of shorter wavelength, generated in the small regions of the solar flares themselves. The wave-

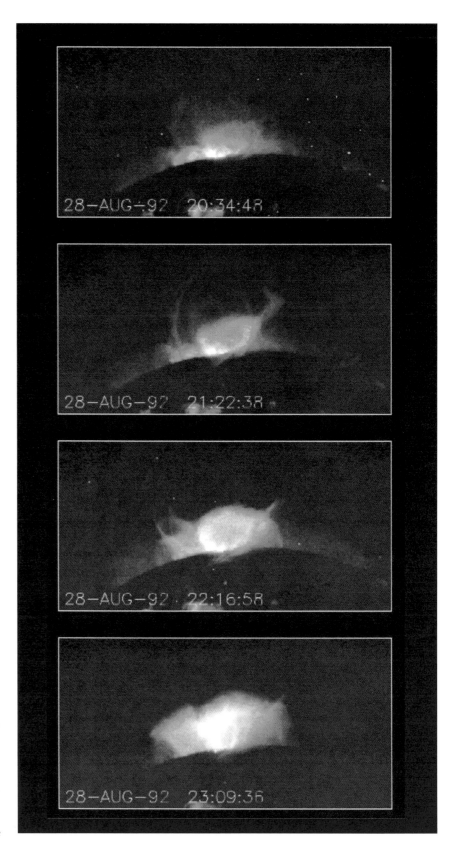

Two kinds of outbursts linked. Above the Sun's western edge, dark in these X-ray images, a mass ejection is followed by a brilliant flare. With unprecedented pictures like these, the Yohkoh solar satellite confirmed that the same magnetic explosion in the Sun's atmosphere could cause both events. The mass ejection makes a bubble in the second image and then expands out of the frame, while the flare intensifies to dominate the scene.

Yohkoh Team

lengths of the X-rays, analysed by special spectrometers aboard Yohkoh, revealed details of the flares. Bursts of gamma rays, which were super-hard X-rays, could be detected for about a minute at the crisis of a major flare.

A movie of the whole Sun by X-rays, made from a succession of Yohkoh images, showed knots of hot gas in the solar atmosphere, sprawling like clouds over spotty regions of the surface. These clouds continually brightened, faded or changed their shapes. Large areas of scanty emission, the coronal holes, made dark pools and lanes in the X-ray images. As the Sun slowly rotated, the bright and dark features swung across its face. They disappeared around one side, and sometimes reappeared still recognizable a couple of weeks later, on the opposite side.

It was like watching a thunderstorm in slow motion. Every few days, a hot cloud-like region would flash with a flare that outshone the X-rays from the rest of the Sun for some minutes or several hours. Yohkoh recorded hundreds of flares, large and small, and gradually established a clear picture of what happened. Magnetic energy accumulated in the Sun's atmosphere near a sunspot and suddenly broke free. A solar flare was a by-product of a violent rearrangement of the Sun's magnetic field.

Attention focused on the multiple loops that formed in the vicinity of sunspots and sometimes looked like a plate of spaghetti. These X-ray emitting loops were coverings of hot gas on magnetic field lines that arched from the Sun's visible surface. Amid the ceaseless turbulence of the surface and the atmosphere, the loops tangled with each other.

If two loop-tops became crossed in an X, with their magnetic field lines running in different directions, the X could short-circuit and break into two new parts. Field lines of each loop reconnected with field lines of the other, producing new loops > and <. These were kinked like taut bowstrings, and as soon as the reconnection was made the bowstrings straightened, releasing unimaginable amounts of energy.

The resulting magnetic explosion produced a flare by shooting accelerated atomic particles downwards from the loop-tops into denser regions of the atmosphere. Slamming into the gas, the energetic particles heated a small region of the atmosphere, called the footpoint, to 30 or even 50 million degrees C. This was far hotter than the core of the Sun. The footpoint emitted the intense X-rays of a typical flare. Sometimes the particles reached the Sun's visible surface and produced intensified visible light of the kind that Richard Carrington first spotted from Redhill in England in 1859, when he discovered solar flares.

While some energetic particles plunged inwards from the loop-top scene of the magnetic reconnection, others raced outwards as the burst of solar protons often associated with a flare, which posed a threat to astronauts. More remarkable, and more influential for the weather of the heliosphere, was the dislodgement of a huge volume of gas from the Sun's atmosphere, by the force of the magnetic reconnection. Yohkoh's pictures gave the first clear-cut evidence that the well-known mass ejections, in which billions of tonnes of gas rushed into the heliosphere at some 550 kilometres per second, were produced by the same kind of magnetic event as that which made the solar flares.

Not every mass ejection was accompanied by an obvious flare, nor every flare by a detectable mass ejection, but the dual event happened often enough to sustain the general picture. It was conceptually similar to the theory of far smaller events in the Earth's magnetic tail. There a sudden magnetic reconnection could fire off an egg-like plasmoid, equivalent to a mass ejection from the Sun, while shooting energetic particles back towards the Earth where they caused, instead of a flare, auroras near the magnetic poles.

The Washington journal *Science* published on 1 November 1991 the paper by Eigil Friis-Christensen and Knud Lassen linking the global warming to the changing length of the sunspot cycle. Its title was 'Length of the Solar Cycle: An Indicator of Solar Activity Closely Associated with Climate.' The main result on the solar warming of the twentieth century used measured temperatures going back to 1861.

'A set of data that supports the suggestion of a direct influence of solar activity on global climate is the variation in the solar cycle length,' the authors wrote. 'This record closely matches the long-term variations of the northern hemisphere land air temperature during the past 130 years.'

Friis-Christensen and Lassen also returned to the sea ice of the North Atlantic, for climate data that took them back to 1740, before widespread temperature records existed. They used reports from Iceland rather than the Davis Strait, telling of the number of weeks per year during which drift ice was visible at the coast. The wiggles of Iceland ice went in the opposite directions to the wiggles of sunspot cycle length. When the sunspot cycles were fast, around 1770, 1850, and 1940, the sea ice around Iceland dwindled.

Commenting on the warming in the twentieth century, Friis-Christensen and Lassen concluded that the natural variability of the Earth's climate had to be estimated before making any firm conclusions about the effects of human activity. They stressed the cooling at mid-century, which contradicted the ever-rising levels of carbon dioxide but matched the changes in solar activity. The result would not necessarily indicate that a greenhouse warming did not exist.

'It could just mean that other effects may be counteracting the greenhouse effect,' Friis-Christensen and Lassen wrote. 'In particular it has been debated whether increased cloudiness due to global pollution could have a cooling influence on the climate.'

The paper in *Science* acknowledged the lack of a clear-cut explanation of the link between solar cycle length and temperatures on the Earth. Friis-Christensen and Lassen referred to the possibility that the speed of the solar wind had increased since the beginning of the twentieth century, as mooted by other scientists in 1978.

'A plausible physical mechanism for a direct effect on climate of a varying solar wind has not yet been demonstrated, however,' the authors admitted.

That left them appealing to the idea that the speed of the solar cycles was an indicator of other activity in the Sun, perhaps especially of its output of light.

Friis-Christensen and Lassen estimated that a 1 per cent change of intensity of sunlight might be involved, in the period 1890 to 1984. In view of the way subsequent arguments proceeded, the Danes exposed a weak flank by seeming to rely on a change in solar output.

In other circumstances, the result about the Sun and climate would have been hailed at once as an important discovery. Twenty years earlier, when climatologists were more free-ranging in their ideas and the Sun was the prime suspect for climate change, many experts reading such a paper in *Science* would have said 'Aha!' They would have rushed to follow up its implications, on behalf of all two-legged creatures trying to make sense of their mysterious universe. But in 1991 it was inopportune.

A few alert journalists picked up the story from *Science*. It appeared for example in the *New York Times* and *Business Week*, and on Danish television. Some politicians and officials, already uneasy about what they would be asked to sign up to at an intergovernmental conference in Rio in the following year, filed the reports, and so did industrial lobbyists. But solar warming was a nine-day wonder. To judge by the routine and widespread reporting of the greenhouse warming, which continued unabated, the media in general had registered no message from Copenhagen.

Professional reactions to the Danish paper were troublesome for Bert Bolin's Intergovernmental Panel on Climate Change. The science working group, under John Houghton's leadership, was busy preparing an update of its 1990 report. Houghton himself was now Sir John, having been knighted by a grateful government still handing out quaintly feudal honours. This narrative continues to refer to plain John for the sake of parity among the scientists – otherwise we should be into Professor Doctor Friis-Christensen and all that.

The update had to be ready in time for the United Nations conference in Rio de Janeiro scheduled for the summer of 1992. As a result of the panel's 1990 *Climate Change* report, the conference was meant to produce a Climate Convention. Diplomats were rallying those who feared the greenhouse warming, and dealing with opposition from nations and industrial groups who feared restrictions on the use of fossil fuels. For better or for worse, the science of climate change was married to politics. Many faces would be red if Houghton's group altered its story very much.

Moderate adjustments to the 'scientific assessment' of the greenhouse were already in progress. The small warming effect of chlorofluorocarbons in the lower atmosphere was offset by cooling due to the loss of ozone in the ozone layer. And there was no resisting pressure from within the climate modelling community to take more account of sulphur dioxide emissions from fossil fuels. These could make dust and exert a cooling effect, especially in the industrialized northern hemisphere.

Central to Houghton's task was the nuancing of climate estimates in view of this new attention to sulphur dioxide. In simple computations, it already helped to explain why the warming so far was less than previously calculated.

But as the dust had not yet been taken into the major computations of future climates, there was no need to reduce by very much the published estimates of the major changes in global temperature that were pending.

Friis-Christensen and Lassen posed a more serious threat to the greenhouse warming story. They gave comfort to sceptical scientists around the world. Some experts were already suggesting that half of the global warming of the twentieth century might after all be blamed on the Sun, in which case the effect of carbon dioxide had been greatly overstated.

An eminent crystallographer, the late J. Desmond Bernal of London, characterized the declension of responses that original scientific ideas often suffered.

> It can't be right.
> It might be right but it's not important.
> It might be important but it's not original.
> It's what I always thought myself.

There was nothing self-evidently stupid in what Friis-Christensen and Lassen said, or it could not have survived the refereeing by peers which papers in *Science* underwent before publication. So Houghton's group moved directly to the second response. It assimilated the idea that there could be a role for the Sun in climate change, but demonstrated to its own satisfaction that the effects were small compared with the greenhouse warming. Solar warming might occur, but wasn't important.

Tom Wigley, head of a climate research unit in Norwich and a prominent participant in Houghton's group, was the natural person to downplay the Sun. In the 1980s, with his colleague Mick Kelly, he had assessed the possible effects of solar variation, compared with the greenhouse warming, and judged them to be small. The Norwich scientists had also looked, with moderate success, for matches between prehistoric and historic climate changes and variations in the Sun recorded by radiocarbon wiggles. In that sense they were solar men themselves.

Kelly and Wigley tried mixing a solar warming with a greenhouse warming in varying proportions. Using a simple computer model they calculated the course of global warming since the nineteenth century, for each admixture. And they tested statistically how well the evolution of the computed warming matched their own unit's record of the temperature changes in the observed global warming.

Oops. The best fit occurred when the solar warming's role was 100 per cent and the contribution of the enhanced greenhouse effect was zero. That would not do at all. Wigley therefore found another argument against a significant solar warming. Everyone knew, he said, that the greenhouse gases added to the atmosphere since the Industrial Revolution had increased the warming of the Earth by about 2 watts per square metre. Everyone knew that variations in the Sun's intensity were much less than that. Therefore, if the solar warming was remarkable, the greenhouse should be even more so. As the greenhouse warming was not yet huge, the solar warming had to be small.

The Kelly and Wigley study could not be published in time to be quoted directly in *Climate Change 1992*. It was against the rules of the intergovernmental panel to refer to unpublished scientific work. A watered-down version of the argument nevertheless remained. 'A physical model that includes both the hypothesized forcing and the enhanced greenhouse forcing must be used to make further progress,' the report's authors declared.

The 'hypothesized forcing' meant the solar warming of Friis-Christensen and Lassen, or any other proposition about the causes of climate change. All were to be judged against the supposed effect of the greenhouse warming. Another chapter of the report, where Wigley was a lead author, countered the Danish findings in the same way. 'They have yet to be fully evaluated in terms of the implied changes in solar forcing compared to the greenhouse forcing.'

That chapter continued the reasoning, as in the 1990 *Climate Change* report, that the Sun had little scope for varying its output of light. It still relied on the evidence of satellite measurements showing increases of only about one part in a thousand, or a quarter of a watt per square metre, during a maximum of sunspot activity compared with the solar minimum. That was one-tenth of the assumed greenhouse enhancement.

The satellite data went back to about 1980. According to the Swiss space scientist Claus Fröhlich, a change four times greater occurred in a ten-year period preceding 1980. Measurements of the Sun's output by earlier rocket and balloon flights led him to this suggestion. The Houghton group's adjudication was that the measurements were too brief and the instruments' accuracy too uncertain.

The report's authors preferred a more modest conclusion from a study of other stars like the Sun. This said that even if sunspot activity went to a prolonged minimum, as in the Little Ice Age, the cooling would be about 0.6 watts per square metre. That was still far less than the supposed warming due to the enhanced greenhouse effect. When the authors had thus circumscribed the changes in the Sun, the verdict on the Danish solar cycles result, in the draft of the overall scientific assessment, was 'unproven'.

In January 1992 Friis-Christensen went to China, hoping to achieve a more open-minded verdict. In the ebullient seaport of Canton (Guangzhou), Houghton's working group met with 130 delegates from 47 countries to review the report. Months of combative correspondence between authors and critics were over and the technical chapters of *Climate Change 1992* were to be 'accepted'. The overall scientific assessment still required line-by-line 'approval' by the delegates.

In winter sunshine beside the Pearl River, the light in the sky was a minor item in the discussions. Friis-Christensen's inclusion in the Danish delegation had raised eyebrows even at home in Copenhagen. Some greenhouse aficionados gathered in Canton told him that his unhelpful paper in *Science* would not have been published if they had had anything to do with it.

As a lonely solar-terrestrial physicist in a crowd of meteorologists and computer climate-makers, Friis-Christensen wanted to communicate an elementary point of science. The report asserted that variability in the Sun's output of light was the only likely explanation of any solar warming. But the Sun might also affect the Earth's climate through changes in the solar wind.

The Danish delegation formally proposed that the verdict on the solar warming hypothesis should be amended to 'unproven, but cannot be excluded'. The wording finished up as 'unproven, but is a possibility', which was subtly weaker. Less understandable was the rejection of Friis-Christensen's request that 'solar forcing' be added to the key uncertainties listed in the report. As these already included clouds, ocean circulation, polar ice sheets and land-surface processes, it seemed that everything in the Earth system was accessible to scientific doubt except its power supply. The Danish proposal that future research objectives should include solar dynamics and its possible link to climate was also turned down.

Houghton was personally involved in the put-down of the Sun. In defiance of Friis-Christensen's urgings as an official delegate of Denmark, he insisted in the overall scientific assessment that only variations in brightness were 'immediately plausible' as an explanation of solar effects on temperature. In his own book *Global Warming* (1994) Houghton included a special box dealing with the Sun. His conclusion was that the Sun was unlikely to have any more effect on climate than ten years' increase in carbon dioxide.

Friis-Christensen's and Lassen's names nevertheless appeared in the published report, *Climate Change 1992*, both as contributors to the text and as reviewers. The explanation appeared at the top of the list of reviewers.

'Whilst every attempt was made by the Lead Authors to incorporate their comments, in some cases these formed a minority opinion which could not be reconciled with the larger consensus. Therefore, there may be persons below who still have points of disagreement with areas of the report.'

'Let me decode that,' a journalist commented when he read the caveat. 'It says, "If you didn't go along with us we overruled you."'

After a trip of sixteen months, a record time to Jupiter, the spacecraft Ulysses arrived at the giant planet on 8 February 1992. It closed with the northern hemisphere, passing at a distance of 376,000 kilometres. The planet's strong gravity tugged Ulysses southwards, altering its course through nearly 90 degrees so that the spacecraft would go hurtling into unknown space, and eventually over the poles of the Sun.

Jupiter had radiation belts like the Earth's, nourished by the solar wind, but the streams of atomic particles were far more intense. The instruments aboard Ulysses were designed to withstand the radiation, and the Jupiter manoeuvre brought scientific bonuses. Plunging closer to the giant planet than any previous spacecraft, Ulysses registered intense electric currents in Jupiter's magnetosphere. The scientists also learned that the solar wind had far more influence than expected on Jupiter's magnetism. It prevented the magnetic field rotating with the planet and instead peeled off magnetic lines of force and swept them away downwind.

The manoeuvre around Jupiter was more important than the local science, in relation to the mission as a whole. Near-perfect navigation by the spacecraft operations and flight dynamics team sent Ulysses on its way to visit the south polar regions of the Sun and its heliosphere. For the first few months, nothing very remarkable happened, because the spacecraft was still in the familiar equatorial regions of the heliosphere dominated by the slow solar wind from the equatorial zone of the Sun, blowing at about 400 kilometres per second.

By June 1992, Ulysses was at about 13 degrees south latitude in relation to the Sun. It was struck by a much faster solar wind coming from the south polar region. At that time the magnetic polar regions were canted by about 30 degrees from the Sun's axis of rotation. As the Sun turned, the fast wind, blowing typically at 750 kilometres per second, appeared and disappeared again at intervals of 26 days. The novel exploration of the heliosphere had started in earnest.

The greenhouse experts liked to imply that only oddballs and Danes disagreed with their ideas. Yet the datelines on the scientific papers told of questions raised from such non-negligible places as the Massachusetts Institute of Technology and the Scripps Institution of Oceanography. Nor were the opponents nonentities. Roger Revelle, who had initiated the routine monitoring of carbon dioxide in the air in 1958, co-authored a paper saying that action concerning the warming should be delayed because current knowledge was totally inadequate. The same unwelcome opinion was published by a former head of the US weather bureau, Robert White.

In the wider world of real meteorological science and kindred subjects, as opposed to the pressure cooker of the Intergovernmental Panel on Climate Change, there was never anything remotely like a consensus that the world was overheating because of human action. But the explosion of secondary research into the consequences of the greenhouse warming meant that an increased research budget had to be shared among a lot more people. Mainstream academic climatologists found funding harder to come by.

Politics and public debate were not like science, in its endless give-and-take and demands for hard evidence from Nature. All that mattered for the greenhouse campaign was the appearances. One arch-critic had recanted, so the story went, because Richard Lindzen had retracted his opposition to the warming scenario. He had done no such thing, but the newspapers and politicians said he had, so that was all right.

Lindzen the professor of meteorology at the Massachusetts Institute of Technology, as opposed to the other Lindzen of the journalists' imagination, continued to denounce the Intergovernmental Panel on Climate Change. He was forthright in complaining that participants in Houghton's working group were placed under pressure to emphasize results supportive of the current scenario and to suppress other results. 'This pressure was frequently effective,' he said. He also reflected on the motives.

'The remarkable centrality of carbon dioxide,' Lindzen commented in 1992,

Looking down on Brazil. When the Earth Summit was in progress in Rio de Janeiro in June 1992, the watch on the weather of the western Atlantic sector was the temporary responsibility of a spare Meteosat spacecraft from Europe. The US spacecraft had been damaged by solar particles.

Eumetsat

'means that dealing with the threat of warming fits in with a great variety of agendas – some legitimate, some less so: energy efficiency, reduced dependency on Middle Eastern oil, dissatisfaction with industrial society (neo-pastoralism), international competition, governmental desires for enhanced revenues (carbon taxes), bureaucratic desires for enhanced power. … It may not be fortuitous that this issue is being promoted at just the moment in history when the Cold War is ending.'

The apparent scientific consensus at Canton continued to impress politicians, environmentalists and the media. Habitually they added a nought to the number of experts involved in the Houghton exercise, taking it from hundreds to thousands. The tally did not matter, because consensus was neither a method nor an aim of scientific enquiry. A result that was worth zero, scientifically, was still zero no matter by what number you chose to multiply it.

Politically it was worth a lot. The Earth Summit in Rio de Janeiro in June 1992, formally called the UN Conference on Environment and Development, attracted 25,000 people, either to the sessions or to the large fringe festival of environmental activists. Many presidents and prime ministers attended. One outcome was that 160 countries signed the Climate Convention.

In the preamble the signatories expressed their concern that increasing greenhouse gases 'will result on average in an additional warming of the Earth's surface and atmosphere'. They were determined, they said, to protect the climate system for present and future generations. The signatories agreed to adopt national policies to limit emissions of greenhouse gases, and to aim to return individually or jointly to the 1990 levels of emissions. 'Adopt policies' and 'aim' were vague commitments, but Article 3 of the Convention specified that scientific doubts were not to be used as a reason for postponing action.

John Houghton was gratified. 'It has often been commented,' he wrote later, 'that without the clear message which came from the world's scientists, orchestrated by the Intergovernmental Panel on Climate Change, the world's leaders would never have agreed to sign the Climate Convention.'

The climate savers had two arguments that even doubters could accept. As long as the physical cause of the global effect was undecided, it might be sensible to play safe and assume that the enhanced greenhouse warming was to blame in whole or in part. And excellent reasons for being more frugal with fossil fuels had nothing to do with the greenhouse. They ranged from saving money and conserving exhaustible stocks to protecting children's lungs from air pollution.

The hidden danger was that if, after all the fuss, the central attack on fossil fuels turned out to be based on a false premise, other environmental causes could suffer collateral damage. So could scientists, in their open-minded efforts to make sense of global change and the human impact, and thus help to guard the planet Earth as the only habitable place they knew in the whole wide universe.

At the Earth Summit in Rio. Old enemies, including George Bush and Fidel Castro, put their differences aside in June 1992 to discuss safeguarding the planet. One result was a treaty about the climate, based on the dire warnings concerning the greenhouse effect.

Popperfoto

The world's most exclusive party took place on the summit of the Greenland ice sheet on 12 July 1992. Forty people from eight countries celebrated as the drill of the GRIP project returned to the surface carrying not only ice but dirt. It had reached land 3029 metres beneath their feet, where a long-lost Greenland lay buried under the compacted snow of 200,000 years.

The ice from earlier stages of the drilling was already being analysed layer by layer in European laboratories, with startling results. The word from Copenhagen was that Earth was capable of unbelievably rapid changes in temperature, as revealed by changes in the amount of heavy oxygen in the ice from year to year. Abrupt temperature swings, up or down by 5 to 7 degrees C in a few decades, occurred about twenty times in samples from the last ice age, and similar events were apparent in the previous warm interval around 120,000 years ago. It looked as if the absence of such violent climate swings was a peculiar feature of the warm interval since the last ice age ended around 8000 BC.

To explain the events, climatologists had to contemplate major switches in the Earth system. One candidate was the Gulf Stream, which usually kept the temperature of the North Atlantic several degrees warmer than it would otherwise be. The Gulf Stream was always liable to be suppressed by a plague of icebergs smothering the northern ocean with fresh water, and this was the favoured explanation for the sudden chillings seen during the last ice age. The record of past changes continued to demonstrate that you didn't need human activity to alter the climate.

The snows of yesteryear. In the midst of Greenland's huge ice cap, which was made by accumulated annual snowfalls, drilling retrieves dateable data on the ever-changing climate going back nearly a quarter of a million years.

I. Silis and GRIP, Copenhagen

The Japanese Geotail satellite went into space on 24 July 1992, to begin a two-year exploration ranging far down the Earth's magnetic tail, which was drawn out by the solar wind on the planet's dark side. It discovered the site where magnetic reconnections occurred, similar to those seen by Yohkoh in solar flares. Contradictory magnetic field lines, stretched and squeezed close together by the stress of the solar wind, were prone to reconnect explosively 200,000 kilometres downwind from the Earth. The products included the magnetic eggs, the plasmoids, which shot off further downwind. Geotail registered the escaping plasmoids out to the maximum range of its orbit, 130,000 kilometres from the Earth. The new multinational effort to make sense of the solar wind's actions had begun.

Geotail confirmed the suspicion of solar-terrestrial physicists, that auroras seen in events called substorms were provoked by activity far out in space. Other spacecraft in preparation, NASA's Wind and Polar, Russia's Interball and Europe's Cluster, would inspect other weak points in the Earth's magnetic defences, on the sunlit side and over the magnetic poles. If, as some experts suggested, auroras affected the weather at ground level, these explorations of the space environment might have a direct bearing on the climate question. But there was no proof of any such link.

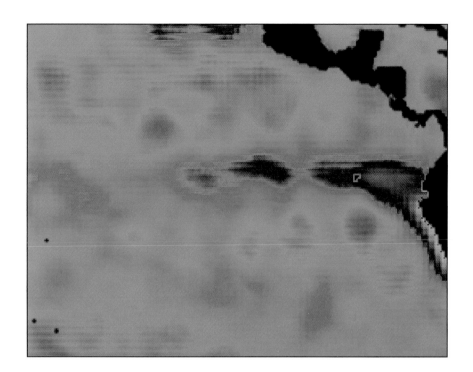

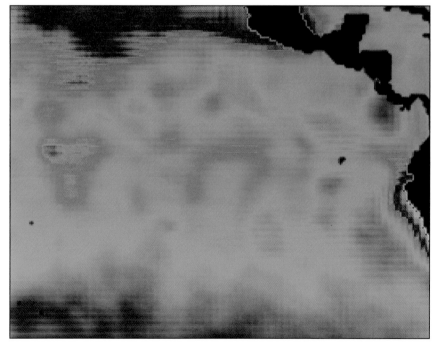

El Niño complicates the climate. The ERS-1 satellite saw sea surface temperatures peak in the equatorial Pacific in April 1992, in the warming event called El Niño, which occurs every few years. Orange denotes water 3 degrees C warmer than usual. Just 28 days later (lower image) temperatures in the region were back to normal.

ERS-1/ESA and ATSM/Rutherford Appleton Laboratory, Didcot, UK

214.2   229.3   244.5   259.7   274.8

Cloud-top temperatures in Hurricane Andrew. The image from the ERS-1 satellite shows the hurricane just clearing the Florida coast after its devastating pre-dawn assault on 24 August 1992. The colour scale is in degrees Kelvin, where 273K = 0°C. As the cloud tops increase in height towards the central eye, their temperature falls to about minus 70 degrees C (purple). In the eye itself the clouds are about 30 degrees warmer (yellow-brown). Advocates of the greenhouse warming theory cited such events in support of their predictions of a man-made climate catastrophe.

ERS-1/ESA and ATSM/Rutherford Appleton Laboratory, Didcot, UK

Chapter Six

HEATING THE CLOUDS

B Y THE SUMMER OF 1992, the Sun had scalped a few more satellites, but was past its sunspot peak. It still had the Earth's oceans to play with. From high in the tropical sky it pumped photons into the water, which absorbed them like a huge blue leaf. The sea then heated and moistened the ocean air, and powered the winds of the world.

A cloud cluster off West Africa found a nice warm ocean to graze on, and just far enough from the equator to gain a bit of spin from the Earth's rotation. It wound itself up into a hurricane, building a Colosseum of towering clouds around a central eye. The eyewall pumped air upwards and created a partial vacuum at the surface. Air from all around rushed in on spiral paths to try to fill the vacuum, but only made matters worse. Its cargo of moisture carried latent energy to drive the pump faster.

The hurricane headed westwards towards the Caribbean. It was an alarming yet commonplace event on a planet with warm tropical oceans, occurring once a week on average under one alias or another. The typhoons of the Pacific were the most violent. The cyclones of the Bay of Bengal were particularly deadly because they could swamp smallholdings in the Ganges delta and drown whole families. In May 1991 a cyclone killed more than 100,000 Bangladeshis. In an unequal world, Hurricane Andrew 15 months later won far more headlines by beating up Florida.

Hurricanes were easy to recognize in images from space because they looked like spiral galaxies. Normally there was a division of labour across the Atlantic, such that Europe's Meteosat over the Gulf of Guinea watched hurricanes forming in the eastern Atlantic, and the American GOES-East satellite stationed over Brazil tracked their arrival on the western shores. It was a wonderful lifeguard.

Solar particles in the space storms of 1989–91 brought premature death both to GOES-East and also to a spare GOES spacecraft. Europe had in reserve an old Meteosat in orbit, and it shuffled over to Brazil to fill the gap for a few years. Pictures relayed from the European Space Operations Centre at Darmstadt, Germany, showed the Americans that Hurricane Andrew was swerving their way.

Despite clear warnings based on the satellite observations, 74 people lost their lives. Winds of more than 200 kilometres per hour slammed into Dade County, Florida, and 300,000 people found themselves homeless. The damage was estimated at $30 billion, making it the most expensive storm on record.

Like a spiral galaxy. A hurricane photographed from space is easily recognizable by its elegant shape, which conceals the violence of the winds spiralling in towards the low pressure eye, surrounded by towering clouds. Against the contentions of the greenhouse advocates, intense Atlantic hurricanes have become rarer during the recent phase of global warming.

Silvestris/FLPA

The US National Hurricane Office pointed out that if Andrew had tracked a mere 30 kilometres further north, the bill could have been $100 billion because of wind damage and flooding in Miami and New Orleans.

The greenhouse lobby seized on Hurricane Andrew as their best horror story. Here the warming hit governments, insurance companies and the general public where it hurt most – in their wallets. The environmental pressure groups were not alone in relishing the event. When John Houghton wrote his popular book *Global Warming,* he started with Andrew and other windstorms to illustrate the terrible effects of an overheating world. Later in the book he said that calculations at the UK Meteorological Office hinted that, with a doubling of carbon dioxide, tropical cyclones might increase by 50 per cent.

Except for frosts, all remarkable weather, whether wind, hail, flood or drought, was a symptom of the greenhouse warming for some spokesperson or other, as if such things had never happened before. Tiresome people with long memories recalled that the same tally of extreme weather (except heatwaves) had been advertised in the 1970s as symptoms of global cooling. And when, in those days, people said that nasty hurricanes betokened a chillier world, they were probably nearer the truth.

In Hamburg, Lennart Bengtsson and his colleagues conducted a special study of tropical cyclones a couple of years after Hurricane Andrew. They used a computer model running on a standard greenhouse scenario, and they found the number of storms decreasing. Elementary climatology predicted the same thing. The vigour of the world's winds came, in the final analysis, from the difference in temperature between the tropics and the polar regions. This contrast would diminish if the world warmed.

The greenhouse claims about Hurricane Andrew were not just scientifically debatable among competing modellers. Observations of the real world showed them to be categorically wrong. The argument that a warmer world necessarily meant warmer oceans, of the kind that nourished Andrew and its kin, collapsed in the face of the data. The sea surface in the western tropical Atlantic and the Caribbean was cooler in the 1990s than it had been thirty years earlier. As for the count of Atlantic hurricanes, during the general warming from 1970 to the late 1980s, the number fell by 50 per cent.

Never mind, good news about the climate attracted no attention from the media, and tropical cyclones would still thrill environmentalists and horrify insurance companies four years after Florida had cleared the debris. For those demanding curbs on carbon dioxide, Hurricane Andrew remained the costliest proof of the human species' recklessness with the climate.

On 2 November 1992, just when the science team of the Japanese satellite Yohkoh thought the Sun was quietening down, the X-ray telescopes saw a gigantic flare. It was the largest event of Yohkoh's career, and it occurred in the Sun's atmosphere a little beyond the western horizon of the visible surface.

The far-ranging spacecraft Ulysses was more than five times further away from the Sun than Yohkoh, which was in orbit about the Earth. Ulysses felt the shock of that solar explosion, as the spacecraft continued its journey, southward bound for its first visit to the solar-polar regions. It registered a record solar windspeed of nearly 1000 kilometres per second as a mass ejection from the Sun washed over the spacecraft.

By that time Ulysses had descended some 20 degrees below the Sun's equator. It was still experiencing the alternation of fast and slow solar winds every 26 days, and with this mixture came shock waves due to collisions between the fast and slow windstreams. The shock waves were features of 'corotating interaction regions', so called because their positions changed with the rotation of the Sun. John Simpson, in charge of the cosmic ray experiment on Ulysses, had helped to define, back in 1955, the near-monthly variations in cosmic rays at the Earth, for which the corotating interaction regions were responsible.

The intense magnetic and electric fields in the shock waves had other effects. They accelerated atoms from the interstellar breeze and turned them into fake cosmic rays. As the Sun quietened after the sunspot maximum of 1990, mass ejections were becoming rarer. Their role in scattering cosmic rays coming from the Galaxy would be largely superseded by the corotating interaction regions.

Cloud hunter. RV *Vickers* investigated the interplay of Sun, sea and clouds.

Courtesy of Center for Clouds, Chemistry and Climate. University of California, La Jolla

The good ship *Vickers* checked the energy of the Sun's rays once every muggy minute as she slowly cruised the Pacific north of the Solomon Islands, in February and March 1993. The research vessel also measured the cooling flow of infrared rays upwards from the sea surface. It was the kind of patient observation of Sun and Earth in action that could make a climate modeller yawn, who might change the weather with a few keystrokes and call a press conference.

The Sun was not often in clear view. Even when low, thick, clouds were not present, which they usually were, veils of high tropical cirrus were often doing their thermostatic duty for the planet. They were much thicker than the thin and fibrous cirrus of mid-latitudes. The American and German meteorological researchers aboard *Vickers* were not in the Pacific to sunbathe, but to check the clouds of the Warm Pool and how they affected the imports and exports of heat.

Straddling the equator for 3000 kilometres eastward of New Guinea, the Warm Pool was the hottest region in the world's oceans. It operated at the heart of the Earth's central-heating system. To the east it was implicated in the intermittent warming of the ocean surface off South America, El Niño. To the west, a great conveyor belt carried warm water across the Indian Ocean, past South Africa and Florida and all the way to Greenland and Europe.

The research vessel was only one element in elaborate investigations spanning six months. *Vickers'* measurements were combined with reports from automatic instruments in buoys spaced out along the Warm Pool, with overflights by meteorological research aircraft, and with observations by satellites as they passed over the region.

More than twenty-five scientists from United States and Germany played important roles in the experiments. The leader was V. Ramanathan, formerly of Chicago, but by this time at La Jolla, California. His earlier research had explained how clouds prevented the sea becoming hotter than 29.5 degrees C, even in the Warm Pool. Ramanathan's Thermostat Hypothesis had already irritated John Houghton's group, but the new observations would be even more troublesome for the climate modellers trying to meet deadlines for updated forecasts of the greenhouse warming.

The numbers didn't add up. *Vickers* registered remarkably little flow of heat into the air from the ocean surface. The shortfall was equivalent to perhaps one-half the heat exported from the tropics to power the winds of the world. Too little sunshine was reaching the ocean surface and it seemed to be absorbed in the clouds. The missing energy was about 35 watts per square metre.

Every student learned that the Earth's atmosphere was heated like a saucepan, from the bottom up. Sunlight not reflected back into space by the clouds travelled almost unimpeded, it was said, to the sea or the ground, where it was absorbed. Moist air then travelled upwards into the sky, releasing heat in clouds by condensation of the water vapour. But the new research showed that clouds filtered energy from the sunlight passing through them, at a high enough rate to create an important heater in the sky. It was like finding an embezzler in a bank. The clouds were pocketing about one-sixth of all the solar energy passing through them.

Back home in La Jolla and Hamburg, the flaw in meteorological bookkeeping kept the scientific auditors fretting for a year. The problem was aggravated because there was no physical explanation of how the clouds managed to filch the sunlight. Ramanathan and his colleagues knew their measurements were right when Robert Cess at Stony Brook, New York, and Jeffrey Kiehl at Boulder, Colorado, compared satellite data with ground measurements of sunlight in places far from the Warm Pool. In Tasmania, Colorado, Wisconsin and Alaska, the heater in the sky showed up everywhere they looked.

The textbooks of meteorology were wrong, and all computations of the Earth's climate would have to begin again. But so important a finding, simple in essence but complex in observational detail, needed careful preparation for publication. It would not appear in print until 1995.

The solar warming theory languished. Since its rejection by the Intergovernmental Panel on Climate Change at Canton, the link between the the length of the sunspot cycles and global temperatures remained a tantalizing curiosity for scientists who were sceptical about the greenhouse or interested in the Sun. For any effort to find out what was really happening to the Earth's climate, a lack of objectivity in the media was part of the problem.

Clouds absorb sunlight. The blackout effect of clouds was supposed to be due almost entirely to the scattering of light, as seen on the sunlit side. The discovery in 1993 that the particles in clouds extract significant amounts of energy upset meterological theories and climate computations.

M. Nimmo / FLPA

Most editors in Europe and North America had accepted the greenhouse warming. They seldom gave column space or air time to any contrary opinion. A general decline in the attention paid to hard science in the media, and a swing towards anti-technological and pro-environmentalist attitudes among science reporters themselves, contributed to the state of mind. So did the rise of a new profession of environmental journalists. The greenhouse warming was virtually written into their job descriptions, as the most reliable big story.

'Now does seem to be the time for rethinking some of our journalistic canons,' said Teya Ryan of the Society of Environmental Journalists in the United States, making the case for advocacy in the media. 'The "balanced" report in some cases may no longer be the most effective.'

Trying to get a hearing was hard enough for contrarian scientists in the United States, where the conservative and business press provided outlets. For the Danish solar-terrestrial physicists to communicate their opinions to the public outside Denmark was almost impossible. Science writers in Europe typically reported what happened in the United States and in their own countries, but seldom in other European countries.

Anyway who would expect anything much from Denmark, a country with the same population as North Carolina? Only, perhaps, reporters with a sense of history. They might know, for example, that in the 1930s Copenhagen was the mecca of theoretical physics, or that Danish lager achieved its quality by the discovery of enzymes – and so paid for the oceanography that charted the Carlsberg Ridge in the Arabian Sea.

Early in 1993, a bid to alert the world's media to the results of Eigil Friis-Christensen and Knud Lassen came in a proposal for a multilingual TV series about the science of the Sun and its importance in human life, to be filmed world-wide. The European Space Agency, with a succession of solar missions under way, had told a Dutch producer and a British scriptwriter that it would contribute money towards sponsoring the series if they could find a quorum of broadcasters in Europe and elsewhere.

In the increasingly shrill world of multi-channel TV, where the zapper ruled and audience attention spans were deemed to be of the order of a couple of minutes, the idea of 100 minutes devoted to the Sun was not easy to market. In response to a request from the producer's agents for the strongest selling point, the scriptwriter picked out the Danish science. On the first page of the treatment, magnified typographically for shock effect, the following words appeared.

> The greenhouse warming may be fiction! So say some leading scientists who study the dominant feature of our climate and our lives, namely the Sun. The Earth has grown warmer – that's not disputed. But the latest research casts doubt on the popular theory that man-made 'greenhouse' gases are to blame. Instead, so the story goes, the light and heat from the Sun have increased. That means the current political thinking and public concerns about carbon emissions may be completely wrongheaded. It's a big story, which will resonate around the world.

The treatment evoked interest, apparently keen, from more than a dozen TV stations in different countries. But no one would sign up first, as primary broadcaster. By the end of 1993, with nothing decided, the European Space Agency had withdrawn its offer of support and the project fizzled out. Although the treatment itself had alerted many broadcasters to the Danish discovery, they did nothing else about it.

After his retirement in 1991, Knud Lassen had more time than Eigil Friis-Christensen to devote to their sunspot hobby. Coming into the Danish Meteorological Institute for a few days each week, Lassen continued to harvest information on the changing lengths of the solar cycles. He worked backwards through the eighteenth century and into earlier historical periods, when both the solar data and the climate data had to be treated with care. Although Friis-Christensen was busier than ever with other work, he continued in his spare-time role as Lassen's discussion partner. He used the computer to analyse and plot the increasing number of sets of data.

They had a fortunate haven in their institute. In accordance with the views of its own climate specialists and other Danish participants in the intergovernmental exercise, it endorsed the greenhouse warming. But in addition, the search for the Sun's role in climate change was written into the tasks of Friis-Christensen's solar-terrestrial physics division. In the institute's brochure for the public, the matching graphs of global temperature and solar cycle length appeared without comment alongside paragraphs referring to the institute's work on the greenhouse warming. In Copenhagen, at least, the possibilities were not mutually exclusive.

That was Knud Lassen's view too. For scientific reasons he was more cautious than Friis-Christensen about the implications of their work. Although in his retirement he was a freer agent, Lassen made a point of becoming involved in no arguments about science and public policy. As a lifelong observer of scientific disputes he knew that opinions which at first seemed totally at odds were often reconciled. He expected a compromise between the solar warming and the greenhouse warming.

'We have our own idea,' Lassen said to Friis-Christensen, 'but I don't think it's the whole story.'

Friis-Christensen, on the other hand, was already sure that the Intergovernmental Panel on Climate Change had seriously understated the solar warming.

The eighteenth-century data compiled by Lassen extended the sunspot cycle lengths and climate variations back to before the start of the Industrial Revolution. If the later outpourings of carbon dioxide from the burning of fossil fuel had the significance accorded to them by the greenhouse theory, there ought to be a discernible shift in the wiggles between the early eighteenth century and the late twentieth century. Yet the temperature trends and the sunspot cycle lengths followed each other faithfully.

Friis-Christensen suspected that the observational data on the solar warming left very little room for the greenhouse warming. He was not yet ready to go public with this opinion. But he was more exposed than Lassen to attacks, and was therefore more outspoken about the scientific implications of the solar warming.

'Science is diversity not consensus,' Friis-Christensen said. 'I should not hide what I believe as a scientist, just because it is not politically correct.'

A platform for the solar warming was hard to find. The Swedish electrical industry created an opportunity when, at a centenary event, it invited Friis-Christensen to speak at the same meeting as Bert Bolin, chairman of the Intergovernmental Panel on Climate Change. Bolin stuck to the greenhouse story, and Friis-Christensen showed the graphs indicating a solar warming. Although Bolin complimented Friis-Christensen on his paper, there was no meeting of minds.

A by-product of that event was a booklet written by two Swedish experts and Friis-Christensen. Called *The Earth's Climate – Natural Variations and Human Influence*, it was published by Elforsk, the Swedish electrical utilities' joint company for research and development. Summarizing human knowledge about climate change, the booklet gave a more balanced assessment of global warming than was then generally available. Friis-Christensen's contribution did not discount the greenhouse warming entirely. But he took the opportunity to turn around the argument that Tom Wigley and Houghton's group had used against him, namely that solar and greenhouse effects had to be considered jointly.

'The model calculations,' Friis-Christensen wrote, 'show that the calculated temperature rise resulting from a doubling of the concentration of carbon dioxide would be drastically reduced (to about a half) if the effect of the Sun is incorporated in the model.'

'So!' said environmental lobbyists and greenhouse scientists when they saw the Elforsk booklet, 'the solar people are getting help from the bad guys, from the energy companies who are pouring out all that carbon dioxide which is going to roast us.' Similar complaints were made in the United States, where oil and coal companies created an anti-greenhouse lobby and publicized scientific work that they thought helpful to their cause.

Bolin's Intergovernmental Panel on Climate Change was a political entity. Instituted and executed by intergovernmental and governmental agencies, its work was coupled to the fevered politics of the Climate Convention. Government policy in many countries ensured that the greenhouse warming had the lion's share of the research funding. Yet Bolin's panel and Houghton's working group claimed to be strictly scientific. The most reasoned questioning of the greenhouse scenario came to be labelled as 'politically motivated'.

The solar-terrestrial physics that earned Friis-Christensen's salary had almost eliminated any spare time for thinking about the solar warming. He had gone into the satellite business. For several years he had led a group of scientists from Copenhagen wanting to persuade the Danish government to fund a baby satellite called Ørsted. Weighing only 60 kilograms, and the size of a fat suitcase, it was to deploy in space a boom eight metres long, pointing away from the Earth. The key scientific instruments would cling to the tip of the boom like sailors on a mast.

Ørsted would map and monitor the Earth's magnetic field more accurately than ever before. Magnetic sensing coils, combined with a star mapper, were designed at the Technical University of Denmark. Among the many uses of the satellite's results, Friis-Christensen himself expected new insights into the interactions of the solar wind and the Earth's magnetic field, relevant also to the climate question.

The campaign succeeded. The Danish government backed Ørsted, and the rush was on to prepare it for flight in 1996. NASA undertook to launch the satellite into an orbit over the poles without charge. The French space agency offered a calibrating instrument. This approval of Ørsted was a token of the professional respect that Friis-Christensen commanded both at home and abroad.

To get the satellite built, equipped and launched, Friis-Christensen had to deal with three Danish ministries, with NASA and the French and European space agencies, and with eighteen companies and institutes involved in the spacecraft. At his own institute he would have to create a science data centre for Ørsted, linked via mission control at Birkerød to three ground stations. Then there was the Argentine connection. At NASA's suggestion, the Technical University of Denmark's magnetometer would also fly in an Argentine satellite SAC-C, due for launch in 1998.

Friis-Christensen's space commitments, as project scientist for Ørsted, came on top of his regular responsibilities concerning his ground-based auroral and magnetic observatories. For those, another raft of responsibilities involved joint observations to be made with the European Space Agency's four-satellite Cluster mission, due to be launched in 1995. In addition he was a part-time professor at Copenhagen University.

It was surprising that he found any time at all to interact with Lassen about the solar warming. But the two men met once or twice a week, usually in the evening. Friis-Christensen was happy to be Lassen's sparring partner for ideas, and his typist too, although he felt he was the bottleneck in the partnership and kept urging his former boss to get a personal computer of his own. Lassen was amassing more and more historical evidence to confirm that the length of the solar cycle affected life on the Earth significantly. Effects of solar warmings and coolings showed up all over the place, especially when other scientists who had read the Danes' *Science* paper of 1991 began making connections.

An excellent example concerning China arrived on Lassen's desk as a preprint from Stony Brook, New York. There Sultan Hameed and Goafa Gong had compiled a climatic record for the onset of spring in the Yangtze River valley extending from 1580 to 1920. Lassen was gratified to find that the scientists had superimposed on their wiggles the graph of solar cycle lengths from 1740 onwards.

Contemporary diaries and other documents that noted the dates of spring blossom provided Hameed and Gong's basic climatic information. Eighty years of official records from the eighteenth century giving the dates of the last snow of the year supplemented the data. From this quarry the Stony Brook scientists deduced by how many days spring came early or late in southern China, compared with the average date.

The onset of spring was typically three weeks earlier in the eighteenth cen-

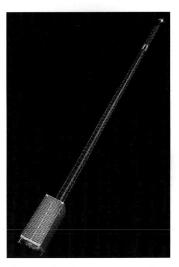

The Danish microsatellite Ørsted. Conceived to orbit over the Earth's poles and measure the Earth's magnetism with high accuracy, its main feature is the lightweight boom extended in space to carry the instruments well away from any magnetic fields in the body of the spacecraft. Effects of the solar wind on the magnetosphere are among the main interests of scientists from many countries participating in the Ørsted mission. The project scientist is Eigil Friis-Christensen.

Danish Meteorological Institute

tury than in the trough of the Little Ice Age near the end of the seventeenth century. And the graph was extendable through the late twentieth century by weather-station data, showing early springs at the optimum around 1950 and delays in the subsequent climatic downturn.

There was already a good match between the wiggles of the Yangtze climate and Friis-Christensen and Lassen's solar cycle wiggles. When the preprint arrived, Lassen was working with estimates of the solar cycle length going back to 1500, albeit with a gap in the late seventeenth century during the Maunder Minimum when sunspots were scarce. He was therefore able to take the comparison further back in time that Hameed and Gong could do. In particular he could match the very early springs in China around 1730 to short sunspot cycles of about 10 years.

Political correctness made life awkward for anyone trying to discover how Nature really ran the planet and might actually react to the misdeeds of its human population. If you so much as queried the greenhouse warming, you were an enemy of the environment. You probably panelled your study in fresh mahogany, ran your car on leaded fuel and hunted endangered species for relaxation. You were undoubtedly in the pay of an oil company.

Activists called carbon dioxide a pollutant that was going to suffocate the planet. This was painfully sloppy language for anyone who grasped that plants and people were made of carbon dioxide and water. The criminal gas was the foundation of life itself and the plants loved it, as every grower knew who added carbon dioxide to the glasshouse air for the sake of higher yields.

One of the lead authors of John Houghton's *Climate Change* stepped out of line to suggest that the greenhouse world advertised by the climate modellers might be a nice place to live. James Melillo of Woods Hole, Massachusetts, was no crank. He was vice-chairman of the scientific committee of the International Geosphere-Biosphere Programme. Melillo's ecosystems centre at Woods Hole joined with a complex systems research centre at Durham, New Hampshire, to make a computer model of global plant life on land. They assumed that carbon dioxide had doubled, and other changes had come to pass as predicted by four different climate models.

Climate change by itself had surprisingly little influence overall. A decrease in productivity in the tropical forests was balanced by an increase in the northern forests and tropical savannas. The boost from the direct effect on plant growth of the added carbon dioxide was 16 per cent. Taking the direct and indirect effects of the carbon dioxide together, all types of vegetation showed increases in productivity.

The global gain for plant life was 20 per cent with the least favourable climate model, and about 26 per cent with the rest. It was heresy, of course, to suggest that carbon dioxide might be good for life on the planet. Some details were particularly unwelcome to environmental activists, for example a 50 per cent increase in plant growth in deserts because the richer air meant that plants lost less water while acquiring their carbon dioxide.

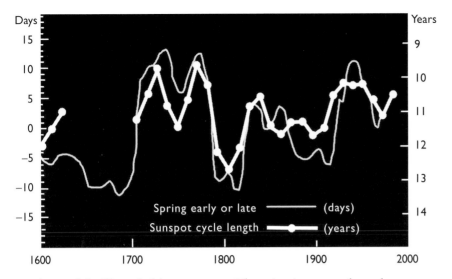

Days / Years

Spring early or late ——— (days)
Sunspot cycle length ——●—— (years)

Chinese fortunes at the Sun's mercy. A change of one year in the length of the solar cycle brings springtime to the Yangtze River one week earlier or later. In historical data (thin line) analysed at the State University of New York, the researchers in Copenhagen saw fluctuations that closely matched their reconstruction (thick line) of the speeding and slowing of the Sun's magnetic motor in past centuries, as represented by the cycle length.

After K. Lassen & E. Friis-Christensen, 1995

The model still needed improvement. The scientists wanted to take account of alterations in vegetation type, effects on cultivated crops and possible limits set by the availability of phosphorus in the soil. So they were properly cautious about drawing any grand conclusions.

'It's just a preliminary analysis to motivate discussion,' David Kicklighter, who ran the model at Woods Hole, said to an inquisitive reporter. The story, based on work by a leading scientific ecologist, appeared in a London newspaper. The founder of *The Ecologist* magazine hectored the reporter for half an hour about his irresponsibility in giving credence to any idea that carbon dioxide was good for you.

While the Danes themselves were sure that an additional physical mechanism was needed to explain their solar warming, some American astronomers did their best to vindicate them by variations in the Sun's brightness alone. In the journal *Energy* in 1993, Sallie Baliunas of Cambridge, Massachusetts, and Robert Jastrow, affiliated to Mount Wilson Observatory in California, reviewed many years of studies of other stars resembling the Sun. These stars showed magnetic cycles similar to the Sun's sunspot cycle. They too varied the length of their cycles, and with those variations came changes in brightness. They helped to explain the prime result of Friis-Christensen and Lassen, linking changes in northern hemisphere temperatures to changes in the length of the solar cycle.

Mount Wilson Observatory was once the the most famous astronomical centre in the world, where Edwin Hubble discovered the expansion of the universe in the 1920s. The street lights of Los Angeles and the siting of larger telescopes elsewhere left it better suited to routine studies of relatively bright stars – exactly what was needed for watching their long-term fluctuations. Since 1966 Mount Wilson had monitored magnetic activity in about a hundred stars, including ten similar to the Sun in mass and age. The observations relied on characteristic light from calcium ions, excited by magnetism at the surface of a star.

After a quarter of a century of observations, most of the sun-like stars showed cycles of magnetic activity very similar to the sunspot cycle. Pronounced short-term fluctuations resembled the effect of groups of sunspots moving across the face of the Sun, so presumably there were starspots too. One well-studied star was 107 Piscium, lying 24 light-years away in the constellation of Pisces. It had gone through three peaks of activity since 1966, in a magnetic cycle lasting nearly ten years. In eight stars, the cycles ranged in duration from eight to twelve years.

From 1984 onwards, Sallie Baliunas and collaborating astronomers started monitoring the intensity of the sun-like stars that were being scrutinized magnetically at Mount Wilson. They made the brightness measurements at the Lowell Observatory in Arizona. In 1984 the star 107 Piscium was rising to a peak of magnetic activity, and it declined to a minimum in 1991. During those years, the Lowell measurements showed the output of light from the star falling gradually by 0.6 per cent. That was much larger than any change measured in the brightness of the Sun.

Although nothing quite so apposite as a clear change in cycle length had yet shown up in the stars, one event was more dramatic. A little farther away than 107 Piscium was the star 54 Piscium. Between 1966 and 1977, the Mount Wilson observers saw magnetic activity in 54 Piscium fall from one peak and rise to another, just like the other stars with their magnetic cycles. But in 1980 the magnetic activity slumped, rapidly and without warning. It thereafter remained low.

The disappearance of the magnetic cycle in 54 Piscium seemed to Baliunas and Jastrow an imitation of what happened to the Sun at the onset of the Maunder Minimum in the seventeenth century, when astronomers became frustrated by the rarity of sunspots and the Little Ice Age reached its climax. And another of the sun-like stars seemed locked in a Maunder-like minimum. Tau Ceti, 11 light-years out in the constellation of Cetus, had since 1966 exhibited scarcely a flicker of magnetic variation.

Baliunas and Jastrow established a link with the length of the magnetic cycle. First they showed that the brightness of their sun-like stars varied most when there was the greatest variation in magnetic activity. Then they showed that the changes in magnetic activity were much greater when the magnetic cycle was only 6 years in duration than when it was 12 years long. Baliunas and other colleagues had already arrived at a similar conclusion about the Sun's magnetic activity in relation to the changing length of the sunspot cycle.

'This result suggests,' Baliunas and Jastrow wrote, 'that the observed correlation between changes in the Sun's cycle and changes in global temperature observed by Friis-Christensen and Lassen is a significant physical relationship rather than a fortuitous correspondence.'

The conclusion of Baliunas and Jastrow was that even a moderate change of 0.4 per cent in the solar brightness since 1700 would explain all or most of the Earth's recovery from the Little Ice Age, and most of the global warming of the twentieth century. As other stars similar to the Sun showed changes of up to 0.6 per cent, the impressions from a short run of satellite observations of solar brightness might understate the Sun's ability to change at other times or over longer periods.

Imperial reverence for the Sun. The red robe worn by the Crown Prince of Japan at his wedding in June 1993 symbolized the glow of the solar goddess Amaterasu, or Heaven Shining, to whom he and his bride dedicated themselves. The Shinto cult sustains the natural worship of the Sun that was commonplace elsewhere before later religions displaced it.

Popperfoto

Indirect physical evidence for a link between the Sun's brightness and the length of the sunspot cycle was gratifying for supporters of the solar warming. If Friis-Christensen and Lassen had not discovered the importance of the cycle length from the climate record, the results from the stars could well have prompted someone else to look for such an association. And the shutdown of the starspot cycles in 54 Piscium and Tau Ceti gave impressive support to the idea that a similar event occurred on the Sun in the seventeenth century.

Yet the numbers offered by Baliunas and Jastrow, for changes in the Sun's output of light, were hardly earth-shattering. They were broadly in line with estimates of solar changes that the Intergovernmental Panel on Climate Change had already contrived to live with. Another mechanism besides changes in brightness would still be needed, to dislodge the greenhouse warming.

A reprise of the questionnaire first offered for 1989, but with answers updated to 1993, may help the reader to appraise the course of the contest, in the middle of our story.

About the Sun

Does the Sun control changes in the Earth's climate, over decades and centuries?
Possibly. The best evidence (by 1993) comes from Friis-Christensen and Lassen's graphs matching decade-to-decade temperature changes to solar action, as indicated by the speed of the sunspot cycles.

Is the physics of the solar warming persuasive?
No. Although the Sun is evidently in a manic mood, there is no explanatory link between solar action and the decade-to-decade changes in temperature in the twentieth century.

Are variations in solar brightness sufficient to explain the global warming of the twentieth century?
Some of the warming, but not all.

Is there another solar mechanism that is sufficient?
Who knows?

Can the new solar spacecraft discover this mechanism?
Possibly. Yohkoh, Ulysses and Geotail are already giving information about the Sun's eruptions and the solar wind, not previously available.

What is the solar prognosis for climate in the twenty-first century?
There is still no evidence that solar effects can be large enough to alter significantly the anticipated greenhouse warming.

About the greenhouse warming

Are man-made greenhouse gases warming the Earth?
Yes, in principle they should be doing so, though the intensity of the warming and its contribution to climate change are, by 1993, seen to be reduced significantly by man-made dust.

Is the physics of the greenhouse warming persuasive?
The neat story of 1989 turns out to have been oversimplified. Issues about dust, and about the feedbacks involving water vapour and clouds, have made everything complicated and questionable in detail. Perseverance is the watchword, rather than persuasiveness.

Is the meteorology of clouds understood well enough for assessing human impacts on climate?
Probably not. The discovery of light absorption by clouds casts grave doubts on the aptness of assumptions about clouds in the climate models.

Are the predictions of the computer models of climate credible?
The greenhouse models are being thoroughly revised to make them more realistic by considering other influences, particularly man-made sulphate dust.

This means that the predictions of 1990 should not have been considered credible.

Can the Earth-observing spacecraft prove the greenhouse warming?
It is still seen as their most important task, but results so far are unfavourable to the greenhouse theory.

What is the greenhouse prognosis for climate in the twenty-first century?
The official projection (1990) of a global warming by 2100 of more than 3 degrees C will be revised downward in the light of the new attention to man-made dust.

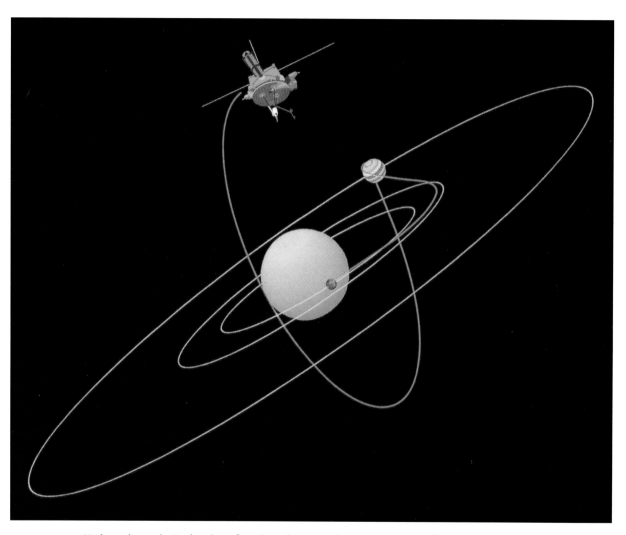

Under and over the Sun's poles. After a long detour via the planet Jupiter, the Ulysses space project came to a climax in 1994–95 as it passed through each polar region of the heliosphere in turn. Discoveries about the Sun's magnetism and solar influences on cosmic rays astonished the European and American scientists participating in the mission.

ESA

Chapter Seven

WHAT SOUTH POLE?

EXACTLY HOW THE SUN worked its climatic mischief was, for Eigil Friis-Christensen, still the big question. It mattered more than any public debate, more even than Knud Lassen's diligent search for historical evidence linking the length of the solar cycle to climate changes. If the Sun caused most or all of the global warming since the eighteenth century, and if the Sun's scope for varying its output of light was as limited as respected astronomers suggested, then another strong physical mechanism must couple the Sun's weather to the Earth's weather. What was the missing link?

A colloquium in Boulder, Colorado, in June 1993 brought Friis-Christensen's mind into a fresh focus on the question. Astronomers were discussing the variability of the light output of the Sun and sun-like stars. Several of them were sceptical about the greenhouse story. At the meeting Friis-Christensen encountered an astronomer from Northern Ireland, John Butler of Armagh, who had cheering news for him.

At Armagh Observatory, manuscript records of air temperature dating back to the end of the eighteenth century had come to light in an untidy heap. This unlooked-for source carried the instrumental record of temperatures in that corner of the world back 200 years. Here too, the fluctuations neatly matched the Danish graph of variations in the length of the sunspot cycle, most conspicuously in a warming in Ireland between 1840 and 1860, coinciding with a modest peak in speed of the sunspot cycles. The warming, Butler thought, might have been in part to blame for the fungal blight of the potato crop, which initiated the Great Famine in Ireland in 1846.

Butler urged Friis-Christensen to join him in applying to the European Commission for a multinational research contract to investigate the missing climatic links with solar activity. The idea was to calibrate the response of trees to climate in the island of Ireland back to the eighteenth century. Weather data, to be assembled in Armagh and Cork, could then feed into the interpretation of tree-rings in bog oaks by Michael Bailey in Belfast. The tree-rings gave information by growth about how the trees had fared, and by radiocarbon about what the Sun had been up to.

With a contribution on solar-terrestrial physics from Copenhagen, Butler thought there could be a neat UK-Irish-Danish contribution to propose for the environmental component of the Commission's fourth framework programme for research. Friis-Christensen was far too busy to promise much personal participation, but he foresaw that, with outside funding, someone else in the Danish Meteorological Institute might do the work under his supervision.

Even the form-filling required by the European Commission was daunting, but Butler promised to take care of that. Friis-Christensen said he would contribute his thoughts from the point of view of solar-terrestrial physics. Back in Copenhagen he opened the drawer in his desk where he kept his worries and his information about the climate, and pondered once more the question of the missing link.

Some physical mechanisms linking the Sun to the Earth's climate operated over too long a timescale to be relevant to changes in climate over decades, which were the concern of the solar warming hypothesis. The Earth's orbital wobbles varied the altitude and distance of the summer Sun and drove the ice age cycles, but they took thousands of years. The Sun's wanderings through the Milky Way Galaxy could expose the heliosphere to severe compression by dense patches of interstellar gas. Again the timescale was protracted.

Most ideas up till then, for linking the Sun and changes of climate over decades and centuries, boiled down to two well-known possibilities and a long shot. Apart from the variation in the Sun's output of light, the other main possibility concerned direct interaction between the solar wind and the Earth, made visible by auroras. When gusts in the solar wind rammed its atomic particles through the Earth's magnetic shield, it dumped enough energy into the air to cause spectacular auroras, inflate the outer atmosphere and create the electric currents observed by Friis-Christensen's magnetometers.

But auroras occurred at very high altitudes, typically 100 kilometres up, where the air was extremely thin. The energy deposited was only one ten-thousandth of the energy of sunlight. To influence the climate, any auroral effect had to be transmitted to the lower atmosphere and greatly amplified. People had imagined, for example, the creation of anticyclones in the auroral zone which could push warm air towards the poles. After many years of thought and observation no one had been able to confirm any persuasive link between auroras and the climate. Friis-Christensen was nevertheless convinced that the hunt for a connection should continue.

The long shot that interested him concerned the cosmic rays. They were an excellent indicator of the Sun's behaviour on many timescales, from the sudden drops associated with outbursts from the Sun, through the 11-year variations of the sunspot cycle, to the changes from century to century and millennium to millennium as shown by radiocarbon in old wood. But they had attracted little attention as a possible direct link between the Sun and the climate.

Solar experts and climatologists alike thought of variations in cosmic rays as mere sawdust, telling by proxy of the much grander business of the Sun, with more plausible effects on the Earth. Speculations that cosmic rays themselves might affect the weather directly, ran at once into a big difficulty. If auroral effects were feeble, the vigour of the cosmic rays hitting the Earth was far less, being comparable only with starlight. Although it was remarkable that the Galaxy should send in the form of atomic bullets as much energy as in visible light, the

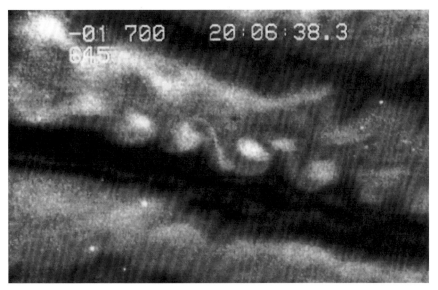

Fantastic shapes in auroras. The typical form of an aurora seen in the photograph (ABOVE) resembles a curtain hanging from the sky, curved in an arc. Harald Frey from Munich captured details (BELOW) with a specially adapted TV camera looking directly up the plunging field lines of the Earth's magnetism, in northern Scandinavia. His videos showed dancing curls developing alongside linear glows that streamed in contrary directions. The features are projected on to the upper air from electromagnetic contortions out in space, by natural electron beams following the magnetic lines of force. An unresolved issue is whether events in the auroral zone affect the weather on the ground.

PHOTO: *Silvestris/FLPA;*
TV IMAGE: *Max-Planck-Institute for Extraterrestrial Physics, Garching, Germany*

total was only a few billionths of the energy of sunlight.

As Friis-Christensen also knew, there was another way of judging the cosmic rays. They penetrated much deeper into the air than the auroral particles ever could. They multiplied in showers of particles, some of which reached the ground. As each particle ploughed through the air it tore electrons out of atoms, leaving a trail of charged atoms and electrons collectively called ions.

The peak production of ions by cosmic rays occurred at an altitude of about 12 kilometres.

Energetic particles resembling cosmic rays came from the Sun itself, from solar flares. They varied in a contrary manner. When the Sun was busy, the flare particles became commoner but the cosmic rays from the Galaxy diminished, both generally and in the Forbush decreases associated with flares and mass ejections from the Sun. So if they affected the weather at all, the solar particles and the galactic particles would work in opposite directions. Some experts thought that the flares might be the key to the mystery of solar effects on the climate.

'We have to look for one-to-one relations,' Jean-Claude Pecker, the doyen of French solar physicists, had declared. 'Say, between some type of flares and some type of meteorological change.'

The lower atmosphere in the Earth's polar regions warmed and expanded after eruptions on the Sun, and Cor Schuurmans of De Bilt in the Netherlands attributed this effect to solar flare particles. Writing in 1965, he summarized the polar warming events seen after fifty-three flares in 1957–58, a period of exceptionally numerous sunspots. Schuurmans also suspected that the Sun's high level of activity during the period 1946–60 was responsible for an unusually high frequency of south-west winds at the surface over the eastern Atlantic.

After a flare, the energetic solar particles were far more numerous than the true cosmic rays, but only for a day or two. Even when the Sun was active, a month might pass before the next flare. Except in the most violent flares, occurring perhaps three times in a decade, the particles were less energetic than the true cosmic rays, and penetrated less deeply into the atmosphere. Bursts of flare particles detected by spacecraft usually failed to register in cosmic ray detectors on the ground. For all these reasons, the rare outbursts of solar particles might be less important than the continuous influx of cosmic rays from the Milky Way Galaxy.

The Earth's magnetism was a partial shield against the cosmic rays. It was less effective than against the much feebler particles of the solar wind, but quite sufficient to exert a strong geographical effect. Measured on the ground, the intensity of cosmic rays in the tropics was about a quarter of that near the magnetic poles. At the top of the atmosphere the difference in particle counts was far greater, but the few cosmic rays that penetrated the magnetic defences in the tropics were extremely energetic and created huge showers of other particles. If there were any effect of cosmic rays on the weather, there should be a geographical factor, linked to the Earth's magnetic field.

But what could the effect be? The peak production of ions occurred near the bottom of the stratosphere, much closer to surface weather than the auroral particles ever came. The cosmic rays might conceivably affect the behaviour of gases and vapours and solids in the air, on a microscopic scale.

In his desk drawer Friis-Christensen had a scientific paper written more than 30 years earlier by Edward Ney of Minneapolis. Ney was famous for exploiting high-flying plastic balloons for scientific purposes, primarily to collect cosmic

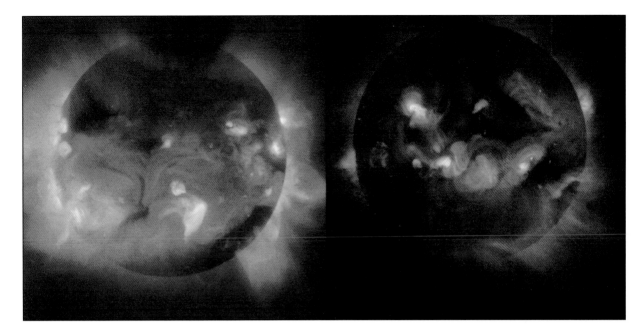

rays before the atmosphere broke them up. In 1959 he proposed that cosmic rays might discourage storminess and reduce the number of thunderclouds by making the air more conductive for electricity. He predicted lower temperatures when the Sun was most active. That was the wrong way round according to the usual supposition, from Herschel onwards, that sunspots brought warmer weather, but Ney's speculation would be worth re-examining.

Cosmic rays thus floated to the top of Friis-Christensen's checklist of things to investigate as the possible new connection between the Sun and the Earth's climate. In his contribution to the proposal for the European Commission contract, he specified auroras and cosmic rays as the solar-terrestrial indicators for investigation, to parallel the work on climate and trees in Ireland. With Butler in Armagh looking after the paperwork, Friis-Christensen put the question aside until the contract was forthcoming. Then he could set somebody else to work on it.

In February 1994, energetic particles from a solar flare reached the spacecraft Ulysses by a circuitous route. To the astonishment of the mission's expert's, the flare occurred at 20 degrees north latitude on the Sun, but affected the spacecraft at more than 50 degrees south latitude as it continued its flight towards the Sun's Antarctica. It was as if thunder in Mexico were heard in Patagonia.

'Ulysses tells us that the regions of the heliosphere are interconnected in ways we had not imagined,' said the project scientist, Richard Marsden.

Ulysses was by this time bathed continuously in the fast solar wind from the south polar region of the Sun. It had its last glimpse of a wind from the northern magnetic hemisphere of the Sun in April 1993, but the alternation of the slow equatorial wind and fast polar wind had continued in their 26-day cycle until July 1993. Scientists had used the opportunity to compare the composition of the two kinds of solar wind.

The quietening Sun. The Yohkoh spacecraft's images of the Sun's hot atmosphere changed as the years passed. At a time of numerous sunspots (1991, LEFT) the atmosphere was unruly. As the sunspot count dwindled (1994, RIGHT) the activity diminished. Large dark, relatively cool areas became conspicuous in the X-ray images. These are called coronal holes, and are the source of a fast solar wind.

Yohkoh Team

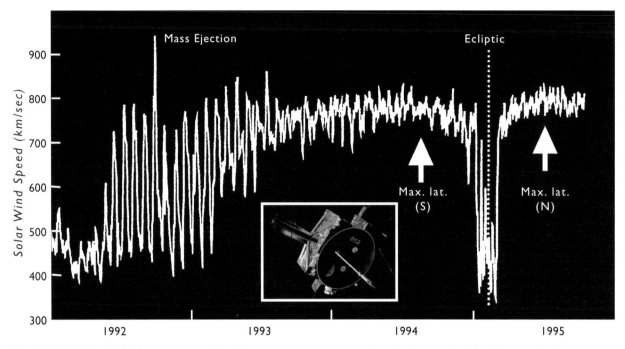

Two kinds of solar wind. Like a sailor discovering prevailing winds on Earth, Ulysses explored winds blowing from different parts of the Sun. Until mid-1992 the spacecraft was in the slow solar wind of the Sun's equatorial regions. Moving gradually towards higher latitudes, it felt a faster wind from the south polar region. The source was canted, so the fast wind came and went as the Sun rotated. By 1994 the fast wind bathed Ulysses continuously. After passing near the south pole (max. lat.) the spacecraft quickly crossed the equatorial zone of the slow wind (around the ecliptic) and entered a fast north polar windstream. Tussles between the fast and slow winds perturb the heliosphere and help to disperse cosmic rays before they reach the Earth.

Ulysses/ESA & NASA, and SWOOPS team

'Our instrument senses a striking difference,' said Johannes Geiss of Bern. 'We can say that the temperature of the solar atmosphere is about 1.8 million degrees at the source of the slow wind, which typically comes from the Sun's lower latitudes. The temperature is hundreds of thousands of degrees lower in the coronal holes where the fast wind originates. Although the slow wind comes from the hotter source, it is poor in elements such as oxygen and nitrogen that are hard to ionize. These elements must be depleted in the chromosphere below the solar atmosphere.'

Shock waves in the solar wind continued to wash over Ulysses at much higher latitudes than expected. The last came in March 1994, at 55 degrees south. Mission planners deemed the Sun's polar region to start at 70 degrees south, and Ulysses was there at the end of June.

André Balogh of London, who was in charge of the magnetometers aboard Ulysses, provided the mission with its road map of where the spacecraft was from day to day in relation to the Sun's ever-changing environment.

'Now the spacecraft is in a high-latitude zone,' he remarked. 'The magnetic field slants out into space in an ever-more southerly direction, but the Sun's rotation twists it into a corkscrew. There are also many waves, travelling out from the Sun, which may be responsible for accelerating the solar wind.'

The work for the Ørsted satellite was still very demanding. Friis-Christensen nursed and chivvied his science team of nine principal investigators in Denmark and France who were preparing the satellite's instruments. In addition nearly eighty proposals came from research groups all over the world, clamouring to join in the Ørsted mission. Even when laborious scrutiny and selection had whittled the number of groups down to fifty, it left a large community of geomagnetists for Friis-Christensen to deal with.

To be the project scientist even for this baby satellite would seem to most people like a full-time job. Nevertheless, he found reserves of adrenalin for the climate issue. Friis-Christensen helped Knud Lassen to finalize a scientific paper in their joint names, which took back to AD 1500 the relationship between the length of the solar cycles and land surface temperatures in the northern hemisphere.

The new paper summed up much of the historical work that Lassen had been doing. In part this was a reappraisal of other people's efforts to trace sunspot cycles back through time. Before fairly good sunspot records became available from 1749 onwards, the best guide to the Sun's activity was the occurrence of auroras seen at relatively low latitudes outside the Arctic. When people saw strange lights in the sky they often mentioned them in written records, which other scholars had amassed.

As an auroral specialist himself, Lassen knew that the peaks in such occurrences need not coincide with the peak in the sunspot count, but he judged the absence of reports of auroras to be a better indicator of a quiet Sun. He was able to settle on many dates for the minima of the sunspot cycle from 1500 to 1749, though he left a gap of 33 years in the mid-seventeenth century when the data were unconvincing. From the intervals between the quiet Suns, Lassen could deduce variations in the length of the sunspot cycles. He checked the method by applying the aurora data in the same way through to the twentieth century. The cycle lengths judged by auroras rose and fell nearly in step with those calculated from the sunspot data.

The graph of five centuries of cycle length changes could then be compared against a graph of assessments by other scientists of annual mean land temperatures in the northern hemisphere from 1579 to 1987. Just as when Lassen had first recognized the similarity between the graphs for the period 1851 to 1987, the match was surprisingly good. High temperatures around 1590 and 1750, for example, corresponded with relatively fast cycles, and a slower Sun brought lower temperatures around 1610 and 1800. Considering all the uncertainties in both the solar and climatic data, the Sun's influence had to be clear and strong to produce such a match in the graphs. And the lead from the Stony Brook scholars, about springtime on the Yangtze River obeying the Sun's moods, embellished the story with an independent regional example.

'The spring temperature in this region of Asia has oscillated in concert with solar activity during the past 300 years,' Lassen and Friis-Christensen were able to declare.

Before they sent the final version of the paper to the *Journal of Atmospheric and Terrestrial Physics,* they added some mild comments concerning the argument with the greenhouse people. They suggested that the computer models were not dealing in adequate geographical detail with effects of a variable output of light from the Sun. And a closing remark showed how Friis-Christensen's mind was running: 'Another possibility is that it is not the variation in luminosity that is important, but rather an effect through energetic particles.'

To nag Friis-Christensen about cosmic rays, a copy of the geophysical news-

Electrifying the air. By an American theory publicized in 1994, the Sun might influence cloud formation by redistributing atmospheric electricity created by tropical thunderstorms, like this one in Australia. Cosmic rays, influenced by the Sun, were the agency proposed. This hypothesis linking cosmic rays and clouds was, in retrospect, a step towards the Danish discovery.

Ecoscene/Dannett

paper *Eos* arrived on his desk in the summer of 1994. Brian Tinsley of Dallas had a prominent article on the front page entitled 'A solar wind mechanism suggested for weather and climate change'. Lassen and Friis-Christensen had already cited a previous Tinsley paper, about a possible connection between energetic particles and atmospheric electricity, and now he was taking his ideas further.

He focused attention on the thousand thunderstorms raging in the tropics at any one time, and on the electric charges that they pumped into the air. The charges spread around the middle atmosphere, at cloud-top height, and maintained over the whole Earth a voltage of 250,000 volts relative to the surface. In Tinsley's opinion, cosmic rays affected the electrical conductivity of the air, and therefore the routes by which electric charge flowed back to the surface. Measurements made by balloons over Minnesota showed the electric currents in the air declining as sunspots increased.

Tinsley therefore envisaged electric charges accumulating at the cloud-top level at high magnetic latitudes, when the Sun was stormy and cosmic rays were weak. The charges could, he thought, promote the formation of ice crystals in clouds, and this process would release heat and encourage convection in the atmosphere. The clouds themselves could also have climatic effects. It was an ingenious but complicated story, with currents in the atmosphere increasing at low latitudes and reducing the effect of changes in the cosmic rays.

The paper went into Friis-Christensen's drawer. Serious attention to such matters would have to wait until the European Commission contract came through and Friis-Christensen would have help on the problem of the mechanism of the solar warming. Meanwhile he could only speculate that the long shot was the best bet after all, and that cosmic rays modulated by the Sun's activity affected the weather on the Earth.

The European Space Agency gave brief but emphatic publicity to the work of Eigil Friis-Christensen and Knud Lassen. A video prepared for Ulysses' approach to the Sun's south pole made use of beautiful computer animations, and the narrator remarked:

> Concern about the Earth's changing climate gives an urgency to solar research. Some experts doubt whether the recent warming of the Earth is really due to carbon dioxide. Danish scientists have discovered that a speeding of the Sun's activity seems to match the changes better. Records of a changeable Sun go back thousands of years. They show repeated variations from one century to the next. Who can understand the Earth's environment without sufficient knowledge of the Sun, which warms it and gives us life?

Similar references to Friis-Christensen and Lassen followed in other videos and brochures produced by the agency, concerning the SOHO and Cluster missions. Despite their wide distribution in English and French to broadcasters and journalists in many countries, the story evoked occasional queries, but no serious attention.

In its exploration of the heliosphere from new angles, Ulysses was due to reach its furthest south solar latitude, at 80.2 degrees, on 13 September 1994.

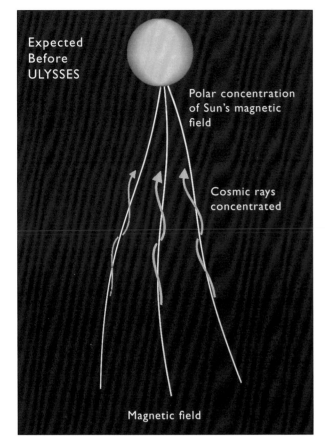

Expected
Before
ULYSSES

Polar concentration
of Sun's magnetic
field

Cosmic rays
concentrated

Magnetic field

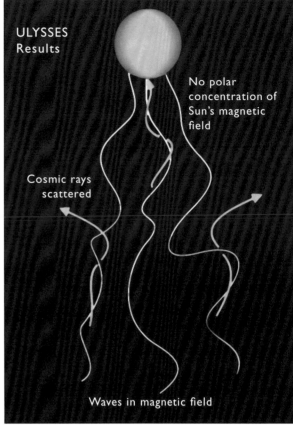

ULYSSES
Results

No polar
concentration of
Sun's magnetic
field

Cosmic rays
scattered

Waves in magnetic field

Like the Earth's magnetic poles, the Sun's were offset from the axis of rotation, which defined 90 degrees latitude, so the expectation was that Ulysses would pass directly over the south magnetic pole at some stage. According to the theories, the magnetic field would greatly intensify over the pole, and cosmic rays would come pouring into the spacecraft's detectors from the Milky Way, almost unimpeded by the Sun's activity.

But as the weeks passed, the average intensities of the magnetic field scarcely changed and the cosmic rays increased only slightly. Instead, the magnetometer in Ulysses continued to detect strong magnetic waves coming from the polar region of the quiet Sun, which helped to scatter the cosmic rays. The waves changed the direction, not the strength, of the local magnetic field.

'It is as if there is a man in the Sun hitting the field-lines with a hammer,' André Balogh commented, speaking for the magnetometer experiment in Ulysses.

When the Ulysses science working team assembled in the Netherlands in September at the European Space Agency's laboratory at Noordwijk to mark the south polar pass, jubilation at the mission's success was matched by surprise about the Sun's behaviour. The textbooks would have to be rewritten, and John Simpson, in charge of the cosmic ray instruments, would not see the pure cosmic rays which he had hoped for during the long years of the mission's conception and flight.

Surprises at the Sun's south pole. Until the spacecraft Ulysses visited this part of the heliosphere in September 1994, scientists imagined an intense magnetic field funnelling copious cosmic rays towards the pole. In reality the influx scarcely changed, because strong magnetic waves dispersed the cosmic rays and no intensification of magnetism occurred.

ABOVE: The American satellite Wind. As its name implies, it was designed to sense the solar wind.

NASA

RIGHT: The Sun's magnetic field made visible. The black dots trace the progress of energetic electrons on 7 April 1995, as they followed a line of the magnetic field out from the Sun. They revealed themselves by broadcasting radio waves, which declined in frequency (kHz) as the electrons lost energy. This 3-D view of a radio burst required observations by two widely separated spacecraft. The trajectory is here charted in the ecliptic plane, where the planets orbit the Sun. The Sun's rotation winds the magnetic field into a spiral, as Eugene Parker of Chicago proposed more than 30 years ago.

Wind/NASA and Ulysses/ESA & NASA; courtesy of R.A. Hoffman, NASA Goddard

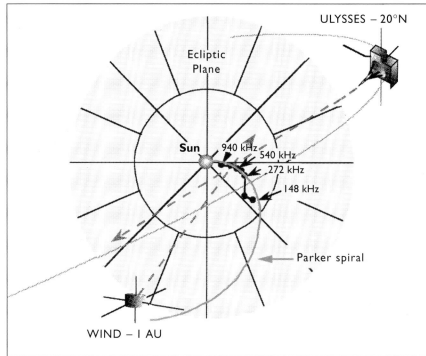

The intensity of cosmic rays had increased while Ulysses flew from the Earth to Jupiter and back towards the Sun's polar region, but that was because the Sun itself had become feebler at the approach to its sunspot minimum. A general lesson from Ulysses was that the Sun was equally effective in repelling cosmic rays, whatever their direction of approach. Although the polar magnetic waves were doing part of the work over the pole, there was a continuing influence from the equatorial regions too, shown by a persistent 26-day variation in the cosmic rays. Evidently the 'corotating interaction regions' spread their influence on cosmic rays even to high latitudes, where the Sun's surface took 36 days to rotate.

Balogh summed up the science team's astonishment succinctly. 'We went to the south magnetic pole of the Sun and it wasn't there.'

NASA's spacecraft Wind went into orbit on 1 November 1994, to observe the solar wind upstream from the Earth. Manoeuvres using encounters with the Moon took it progressively farther and out towards the Sun. Wind was therefore operating in the opposite direction to the Japanese Geotail mission. Geotail had just completed two years' observations far down the Earth's magnetic tail and was about to re-configure its orbit closer to the Earth.

Ulysses and Wind operated in concert, by using their radio instruments to observe simultaneously emissions due to packets of particles emitted from the Sun. The particles travelled, not straight out from the solar wind, but along the spiral arms of the magnetic field, made by the rotation of the Sun. The existence of the magnetic spiral had been known for many years. By giving a stereoscopic view of the radio emissions, Ulysses and Wind together provided the first pictures of it. The pace of discovery about the Sun and its windy empire was accelerating.

The art of climate modelling was also advancing rapidly, as new supercomputers became available. Even as the first rough and ready forecasts were being presented to the world in 1990, groups were hard at work improving matters. The chief requirement was to represent the ocean adequately, both in its interactions with the air and in its ability, with its huge heat capacity, first to delay and then to consolidate any global warming.

Just as the world of golf had its hallowed places like Augusta, Pebble Beach and St Andrews, so computerized climatology possessed a special geography. At a dozen prime sites around the world, supercomputers ran major programs linking the air and the oceans, and making climate predictions. These were the altars of an air-ocean cult, which began at Princeton, spread to Boulder, Bracknell and Hamburg, and by 1995 was active with its supercomputers from Melbourne to Paris. Several were represented in the inner core of lead authors preparing the latest report of the Intergovernmental Panel on Climate Change. All contributed directly or indirectly to the work of Houghton's science working group.

No sooner were the systems running than there were new requirements for treating man-made changes in the atmosphere. Sulphate dust added to the air by human activity gave the modellers plenty of food for thought and fodder for the computers. Sulphur dioxide gas emitted from fossil-fuel burning and smelting became converted into microscopic grains of sulphate salts in the atmosphere. They created a thin haze that reduced the sunlight reaching the surface. The latest estimates for the man-made global warming during the twentieth century dropped by almost 1 degree C, when the sulphate dust was allowed to offset the supposed warming by the greenhouse gases.

The Laboratoire de Météorologie Dynamique in Paris offered a distinctive approach to the sulphate problem, taking account of the effect of sulphate dust on clouds. Robert Charlson in the United States had pointed out some years previously that man-made sulphates made watery clouds thicker, with smaller droplets. Satellite observations showed that droplet sizes were smaller in the polluted northern hemisphere than in the south. The indirect effects on watery clouds, added to the direct effects of the sulphate haze, reduced still further the sunlight reaching the Earth's surface. Hervé Le Treut and his colleagues in Paris were the first to take account of the cloud-modifying effects of sulphate in a major computer model.

The French team found that a certain combination of direct and indirect cooling, due to sulphate, cancelled the greenhouse warming due to carbon dioxide. The resulting computation nicely balanced a warming in the unpolluted southern hemisphere with a cooling in the north due to the thickened clouds, which fitted the satellite results. This was an exploratory trial, rather than an attempt at realism. It aimed at understanding how the climate system responded to different kinds of effects. Nevertheless the mechanisms producing the cancellation were not wildly unrealistic and they illustrated the great uncertainty in assessing the counterbalancing effects of sulphates, compared with the greenhouse gases.

Eigil Friis-Christensen and Knud Lassen, in advancing the solar warming theory, had never ignored the possibility of a greenhouse warming. They had expressed surprise that there was no sign of it in their solar warming graphs, and proposed that added dust might have cancelled the greenhouse warming, leaving the climate free to obey a changing Sun. Cancelling the greenhouse warming by dust was exactly the result from Le Treut and his computer-modelling group in Paris.

Le Treut himself did not want it to be taken literally. It was a deliberate result in an exercise to study the physics of the climate and its modelling, and he knew of big defects in the model. But he was also one of the modellers who acknowledged large uncertainties in the climatic impact of man-made dust and dust-affected clouds.

The work in Paris was far from finished. To advance from the demonstration run showing a cancelled cooling to a more realistic computer model of the man-affected atmosphere required improvements in the cloud modelling and attention to other factors. These included the effects of other kinds of man-made dust, of greenhouse gases other than carbon dioxide, and icy clouds. Even the difference in temperatures between the northern and southern hemispheres, which went so neatly with the effects of pollution on clouds, was very sensitive to changes in sea ice.

Teaching responsibilities, on top of his research, prevented Le Treut finishing a scientific paper on the subject. As a result, his computation with a zero warming would appear without discussion as a line in a table in the next report by Houghton's group, *Climate Change 1995*. It was printed beneath results from other groups that did not take account of the effects of sulphates on clouds, and showed significant warmings.

Le Treut was not opposed to the aims and activities of the Intergovernmental Panel on Climate Change, although he saw them as more of an exercise in risk assessment than of prediction. He was concerned to understand the physics of the changing atmosphere and oceans, rather than to meet any deadline for verdicts useful for policymakers. Yet for Le Treut, as for other agnostics among the modellers, the increase in greenhouse gases remained the one certainty in an increasingly complex climatic picture.

'I am convinced that the climate is going to warm,' Le Treut said. 'A little? A lot? No one knows. I am not convinced of our ability to predict the course of this warming geographically or in time.'

The World Meteorological Organization in Geneva ran a World Climate Data and Monitoring Programme, independently of the Intergovernmental Panel on Climate Change. Starting in 1984, its purpose was not to predict, but to report on the evolution and fluctuations in the climate of the real world. In its review of the global weather of 1991–93, published in 1995, the monitoring programme highlighted short-term changes in the Pacific Ocean that boosted the global temperature independently of other possible causes, whether the greenhouse warming or the solar warming.

An unusually long run of El Niño warmings of the Pacific Ocean began in

1991. It paused in 1992 but quickly resumed, and was still persisting. Other prolonged El Niño conditions prevailed in 1911–13 and 1939–42, but the review commented that a lack of data from the earlier periods ruled out accurate comparisons with the 1990s.

Meteorologists and oceanographers had by this time done well in making sense of the events associated with El Niño. Known initially only as a problem for fishermen, who often found the sea off Peru turning warm and sterile at Christmas, El Niño turned out to involve unusually hot equatorial water stretching across the Pacific, for fully a quarter of the way around the planet. That discovery, made in the late 1950s, led Jacob Bjerknes of Los Angeles to link El Niño with the Southern Oscillation, a see-sawing of atmospheric pressure between the central Pacific and the Indian Ocean.

By the 1990s, scientists understood El Niño as a great eastward expansion of the Warm Pool of the western Pacific. Computer modellers were having some success in simulating these conditions. They associated it with a faltering of the surface winds and ocean currents normally driving from east to west in the equatorial zone. The surface layer of warm water, which in normal years was much deeper in the west than in the east, became more nearly equal all across the ocean. The root cause and possible prediction of El Niño remained elusive.

With sea surface temperatures rising locally by 7 degrees C, El Niño had world-wide impacts in severe cases. Weather observers and analysts associated it with droughts in Australia, Indonesia and India, and it took at least part of the blame for the record-breaking Great Flood of the Mississippi River in 1993. For students of climate change the overall effect was a blip in the global mean temperature, superimposed on any warming trend.

Should the global warmth of the early 1990s be blamed on the persistent El Niño, rather than on a long-term warming process? There were two ways of judging it. The persistent El Niño could be a major event in its own right, and a dominant contributor to the high global temperatures. Alternatively, it might be only a relatively weak addition to a general rise in temperatures due to other causes. In its review of the early 1990s, the World Climate Data and Monitoring Programme seemed to favour the latter opinion.

Whatever the eventual verdict might be, any explanation of climate change would have to take El Niño into account, if only for explaining dramatic variations in global mean temperatures from year to year that did not conform to expected trends. There was no evidence of any direct link between its frequency and the general state of the climate. The extended El Niño period of 1939–42 was in a warm climatic phase, but the other such event, in 1911–13, occurred in the coldest spell of the twentieth century.

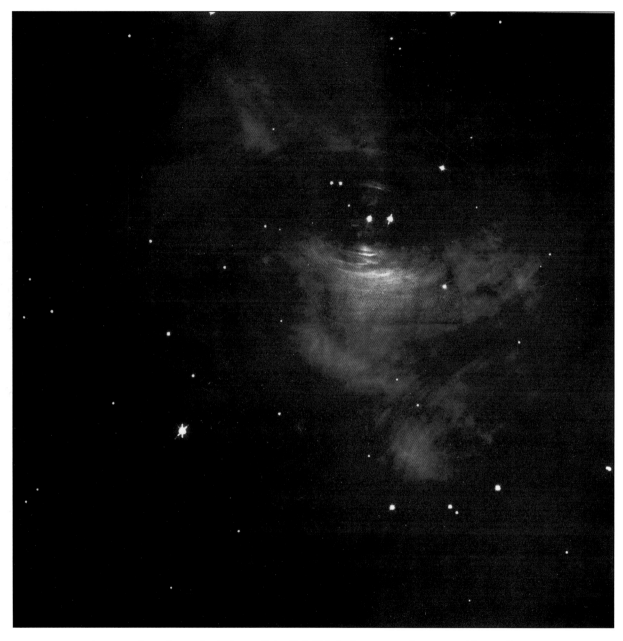

A source of cosmic rays. In the heart of the Crab Nebula the star near the centre, with conspicuous waves beneath it, is a pulsar spinning 30 times a second. As the collapsed core of an
exploded star, it is heavier than the Sun yet only 10 kilometres wide. Its intense magnetic field
slings atomic nuclei into the Galaxy, some of which reach the Earth as cosmic rays. When the
Hubble Space Telescope obtained this picture in 1995, scientists were pondering possible links
between cosmic rays and the weather.

NASA and J. Hester and P. Scowen, Arizona State Uni

Chapter Eight

THE CLOUD CHAMBER

A T ELSINORE, Shakespeare's Hamlet teased the bureaucrat Polonius about the appearance of a cloud. It was a camel, a weasel, a whale. Any layman knew there were thin high clouds and thick low clouds, warm wet clouds and cold icy clouds, cotton-wool fluff and wintry palls, and black towering monsters that attacked the summer landscapes like battleships, with lightning, hail and tornadoes. So how did you tame that lot – in a computer? You couldn't, because the grid boxes used in the computations were far larger than individual clouds, and uncertainties about cloud physics made the necessary averages elusive.

The 1990 *Climate Change* report had said that clouds must (*sic*) not be construed as a possible means of offsetting the greenhouse warming. What could be clearer, or more authoritative? By 1995, the authors of the equivalent chapter were more circumspect.

'The determination of cloud-dependent surface radiative and precipitation fluxes,' they said, 'is a significant source of uncertainty for both land-surface and ocean climate modelling.' The prose was wilting under the scientific onslaught. The original report, confident in a simple greenhouse theory, was admirable for its limpid style. *Climate Change 1995* read like the minutes of a long-winded and tortuous technical argument, as written up by one of the rival participants.

The reports about clouds absorbing sunlight directly, as discovered in the Warm Pool of the Pacific by V. Ramanathan and his colleagues and confirmed in many other places, finally appeared in the journal *Science* in January 1995. Less than two months later, there was irrefutable support for this discovery, which was expected to give the climate panellists food for thought. It came with the publication of results from an experiment in which two research aircraft flew simultaneously above and below the clouds over the Warm Pool of the Pacific, carrying identical instruments to measure radiation both upwards and downwards. The numbers reported by Peter Pilewskie of NASA Ames and Francisco Valero of La Jolla, California, told of huge differences in absorbing power between clouds and clear skies.

The detailed results hinted that the shapes of clouds were crucial to their ability to absorb sunlight. The computer models assumed that clouds were flat, homogeneous sheets, but in reality irregular and even broken cloud could scatter and rescatter the sunlight and might increase its chances of being absorbed.

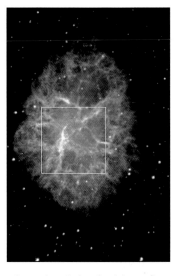

The Crab Nebula. The debris of a star that blew up as a supernova in AD 1054 still disperses in space, 7000 light-years away in the Taurus constellation. The box shows the area of the close-up (OPPOSITE). Astronomers visualize supernova explosions as an intermittent source of cosmic rays, while residual pulsars make cosmic rays continuously.

Palomar image, distributed by NASA

The Prince's teasing of Polonius seemed likely to become all too realistic as an anticipation of the puzzle for the computer modellers. Whether a cloud was a weasel or a whale might be a matter of climatic significance.

The numbers about cloud absorption of sunlight were disastrous for the modellers. They had been overestimating the sunlight reaching the surface by 20–40 watts per square metre averaged around the globe, compared with 2.5 watts per square metres for the supposed warming effect of all greenhouse gases added by human action to the air. The missing energy went directly into the clouds as sky heaters, completely altering the nature of the heat engine that drove the winds of the world.

The discovery reduced by perhaps 40 per cent the energy supplied by the convection of moisture-laden air from the surface. It thereby struck at the heart of the greenhouse proposition, which relied on added moisture to amplify the otherwise meagre greenhouse effect due to the added gases alone. A smaller flux of water vapour, as the more potent greenhouse gas, was likely to reduce any computed greenhouse warming. Meanwhile, every computation of the Earth's climate and its warming, performed by all the world's supercomputers up to 1995, was technically flawed. They would all have to be done again.

'This is such a basic thing – it throws a big monkey wrench into the modelling works,' said a climate expert at Princeton. The modellers were keen to start afresh and make their computations more realistic. But accepting the result could set climate analysis and prediction back by years.

The cloud studies had involved a dozen laboratories, comparable in academic status with the climate modelling institutions. Nevertheless Houghton's authors favoured sparse reports by climate modellers who took issue with Ramanathan and the rest of the troublemakers. In one case they cited a finding that the sunlight budgets might be in error by no more than 15 watts per square metre, as if that would be all right. And they concluded, 'The evidence is weak for the claim that clouds absorb substantially more short-wave radiation than is predicted by models.'

The rubbishing of the discovery of the clouds' embezzlement of sunlight could not possibly survive subsequent scientific scrutiny. But prevarication could still hold the line for the greenhouse warming. By the time the scientific community had digested the discovery and its confirmation, *Climate Change 1995* would be in front of the politicians with its conclusions intact.

Other grave difficulties confronting Houghton's group became apparent as 78 lead authors from 20 countries submitted their drafts early in 1995. The science was becoming more complicated, the quibbles more tiresome and the predictions less awful. Quite independently of efforts by solar people to offer other explanations for the global warming, Nature was shredding the greenhouse scenario before the authors' eyes.

Despite Houghton's own use of hurricane damage in the United States to alert the world to the dangers of climate change, and the agitation of the insurance companies, the authors of the chapter on 'Observed Climate Variability and Change' for *Climate Change 1995* disobligingly concluded that the

Clouds share the sunshine. Light scattered from one cloud can illuminate another, in an intricate contest between brightness and darkness which is familiar to artists but hard for scientists to compute. The fate of a photon of sunlight depends on the shapes and positions of the individual clouds. The picture is oversimplified when climate modellers assume that clouds are flat sheets.

M. Nimmo/FLPA

number of hurricanes crossing the US coast had not really changed since 1900, except that there were more of them during the middle decades of the century.

Another inconvenient report had appeared in 1993 from Jonathan Kahl of Milwaukee and a team which had collated many thousands of weather records from the Arctic Ocean gathered by US reconnaissance aircraft and Russian drifting ice stations between 1950 and 1990. These data were a bonus from the ending of the Cold War. The high spots of the greenhouse warming were supposed to be in the Arctic in winter.

'We do not observe the large surface warming trends predicted by models,' Kahl and his colleagues declared. 'Indeed, we detect significant surface cooling trends over the western Arctic Ocean during winter and autumn.'

Their figures showed a remarkable drop of 4 to 5 degrees C for those seasons. It made a mockery of the model predictions for the region, and onlookers filed the paper to see how Houghton's group would deal with it. The Kahl paper was translated in *Climate Change 1995* as follows: 'No general warming has been observed in the Arctic over the last 50 years or so.'

The scientists and officials of many countries involved in the work of Houghton's group continued to Oo and Ah about the greenhouse warming even though it was not happening. They were too intelligent not to have grave doubts in many cases, but if so they kept their thoughts to themselves.

Loyalty to other scientists was another concern. Over recent years a huge research enterprise had sprung up in Greenhouse Valley. In the United States for example, the federal budget for global change research had soared to $2 billion a year. Much of this science was well worth while, for a better knowledge of the Earth system, but governments funded it in the belief that a major environmental crisis was looming. To change the story about the greenhouse warming might put the research in jeopardy.

It was hard not to feel a little sorry for the greenhouse scientists, after all their energetic work and their long battles with recalcitrant colleagues. If only they had stood back and re-examined the evidence coolly in 1995, they might have saved themselves from further disasters that Nature had in store for them. But throughout that year Bert Bolin's Intergovernmental Panel on Climate Change was again working at full tilt to complete three big new reports on the greenhouse warming. The schedule and organization prohibited any far-reaching objectivity.

The reports had to be ready in time for the next big political conference, scheduled by the United Nations for the summer of 1996. The task was to enlarge and update the original *Climate Change* report of 1990. The all-important scientific working group now had a co-chairman. Gylvan Meira Filho of Brazil sat alongside John Houghton from the United Kingdom. This narrative, intending no slight to Meira Filho, continues to refer to Houghton's group for continuity's sake.

As the circus progressed through meetings in Sweden, the United Kingdom and the United States towards a culminating review in Madrid at the end of the year, sulphate-induced headaches became worse. The problem was to make sulphate dust just effective enough. The greenhouse modellers were on a tightrope. With too little effect from the sulphate, they could not hope to bring the warming calculations into line with the observations. With too much effect they could wipe out the greenhouse warming altogether.

Climate Change 1995 revised the best estimate of the global temperature rise in the twenty-first century from 3 degrees C before 2100 to 2 degrees by 2100. As for the rise in sea-level, the best estimate was cut back from 65 centimetres in the 1990 report to 50 centimetres in the 1995 report. To friends, these seemed moderate enough adjustments in the light of ever-improving scientific knowledge and better computer models.

Some less charitable readers still had on their shelves the 1990 *Climate Change*, which inspired the Rio Climate Convention. Plus 2 degrees by the year 2100, under the 1995 business-as-usual scenario, was the same as the plus 2 degrees achievable, according to the 1990 report, only with curbs on emissions called Scenario B. That envisaged a switch from coal to natural gas, a reversal of deforestation, and all the efficiency increases needed to cut by half the additions of carbon dioxide to the air up to 2100. At a wave of the silicon wand, *Climate Change 1995* reduced the predicted warming by as much as all the rest of the world might have achieved with remarkable effort, according to the 1990 report. And it was done just by remembering the sulphur emissions.

The Danes carrying on about the Sun seemed to be the least of the problems. In the previous year, in an interim report called *Climate Change 1994*, Houghton's group had collated the observations and calculations of the Sun's possible variations in 'output', meaning luminosity. Changes since 1850 were judged to be far less than the effect of carbon dioxide and other greenhouse

December to February

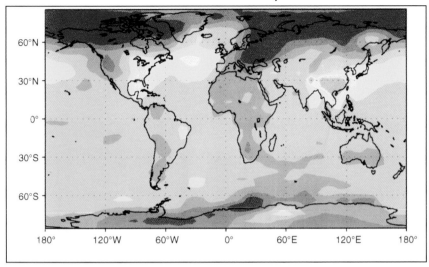

June to August

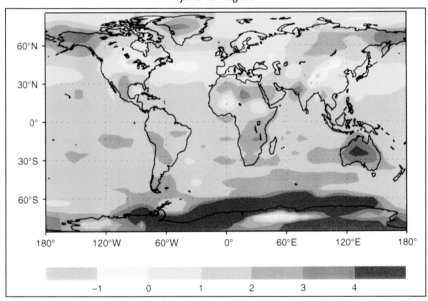

Greenhouse warming predictions, 1995 style. The maps show changes in degrees C over 160 years, between the 1880s and the 2040s, from an air-sea computer simulation at the Max-Planck-Institut für Meteorologie in Hamburg. It takes account of effects of man-made sulphate dust as well as rising levels of carbon dioxide. The greatest warmings (red) are calculated for the polar regions in winter, due to sea ice forming later in the warmer climate. Note the coolings (blue) predicted for China and some other regions. The increase in annual global mean temperature from the 1990s to the 2040s is about 1 degree C in this computer run, or 0.2 degrees per decade.

IPCC/MPIM, 1995

gases. The authors of the new report dismissed as unrealistic any idea that the twentieth century warming might be explained by solar effects that were proportional and in phase with the temperature changes, as proposed by Friis-Christensen and Lassen. The familiar line of reasoning reappeared about man-made effects, or 'anthropogenic forcing'.

'Since the primary area of uncertainty is in the response to anthropogenic forcing,' Houghton's authors declared, 'global mean studies using only a single 'natural' forcing factor and ignoring any anthropogenic component are inadequate.'

Deciphered, that meant: 'We don't know how big the greenhouse warming is. But we believe it's there. So anyone who says it's not, and blames the changes on Nature, is self-evidently off the rails.'

The denouement to the story brought together both of the main challenges to the greenhouse warming, concerning the clouds and the Sun. The Danes had started with sunspots, and found the link between climate and the duration of the sunspot cycles. The cloud investigators, much more numerous and busier with it, had used satellites to correct the assumptions of the computer modellers.

They began with the Thermostat Hypothesis that restricted the oceans to 29.5 degrees C by making clouds. Cloud investigators also pointed out the importance of pollution-made clouds, which greatly increased the cooling effect of sulphates. And they discovered the direct and completely unexpected absorption of sunlight by clouds. In short, the cloud people using satellites kept teaching Houghton's computer people fundamental points of meteorology which they had not taken into account in their computer models.

It fell to a physicist at the Danish Meteorological Institute to make yet another discovery about clouds, as a further piece of basic meteorology. The mechanism was unknown to the cloud experts, never mind the computer modellers. And by linking the clouds to variable solar activity, it provided a physical explanation of the Sun's effects on the Earth's climate already detected in Copenhagen by the studies of the length of the solar cycle.

The path of science was always bumpy, and progress was slow to begin with, because it still relied on spare-time work. Eigil Friis-Christensen had noted cosmic rays as a matter for attention if a research grant from the European Commission enabled him to recruit help for work on the climate problem. Independently, and without Friis-Christensen's knowledge, a scientist in another division of the Danish Meteorological Institute became interested in cosmic rays and climate.

Convergence of ideas when the time was ripe was well known to historians of science. Evolution by natural selection, for example, came independently to Charles Darwin in England and Alfred Russel Wallace in the Moluccas. It was unsurprising because shared knowledge and an awareness of the same riddles posed by Nature defined the frontier of science for active minds anywhere on the planet. But historians might smile about lightning striking twice in the same building beside the Elsinore motorway, and six months elapsing before anyone noticed.

Henrik Svensmark had nothing to smile about. He was unhappy in his work for the Danish Meteorological Institute. With dark hair and eyes he looked young and lively, but at the age of 37 he feared that his once-promising research career was broken.

Svensmark had learned the level and pace of world-class physics when working on high-temperature superconductors at Berkeley, California, with Leo Falicov, a leading theorist. He won a fellowship at the Nordic Institute of Theoretical Physics and a research scholarship at the Niels Bohr Institute in Copenhagen. He built a reputation with controversially original contributions to chaos theory.

Like many of his generation, Svensmark found there was no longer any tenure to be had in those glittering academic surroundings. Having family responsibilities he joined the Danish Meteorological Institute in November 1992 for the sake of a permanent job. But he found himself running big numerical models, computing how the turbulent atmosphere dispersed air pollution. He would have preferred to put his theoretical skills to work on observations or experiments in the real world.

An opportunity to do so came in 1994, when a friend from the Niels Bohr Institute invited Svensmark to help him interpret data from an ice core from Greenland, going back 91,000 years. They were looking for evidence that when the northern lands were smothered by ice and the northern oceans were very cold, the climate fluctuated on short timescales. Working in his spare time, Svensmark applied his mathematics to the wiggles in the Greenland temperature record and was able to confirm a high rate of variability. The research was striking enough to be published eventually in the leading journal *Nature*.

The Greenland palaeoclimatology was still in progress when Svensmark had a crucial thought about the climate of the modern era. He knew the famous graphs that matched the length of the sunspot cycles to the global temperature, so he was pre-tuned to the solar warming hypothesis of Friis-Christensen and Knud Lassen, although he had never discussed it with either of them. Svensmark was also sceptical about the elaborate computer models of climate on which the greenhouse predictions were based.

A chance remark in May 1995 switched Svensmark on to cosmic rays. A colleague had attended a seminar at the institute arranged by Friis-Christensen in connection with a visit by two Russian scientists, and told Svensmark what he had heard. The Russians had suggested that cosmic rays could alter the transparency of the air by provoking chemical action, and perhaps by affecting cloud formation.

Svensmark's mind flashed back to his high-school days in Elsinore. An enterprising physics teacher had built a device called a cloud chamber, and young Henrik had hands-on experience in using the quaint apparatus to make energetic atomic particles reveal their presence. They left tracks of droplets condensed from supercooled vapour, like miniature versions of the condensation trails of aircraft. Svensmark also remembered the photographs in the physics textbooks, of cosmic rays showing up in cloud chambers.

A hundred years had passed since a young Scottish physicist, Charles Wilson, became entranced by the clouds on the mountains. At Cambridge where he worked, Wilson set about making clouds experimentally from moist air in a piston cylinder. Jerking the piston outwards expanded and chilled the air. The air became supersaturated with water vapour and clouds formed, but dust-free air made no clouds, unless X-rays or subatomic particles electrified the air. That discovery distracted Wilson from meteorology, and he perfected the cloud chamber as a particle detector instead, using conditions very different from those of cloud formation in the atmosphere. Yet the cloud chamber retained its name because of the essential similarity of the processes.

Svensmark had a picture in his mind of cosmic rays raining on the Earth's

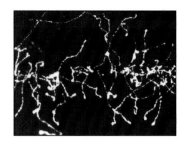

Tracking atomic particles. The cloud chamber (RIGHT) was invented at the end of the nineteenth century, during efforts to make clouds in the laboratory. An early cloud chamber photo (ABOVE) shows electrons forcibly ejected from molecules of the air by X-rays entering the chamber from the left. The energetic particles strip electrons from other molecules to create a trail of ions upon which droplets condense, out of supersaturated vapour filling the chamber. Memories of this obsolete instrument prompted Henrik Svensmark in Copenhagen to wonder whether cosmic rays could influence the Earth's cloud cover.

Univ. Cambridge/Cavendish Laboratory

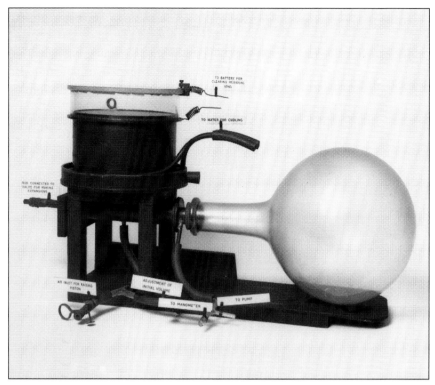

atmosphere and making clouds. Immediately he asked another colleague in the institute how much supersaturated water vapour might exist in the atmosphere at any time, and thus be available to make clouds in response to cosmic rays. The answer was that no one knew for sure, but it might be quite significant, equivalent to perhaps 5 or 10 per cent of the Earth's cloud cover.

Climatic implications were self-evident to Svensmark. Whenever water vapour condensed into clouds it immediately had far more effect on the flows of light and heat through the atmosphere than it did in invisible vapour form. If they influenced the amount of cloud cover, changes in the cosmic rays reaching the Earth could have quite disproportionate consequences for the weather and the climate. Long-term changes in cloud cover due to the Sun's effects on cosmic rays might explain the solar warming.

Although the remarks about cosmic rays from Russia, heard at second hand, set Svensmark's scientific antennas quivering, the idea was not a high priority even for his spare-time work. He was still busy with the ice core and with a technical idea about the statistics of time series. Not until late in the year would he get around to looking for a world-wide link between cosmic rays and cloud cover.

In the summer of 1995 Ulysses made its pass over the north polar regions of the Sun, attaining its highest northerly latitude on 31 July. On the whole, the results confirmed what the spacecraft had seen in the southern regions of the heliosphere. There were hints of lopsidedness, with the solar wind emissions appearing weaker on the northern side of the Sun than they had been in the south.

Steamy planet. An image from Meteosat, high over West Africa, shows the distribution of water vapour in the atmosphere. For the natural greenhouse effect, water vapour is by far the most important gas warming the Earth. For the solar warming theory, spare water vapour can make extra clouds in response to cosmic rays, which vary according to the Sun's mood.

Eumetsat

Since the south polar pass, theorists had scratched their heads over the strange appearance of 26-day fluctuations in the counts of cosmic ray particles over the poles, when Ulysses no longer had any direct encounter with the 26-day 'corotating interaction regions' typical of the equatorial zone. An explanation offered was that some incoming particles could encounter the interaction regions themselves, and then reach Ulysses by a devious route.

Ulysses had helped to clarify the general picture of how the Sun varied the intensity of cosmic rays through a solar cycle. One factor was the vigour of the ordinary solar wind, which pushed the cosmic rays away. The wind's effectiveness was increased by a tilt in the Sun's magnetic equator, which was slight when the Sun was quiet but severe when it was was active. Frequent mass ejections from an active Sun filled the heliosphere with enlarging pancakes of plasma which persisted for months or years and scattered the cosmic rays. When the Sun was quiet, the corotating interaction regions performed a similar role, less effectively but nevertheless influencing huge volumes of space.

The success of Ulysses, in flying over the poles when the Sun was quiet, won an extension for the mission. It was originally due to terminate after the north polar pass in 1995. But its orbit would carry Ulysses away from the Sun, to the orbit of Jupiter, and then return it to the Sun's polar regions in the years 2000–01, at the next sunspot maximum. Keeping the spacecraft alive, to allow it to observe the active Sun creating completely different weather in the heliosphere, would multiply the value of the mission.

In 1995, solar-terrestrial physicists were also waiting eagerly for the despatch into orbit of the four satellites of the European Space Agency's Cluster

Space quadruplets. The Cluster
mission required four satellites to
fly in company and create 3-D
views of the electric weather
around the Earth, stirred by the
solar wind pounding the magnetosphere. Two of the four Clusters
are here seen paired as they would
be during the launch. Each satellite
carried eleven sets of identical
instruments supplied by European
and American scientists. These
masterpieces of science and
engineering finished up in a South
American swamp.

ESA & D. Parker

mission, due in the autumn. That would be the starting gun for years of inten-
sive research. Cluster's unprecedented inspections of breaches made by the
solar wind in the Earth's magnetic shield had to be supported by observations
of magnetic variations, auroras and other solar activity from the ground. But by
the summer of 1995 delays with the new Ariane 5 launcher caused a postpone-
ment of Cluster to the following year.

The schedule for Denmark's Ørsted satellite slipped too. An American satellite on which it was to ride piggy-back into space, in the NASA launch, would
not be ready to go until 1997. That seemed a pity at the time, because the
satellite would miss the solar minimum of 1996, yet it was just as well for Eigil
Friis-Christensen's continuing interest in the climate question. Once Ørsted
was flying, his involvement would be almost total.

Even so, space research brought new distractions. At the beginning of 1995
Friis-Christensen had joined the European Space Agency's solar system working group, where independent scientists from various countries evaluated future
projects. Decision time was approaching for Europe's next choice in space science, and rival ideas for solar system missions were challenging others contem-
plated by an astronomy working group. Would the so-called M3 mission land
instruments on Mars or search for clumps of matter in the Big Bang?

While judging other people's proposals for the science programme, Friis-
Christensen was himself a campaigner for a new project in the agency's Earth
observation programme. It would create the successor to Ørsted. With colleagues from France, Germany and the United Kingdom he wanted the Euro-

pean Space Agency to fly two satellites operating together to measure the Earth's magnetic field at different altitudes, with instruments more sensitive than Ørsted's. But this proposal was in fierce competition with eight other bids for the first Earth Explorer, due for launch early in the twenty-first century, and the case for choosing the Magnetometry Mission needed careful honing.

Like many other scientists at the height of their careers, Friis-Christensen was finding that project proposals, project management, administrative meetings and business travels left very little time for personal research. Every day's sunlight reminded him that he had not solved the problem of the solar warming. Every day's newspapers and journals told him that the greenhouse warming still washed like a rising ocean over the world's scientific institutes, intergovernmental conclaves and media. The drawer in Friis-Christensen's desk at the Danish Meteorological Institute, which might hold the secret of the solar warming, was seldom opened.

To make matters worse, in the summer of 1995 the European Commission rejected the application initiated by John Butler of Armagh, for the research contract on Sun-climate connections. It was too ambitious, the adjudicators said. With the rejection Friis-Christensen lost the funding for a scientist to work on the climate question at the Danish Meteorological Institute. An administrative minuet then began, rehearsing the possibility that a reassignment of personnel within the institute might bring to Friis-Christensen's solar-terrestrial physics team a scientist from another division, either part-time or full-time, suitable for investigating the solar warming mechanism.

By a coincidence stranger than fiction, the administrative finger pointed at Henrik Svensmark. His name had already cropped up as the likely person for the European Commission contract. He was known to be discontented. There was an inquiry into why he always seemed to be doing research that he was not paid to do. He did it in his own time, he said. Svensmark had experience in climate research, having worked with the ice core people in the Niels Bohr Institute. Trading him for someone else in Friis-Christensen's division might solve more than one problem.

The independent weather forecaster Piers Corbyn of London was still beating the UK Meteorological Office in their interactions via the bookmaker, in which he pitted his long-range weather forecasts based on his Solar Weather Technique against the expectations of average climatology. Corbyn had been trying for several years to establish a scientific dialogue with the official forecasters. He believed that if he could feed some solar factors into the computer models used for medium-range weather prediction, the outcome could be 'undreamed of accuracy'. But the prejudice against sunspots and anything of that kind, among mainstream meteorologists, was a stronger barrier to communication than Corbyn's own desire to preserve his commercial secrets.

An opportunity for Corbyn to give some broad hints about his methods came in September 1995, at the European Conference on Applications of Meteorology in Toulouse, France. In a poster presentation he asserted that variations in the solar wind influenced the formation and behaviour of weather fronts, and the tracks of storms. Heating of the outer atmosphere by ultraviolet rays, X-rays and high-energy solar protons created waves penetrating to the lower atmosphere. Another mechanism involved the air-Earth electric currents, as described by Brian Tinsley in 1994, which were influenced by solar particles and cosmic rays and which, in turn, affected the formation of cloud droplets and ice grains.

Ozone magnified solar effects, according to Corbyn, by influencing the temperature of the stratosphere. The active Sun altered the ozone concentration in contradictory ways, with ultraviolet rays creating ozone and solar protons destroying it. The outcome, an increase or decrease in ozone, depended on the timing of the solar events in relationship to a well-known alternation in the direction of stratospheric winds over the Equator every two years or so.

Solar flares showed an increase in occurrence at intervals of about 155 days. An analysis by Corbyn's colleague Kourosh Bamsi-Yazdi detected periodicities of 155 days in air temperatures high above the North Pole, between 1965 and 1994, and also in ground-level air temperatures in central England between 1659 and 1994.

The poster revealed enough to show the assembled meteorologists that Corbyn's Solar Weather Technique owed much more to scientific content than to luck. A limit to his disclosures at Toulouse was set by the conference organizers' time allocation of just 5 minutes for a talk, rather than by confidentiality. Corbyn's offer to say more in an informal meeting afterwards was rejected on the grounds that it would interfere with the social programme accompanying the conference.

Corbyn showed his displeasure by using his limited time to speak about his successes in betting against the Met Office, and to compare the official meteorologists to candlestick makers confronted with Edison's light-bulb. A BBC producer then filmed an argument at Toulouse, between Corbyn and Julian Hunt, the new chief executive of the Met Office. In Hunt's opinion, Corbyn's refusal to disclose all his methods meant that they could not be counted as contributions to science, as normally understood.

An illumination of the underlying beliefs of prevailing meteorology came in a comment, in the same BBC film, from the head of extended weather forecasts in the Met Office, Michael Harrison. He was convinced that variability in the long-term weather was due to chaos. In this context, chaos meant large long-term consequences flowing from small, more-or-less chancy events like the flap of a butterfly's wings.

'All the knowledge and the expertise of scientists around the world,' Harrison said, 'shows very, very strongly that the atmosphere is chaotic. So the idea of weather forecasting using something such as the Sun – with chaos the two are just not compatible with one another.'

In October 1995, the Nobel prize for chemistry was awarded to atmospheric scientists, for their work to protect the ozone layer. Long before the ozone hole was discovered over Antarctica in 1985, Paul Crutzen of Mainz, Germany, in 1970 drew attention to ozone's vulnerability to nitrogen oxides released from the ground. He shared the Nobel prize with Sherwood Rowland of Irvine, California, and Mario Molina of Cambridge, Massachusetts. In 1974, Rowland and Molina jointly identified the man-made chlorofluorocarbons as a special threat to the ozone of the upper air.

Even as the Nobel Foundation announced its award, American scientists at the South Pole were checking the depletion of ozone at the Antarctic spring equinox. It was not quite as severe as in worst season, in 1993, but the scientists were used to variations from year to year and expected 1996 to be bad again. Meanwhile, all manufacture of chlorofluorocarbons in industrialized countries was expected to cease in January 1996. Shoppers' familiarity with the tag 'ozone friendly' showed a remarkable growth in public awareness. The scientists' success in moving the world to take action about the ozone layer carried with it a special obligation to make sure of the scientific facts.

Early theories about ozone depletion underwent drastic revision to acknowledge the role of high-altitude polar clouds, in producing ozone-killing agents from chlorofluorocarbons. Volcanic emissions also participated in ozone chemistry. Even by 1995, atmospheric theories did not fully account for the depletions long observed over Antarctica, and recently over northern Europe too. To help to firm up the atmospheric chemists' story, the European Space Agency's ERS-2 satellite, launched in April 1995, carried a new instrument. Developed by Crutzen's colleagues, it charted the world's ozone every three days. It also detected directly some of the chemical agents, such as nitric oxide, which damaged the ozone layer.

Anxieties about ozone still had nothing to do with the greenhouse warming – except in the negative sense that a shortage of ozone, itself a greenhouse gas, had a cooling effect. Meteorological balloons over Antarctica had detected a high-altitude cooling of 2 degrees C since 1963. The similarity was still at the political level, because of the parallel diplomatic initiatives to curb chlorofluorocarbons and carbon dioxide. If the greenhouse warming turned out to be real, the research into it might win a Nobel prize too. The prospects were not bright.

By that autumn of 1995 Bert Bolin, chief scientist of the planet, was having an uncomfortable time. As overall chairman of the Intergovernmental Panel on Climate Change, the Swedish meteorologist had to ride three horses at once: Science, Impacts and Socio-economic Issues. But while Science was lagging and might be fatally sick, the two other working groups were rushing ahead with their own multinational and peripatetic programmes of drafting and review, to produce parallel reports on a similar timescale to John Houghton's scientific working group. So they had been primed with scientific conclusions about continued global warming, long before Houghton completed his work. Administrative, political and intellectual chaos would ensue, if the scientific story changed very much.

What those other groups did was irrelevant to the scientific arguments. But the Impacts people depended heavily on supposed forecasts of regional climate change, about which the Science group admitted that confidence remained low. And a bust-up in the Socio-economic group gave a glimpse of the fantasy world that Bolin's panel had created for itself, beyond the realm of natural science.

It was black farce around the issue: What is the cash value of a human life? The dispute arose about a chapter on social costs in the Socio-economic report. The overall figure given for the cost of climate change was about 1.5 to 2 per cent of the world's gross product. That was far too low to be very scary. Global warming would delay the world's economic progress by only about one year, if that figure were realistic. Trying to avert climate change might cost far more. When critics looked for a flaw in the arithmetic they found what they thought was an outrageous misreckoning.

A person dying in a rich country as a result of the expected warming was costed at $1.5 million, fifteen times the $100,000 allowed for someone dying in a poor country. There were humanitarian reasons for using such unequitable figures. Costs and benefits of anti-greenhouse measures had to be seen in proportion to other ways of helping poor countries. In an unequal world where 30,000 children died every day from preventable diseases, relatively cheap medical programmes, for example, might bring far more benefit than building expensive dykes to keep out a rising sea. A lead author, David Pearce of London, made the point in a letter to a critic. 'The resources have to come from somewhere,' he wrote. 'If, for example, they come from reduced foreign aid, we may kill more people than we save.'

Comparing the greenhouse warming with infectious disease seemed to belittle it, so prominent environmental scientists and campaigners demanded that the chapter be scrapped. But the real folly behind this public row was that such arithmetic was attempted. While Bolin's panel was being embarrassed by the Socio-economic battle, serious meteorologists were still questioning basic assumptions of the global greenhouse forecasts.

Even the stalwarts of the Science group were prudently noting uncertainties and mapping out large areas of ignorance. The regional forecasts needed to assess impacts on human life were notoriously contradictory. Scientific ecologists (as opposed to the political ones) spoke of improved conditions for plant life in a greenhouse world. So sceptics wondered how the Socio-economic group could have the slightest idea about how many people might die of climate change.

Henrik Svensmark had never had any scientific discussion with Eigil Friis-Christensen. He was unaware of the debate about his future at the Copenhagen institute that had gone on behind the scenes. The first that Svensmark knew about being considered for Friis-Christensen's division was when he received an administrative note early in November 1995 asking him to supply a curriculum vitae.

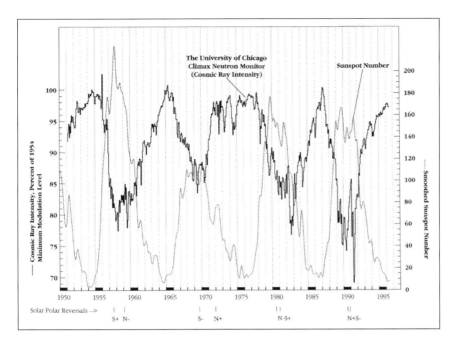

ABOVE: The Climax cosmic ray observatory. In a hut at 3400 metres altitude in the mountains of Colorado is the University of Chicago's station, which **has** operated continuously since 1953. It is the longest-running watchkeeper on variations in the cosmic rays, counted by the neutrons liberated when cosmic rays hit atoms in the air.

J.A. Simpson, Chicago

LEFT: The Sun's moods shown by cosmic rays. The Climax neutron counter recorded the intensities falling and rising through four solar cycles. Roughly speaking, when sunspot counts are high, fewer cosmic rays reach the Earth. But the reductions were less marked around 1970, a time of general cooling and a lazier Sun, as indicated by a longer sunspot cycles. The Climax data for the late 1980s enabled Danish scientists to check the effect of cosmic rays on cloud cover.

J.A. Simpson, Chicago

It was just at that time that Svensmark was returning to the hypothesis that cosmic rays, modulated by the Sun's action, affected the clouds. He had one advantage. He was a highly trained physicist and during three years in a leading meteorological institute he had read a lot in his spare time about weather and climate. But Svensmark had not been schooled as a meteorologist and therefore had no very fixed ideas about what could or could not happen, in the elementary processes of cloud-making.

The water vapour in the atmosphere made clouds when moist air rose, expanded, and cooled to a temperature where the air could no longer retain so much moisture. The supersaturated water vapour needed microscopic dust grains to help it condense into water droplets or freeze into ice crystals. Supposedly there was always plenty of dust in the air, although rainmaking experiments sought to accelerate ice-crystal formation by releasing silver iodide smoke in the clouds to provide additional nuclei.

To test his hypothesis, Svensmark knew he had to put together data about cosmic rays and data about clouds, to see how both varied with time. He might have sought advice from colleagues in the institute, which included a World Data Centre for geophysical information run by Friis-Christensen, as well as experts on meteorological processes. But he had to be careful about talking of his private project during working hours, so Svensmark kept his own counsel and surfed the Internet instead.

Enthusiasts for the system of intercommunicating computers, which had blossomed in an anarchistic fashion in the early 1990s, predicted that it would speed up scientific discovery. Especially, they said, in cross-disciplinary areas it would help to connect branches of science previously considered separate. Sceptics thought that the Internet dropped the user into a swamp of undigested information, without the critical evaluation which only expert knowledge could supply. In Svensmark's case the enthusiasts would be amply vindicated in the end, but he missed the best data to begin with, as the sceptics might have predicted.

From the menus of the World Wide Web, very firm, very clear data on cosmic rays were quite easy to come by. Svensmark took the monthly mean counting rate from a neutron detector at a cosmic-ray station 3400 metres up the Rocky Mountains at Climax, Colorado. He had no reason to know that the Climax station belonged to John Simpson of Chicago, who at that time was digesting information from his cosmic ray experiment on the Ulysses spacecraft over the north polar regions of the Sun.

Then Svensmark needed data on clouds. The Web led him to records of global cloud cover as observed by the Defense Meteorological Satellite Program of the US Air Force. 'It was not the best data set,' Svensmark commented later.

Orbiting over the polar regions, each satellite scanned every part of the world at local noon and local midnight, as the planet turned. Computations of cloud cover relied on a single daylight observation at each place every 24 hours, and even laymen knew that clouds came and went on much shorter timescales. But such were the sketchy data that first came to hand.

The information on cloud cover started from July 1987. At that time the Sun was beginning to rage after the sunspot minimum of the mid-1980s, and the cosmic ray count was declining. The graph of cloud cover wiggled up and down indecisively on Svensmark's computer screen. There was a gap in the cloud data from December 1987 to July 1990 when the US Air Force satellite awaited a replacement. But then the two graphs climbed up together in the early 1990s, as the Sun became quieter after its sunspot maximum and the cosmic rays and cloud cover increased.

At this initial inspection, cosmic rays might affect the Earth's cloud cover. Not by much – perhaps a couple of percentage points between the quiet Sun and the active Sun. Svensmark kept his finding to himself, because he knew there was still a great deal to do before it could be checked out and presented in a scientifically acceptable form. And it was still unofficial, spare-time work.

Svensmark's first talk with Friis-Christensen was at a formal meeting about his job, when his prospective new research leader explained the history and work of the solar-terrestrial physics division, and sketched the climate study that he had in mind for Svensmark to do if he joined. He had studied the c.v. carefully, and Svensmark was able to explain his ice core work. Friis-Christensen also expounded his philosophy of science. Theory, he said, had to be verified by observations and experiments, not only by models. That was just what Svensmark wanted to hear.

Friis-Christensen asked Knud Lassen for a second opinion on Svensmark. Lassen spoke with one of Svensmark's teachers at the Technical University of Denmark who was an old friend. And he had a chat with Svensmark, in the course of which Svensmark asked his opinion about the cloud chamber and whether there could be any connection with clouds in the atmosphere. Although Lassen was cautious about it, Svensmark left thinking that he must work harder on the idea.

He had another formal meeting with Friis-Christensen to discuss the climate project in more detail. Svensmark still said nothing about his personal interest in cosmic rays. It might have seemed brash. But the transfer was agreed, and he was due to join Friis-Christensen's division from the start of the New Year.

Friis-Christensen remained an official Danish reviewer for the scientific working group of the Intergovernmental Panel on Climate Change. Out of a sense of duty to the international community, he made his usual comments about there being other manifestations of solar variability, besides changes in the intensity of sunshine. As usual these were ignored. And after his experience in Canton in 1992, Friis-Christensen declined to go to Madrid at the end of November to approve the new report.

A weather balloon ready to soar over Antarctica. Measurements of air temperatures at high altitudes became central to the arguments about whether or not a greenhouse warming was detectable. Here at Halley Bay, where the ozone hole was discovered, the loss of ozone cools the stratosphere.

Graham Neden / Ecoscene

Chapter Nine

COSMIC RAYS AND CLOUD COVER

'IF you're being run out of town,' an American saying of the time advised, 'stride out in front and say it's a parade.'

The greenhouse warming proposition of the Intergovernmental Panel on Climate Change, that the world was overheating and the effects would be disastrous if not ameliorated, had a growing crowd of angry thinkers at its heels. We'd like a warmer world, some said. Others calculated that the costs of averting any ill-consequences were affordable. And those were people still prepared to believe the overall scenario of climate change.

A meteorological posse in pursuit of the scientific working group was saying that the calculations were wrong, or at the very least had to be done all over again with new cloud physics. The observational evidence of ongoing climate change was not merely failing to confirm the greenhouse warming, but was contradicting it. The Danish solar-terrestrial physicists, who had the clearest idea of what was really going on with the world's climate, had not even joined the throng. They had better things to do.

But other laboratories kept coming up with basic points of climatology that the computer modellers of climate had got wrong, or overlooked. The latest was satellite evidence of a broad, cooling cloud of mineral dust covering North Africa, Arabia and the Indian subcontinent like a permanent sandstorm. It was exactly the kind of thing that an enquiry into climate change should be pursuing if it were not fixated on the greenhouse warming.

In the Spanish capital at the end of November 1995, the final session of the official group sought and obtained line-by-line approval of the 'Summary for Policymakers' from 177 delegates from 96 countries, and their acceptance of the rest of the report. Everything depended on Chapter 8, entitled 'Detection of Climate Change and Attribution of Causes' and on the gloss to be put on the subject in the 'Summary for Policymakers'.

John Houghton strode out in front to say that the greenhouse warming was proved. He found a form of words that stopped short of that, but still gave the media and the politicians the impression that it was so, in good time for the conference in Geneva in the summer of 1996, when signatories to the Climate Convention were supposed to agree on tougher curbs on greenhouse gases.

In 1994, an unfriendly intervention by Patrick Michaels of Charlottesville, Virginia, had suggested that the greenhouse warming was disproved. Michaels was both an academic environmental scientist and the state climatologist for Virginia. He and his colleagues compared recent changes of climate with calculations of how the greenhouse world should evolve, coming from the first of the new generation of air-ocean computer models, at the Geophysical Fluid Dynamics Laboratory near Princeton.

The 1990 report on *Climate Change* had called the air-ocean models 'the ones which describe the climate system most realistically'. A chapter devoted to them gave special attention to the pioneering Princeton computations. One advertised virtue of the new models was that you could trace the changes of climate from decade to decade, as carbon dioxide increased. But that left them open to inspection as never before.

If the greenhouse warming had already begun, which was an article of faith, then should not the global patterns of climate change already resemble the early stages of the computed predictions? Michaels' team found no correspondence whatever between the computed changes and the actual changes observed by meteorologists in the real world of the late twentieth century. Others who did the same sort of thing came to the same conclusion, but as they were friends of the greenhouse warming they merely expressed regret and asked for patience. Michaels, on the other hand, said that the fancy Princeton climate model was simply wrong, and so presumably were all similar models.

'There are a number of serious problems with this analysis,' Houghton's authors retorted. As Michaels was an official US reviewer they could not omit his conclusion entirely. But they protested that the expected greenhouse signal in the patterns of actual climate change was obscured by random variations ('noise') in the computations and, in real life, by natural variations and by effects of sulphates which reduced the greenhouse warming. Michaels had considered sulphates, but assumed that their effects should be small, far from the centres of pollution. Not so, was the reply, according to the latest computer experiments showing far-flung effects.

Although they cried foul over Michaels' conclusion that the models failed to depict the real world, members of the group felt obliged to counter-attack. Chief among them was Ben Santer of Livermore, California, the Convening Lead Author of Chapter 8.

The trouble was that Michaels was right. The calculated changes bore little or no resemblance to the actual changes in climate. Computer-as-artist continued to produce coloured maps of the world, but the results were ludicrous, especially for the 1990 assumptions of a pure greenhouse world, on which the political drive to the Climate Convention of 1992 had relied.

When the climate modellers offered geographic patterns of actual climate change from the 1960s to the 1980s, by computations of the greenhouse warming alone, the map in lurid shades of red showed, for example, warmings over Greenland, Amazonia, the Himalayas and the Pacific Ocean, which had in reality cooled. By the greenhouse calculations there should have been a very strong warming by several degrees C in the Southern Ocean around Antarctica. In actuality it was up by half a degree at most.

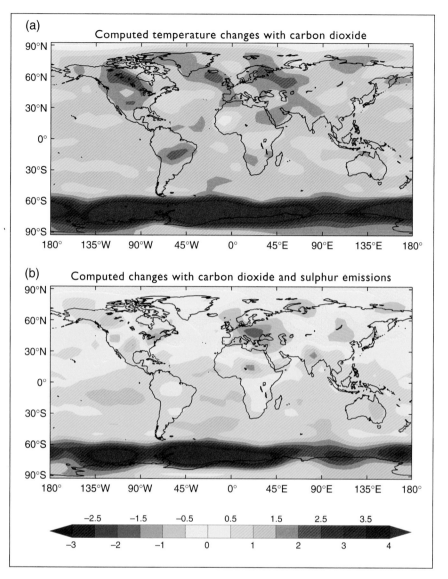

(a) Computed temperature changes with carbon dioxide

(b) Computed changes with carbon dioxide and sulphur emissions

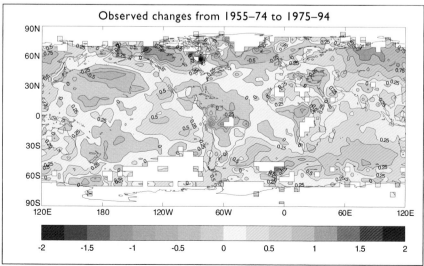

Observed changes from 1955–74 to 1975–94

Looking for the greenhouse warming. The top map (centred on Africa) shows a geographical pattern of progressive surface temperature changes expected from present levels of carbon dioxide, in computations for the Intergovernmental Panel on Climate Change. The second computation takes into account the dust from man-made sulphur emissions, which exerts a cooling effect. The map below (with South America in the middle) shows the real-life changes as measured, in degrees C, between periods centred on the 1960s and the 1980s. In blank areas the data are insufficient.

IPCC Working Group 1, 1995, Figs. 17 and 9

When sulphates were added to the brew, the maps changed completely, with large areas of blue denoting cooling, instead of inexorable warming everywhere. But comparison with the actual climate change showed the errors to be repeated or redistributed. The computations still did not give the coolings over Amazonia, the Himalayas or the Pacific. Nor did they moderate the Southern Ocean warming sufficiently to match reality.

Throwing around its helpful bits of blue like an action painter, the computer sometimes hit the spot: in Greenland, Turkey and Japan for example. But that seemed like luck, because a string of places were condemned by the computer to coolings they did not have: Germany, Novaya Zemlya, Mongolia, East Siberia, Washington State, New England and, bizarrely, Kenya. It seemed like an act of prudence to print the computed maps and the observational maps on different pages of the final report. Only the most diligent reader would notice how absurdly wrong the modelling had been, concerning the geographical distribution of recent climate change.

Ben Santer tried a different approach, and the main scientific evidence for a man-made impact in Chapter 8 of *Climate Change 1995* came from the research of his own group at Livermore. The method was to look for patterns of warming and cooling high up in the atmosphere. Scientists of the US National Oceanic and Atmospheric Administration collated world-wide observations from weather balloons, from 1963 to 1988. They showed the 25-year trend in temperatures at different latitudes and different altitudes, up to 20 kilometres. Plotted not in a map but in a colourful cross-sectional diagram of the atmosphere from pole to pole, the result was a different kind of computer art.

An orange blob for the greatest observed warming, about 1 degree C, hovered in the lower atmosphere over the Southern Ocean at the latitude of New Zealand. A blue blob for cooling occurred at higher altitudes over northern high latitudes, and shades of blue, with purple blobs for the greatest changes, decorated the whole stratosphere. The most intense and purplish chilling, of 2 degrees or more, appeared at 12 kilometres altitude over Antarctica.

The Livermore team then used computer predictions of man-made climatic change to try to match this striking picture of the observations of actual climate change in the atmosphere. The first result was unsatisfactory. The computer model using present-day levels of carbon dioxide put a sliver of blue at 20 kilometres, and a broad red blob of intense heating 8 kilometres above the tropics.

When the team then ran a computer model with man-made sulphate dust added, they managed to reduce the heating and bias it towards the southern hemisphere. Inaccurate warm blobs remained at 2 to 6 kilometres over the polar regions. Relying on the aesthetic rating of this blotchy picture, and its alleged similarity to the observations, the Houghton group suggested that an 'anthropogenic fingerprint' might have been detected.

Santer himself was reluctant to claim so much from his computer artwork. The wording of his chapter concerning the evidence for a man-made climate change was too weak to bolster the Climate Convention. John Houghton took

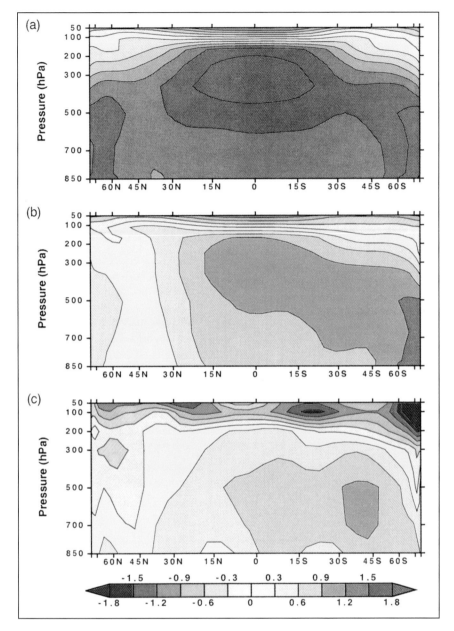

Looking for the greenhouse warming, up in the air. The top cross-section (a) shows computed changes of temperature in the atmosphere from the North Pole (left) to the South Pole (right) and at altitudes up to about 20 kilometres, by the increase in carbon dioxide since pre-industrial times. In the second cross-section (b) a similar computation takes account of cooling effects, especially in the northern hemisphere, of man-made emissions of sulphur compounds. The third cross-section (c) shows actual changes observed by weather balloons between 1963 and 1988.

IPCC Working Group 1, 1995, Fig. 8.7

personal charge of a drive towards a stronger statement implying that the greenhouse warming was proved.

As chairman of the key parts of the plenary meeting of the scientific working group in Madrid, Houghton led the delegates through a lengthy discussion of the draft of Santer's Chapter 8. The aim was to find, as Houghton put it, 'the best and most scientifically accurate wording' for the 'Summary for Policymakers'. The outcome was unanimous approval for a crucial paragraph:

> Our ability to quantify the human influence on global climate is currently limited
> .... Nevertheless the balance of the evidence suggests that there is a discernible
> human influence on global climate.

Lest anyone should still fail to get the message, Bert Bolin, John Houghton and

Gylvan Meira Filho gave it special emphasis in their preface to *Climate Change 1995*.

> That observations suggest 'a discernible human influence on global climate', one of the key findings of this report, adds an important new dimension to the discussion of the climate change issue.

A headline on a news report in the journal *Science* achieved the desired outcome in public information:

It's Official: First Glimmer of Greenhouse Warming Seen

The unfortunate Santer was prevailed upon to modify his scientific Chapter 8 to make it consistent with the 'Summary for Policymakers'. He had his own scientific reputation to worry about, but he obliged as well as he could. The relevant passage in the revised chapter still gave both sides of the argument.

> We come to the difficult question of when the detection and attribution of human-induced climatic change is likely to occur. The answer to this question must be subjective, particularly in the light of the large signal and noise uncertainties discussed in this chapter. Some scientists maintain that these uncertainties currently preclude any answer to the question posed above. Other scientists would and have claimed … that confident detection of a significant anthropogenic climate change has already occurred. … The body of statistical evidence …, when examined in the context of our physical understanding of the climate system, now points towards a discernible human influence on global climate.

Santer's candid acknowledgement of subjectivity, and of differences of opinion among scientists, showed how meaningless was the unanimity that Houghton achieved from his delegates. But few politicians would read the cautious wording that remained even in the revised Chapter 8, preferring the much more concise and emphatic 'Summary for Policymakers'. Even when Chapter 8 became a cause célèbre, on the eventual publication of *Climate Change 1995*, the scientific nuances were too technical for most policymakers, and the political nuances too boring for most scientists.

By mid-December 1995, Henrik Svensmark thought there was definitely a connection between cosmic rays and clouds. If no one knew about it already, he had discovered it. He asked for a meeting with Eigil Friis-Christensen, to find out whether the link was known. This time Svensmark produced the preliminary results from his forays on the Internet.

Friis-Christensen was at once very excited, because his mind was prepared for just such a possibility. He had been thinking about effects near the bottom of the stratosphere, where the count of cosmic rays peaked. What Svensmark described implied a strong effect lower down, but as cosmic rays penetrated all the way to the ground, that was quite conceivable. So it came about, in a suburb of Copenhagen by the Elsinore motorway, that one scientist suggested to another that cosmic rays made clouds all over the world and he was not immediately disbelieved. The human species' understanding of climate change took a step forward.

International Satellite Cloud Climatology Project. Temperatures observed by American and European weather satellites are here collated for the Atlantic region on a July day (273 K = 0 degrees C). Cold cloud tops appear white; warm cloud tops grey. The image illustrates the detailed analysis that went into the climate record of variable global cloud cover used in detecting the effect of cosmic rays.
ISCCP/WCRP/WMO & ICSU; graphics by NASA GISS, courtesy of W.B. Rossow

'We must work very fast,' Friis-Christensen said. They both knew, without having to discuss it, the potential importance of the result for people everywhere. But uppermost in their thoughts were the harsh facts of life in the social system of science. A few weeks of spare-time work had yielded Svensmark's preliminary result, and any other competent person could do the same thing. To win the credit for a discovery you had to be the first to publish it in the formal literature.

That meant first clarifying the findings and then presenting them as a knock-down argument suitable for a scientific journal. Although Friis-Christensen would interact with him and make critical suggestions, Svensmark would have to continue doing nearly all the work. Apart from all his space commitments, Friis-Christensen had to go to San Francisco before Christmas for a scientific congress.

But Svensmark's efforts were now officially approved and he would be able to work on them full time. Well, more than full time. He cancelled his Christmas holiday. When Friis-Christensen returned from San Francisco he took a few days off to see his parents in Jutland, but he interacted with Svensmark via the Internet.

In the quiet spell after Christmas Day the Danish Meteorological Institute was almost deserted except for the duty weather forecasters and that crazy guy upstairs at his workstation. That was when Svensmark located on the Internet much better sets of data on global cloud cover. A series from NASA's Nimbus-7 satellite gave satisfactory results when compared with the counts of cosmic rays, but as with the US Air Force satellites the observation of clouds at any one place were less frequent than the changes in the weather. The source that Svensmark found rather belatedly was the International Satellite Cloud Climatology Project. It gave him more clouds than an Irish bank holiday.

Masterminded by William Rossow at NASA's Goddard Institute in New York City, the project was a large data-processing operation on behalf of the World Climate Research Programme. It collated and tallied the clouds seen by many of the world's civilian weather satellites from mid-1983 onwards, in a common data base providing average cloud amounts month by month over squares of the Earth's surface about 250 kilometres wide. The information also included temperatures and atmospheric pressures at the cloud tops, which gave impressions of the clouds' altitudes. The monthly cloud data existed as electronic files accessible on the Internet, but Svensmark asked the archive centre at NASA Langley for a more convenient compact disk.

The first extended series, called ISCCP-C2, ran from mid-1983 to December 1990, without the gap that marred the US Air Force data. The period conveniently straddled the sunspot minimum of 1986 and continued to the sunspot maximum of 1990. The monthly mean cloud amounts were Svensmark's chief tool after the Christmas break, when at last he found himself working officially and full time on the problem in Friis-Christensen's division. In other words, full time as well as spare time.

The cloud amounts recorded by the International Satellite Cloud Climatology Project naturally varied a great deal from season to season. Svensmark made a twelve-month running average. That meant taking, at monthly intervals, averages of the preceding six months and the following six months. Because of this procedure he had to exclude the period covered by the first six months and the last six months of the ISCCP-C2 data. That left him with the running averages for January 1984 to June 1990.

As for the monthly mean counts of cosmic rays at Climax, Colorado, they rose at the start of the period covered by the cloud data, as the Sun became quieter, and peaked at the end of 1986. From March 1987 the counts fell quite steadily for two years as the Sun became progressively spottier and more active. The graph looked like the Matterhorn, with a gradual slope up towards the summit and a steeper drop on the other side.

Did the cloud averages climb the same mountain? Yes, approximately. The gross rise and fall was there, but the match to the graph of cosmic-ray counts was not close enough to satisfy Friis-Christensen, never mind the real sceptics. There were too many examples in the scientific literature of vague similarities between solar cycles and weather phenomena. If there were a direct effect of cosmic rays on cloud amounts, it ought to be quite precise.

Svensmark wondered if the fault lay, not with the hypothesis that cosmic rays affected cloud formation, but with the cloud data. The intuitive idea that one should use all the available information might be wrong. When he looked more closely at how ISCCP-C2 was compiled, and tracked down Rossow's commentaries on the cloud climatology exercise, Svensmark learned that ISCCP-C2 was not a precise and foolproof compilation.

Results from satellites of different national origins with different instruments and following different orbits co-existed uncomfortably. Like the US Air Force satellites, a pair of American civilian NOAA satellites orbited over the poles, and used the Earth's rotation to scan the whole world's weather. They offered consistent and truly global coverage, with carefully matched instruments, but even with two satellites they visited each place only twice a day in daylight. Clouds could come into existence and dissipate again when the NOAA satellites were not looking.

Much more frequent images came from four geostationary weather satellites that orbited high over the Equator at the same rate as the Earth turned. Each kept a huge area of the Earth under continuous surveillance. Europe's Meteosat for example, from its lofty vantage point over the Gulf of Guinea, sent pictures every half hour of a region stretching from Scandinavia to Antarctica and from Brazil to Arabia, with Africa and the eastern Atlantic Ocean dominating the scene.

Comparable observations came from the American geostationary satellites GOES-East over Brazil and GOES-West over the eastern Pacific Ocean, and the Japanese GMS over the western Pacific. The coverage of these satellites overlapped nicely except over the Indian Ocean sector, where Meteosat and GMS had only slanting views. India's satellite observing that sector did not contribute to the cloud climatology project.

The geostationary satellites could not quite see the poles. The high-latitude regions appeared on an ever-increasing slant in the raw images, until the fore-shortening made cloud assessments difficult. Even so, the high frequency of observations from the geostationary weather satellites made them seem like the preferred source of data, for looking for effects of cosmic rays.

Other question marks about the data, which Svensmark ran into, concerned the identification of clouds. It relied on a difference in temperature between the cloud tops and the surface. Over the tropical and temperate oceans, clouds stood out very clearly in the satellite telescopes against the lukewarm water. But towards the poles the satellite data could confuse sea ice and clouds. Over cold land and mountains, clouds could be missed for similar reasons. Rossow and his colleagues acknowledged that figures for cloud cover over land tended to be too low in ISCCP-C2.

Svensmark decided to edit the cloud data. He would restrict himself to the clearly defined cloud cover over the oceans, as tabulated from the geostationary satellites. The resulting graph of trustworthy cloud data, for the period January 1984 to June 1990, showed the cloud cover over the oceans reducing by 3 per cent, between the peak in the cosmic-ray cycle near sunspot minimum, and the troughs near the surrounding sunspot maxima. The graph followed the mountain-like profile of the cosmic ray graph more closely than before.

'It gets better and better,' Svensmark said. But as an expert on the Earth's magnetism, Friis-Christensen began to stress the importance of geography. If the effect on clouds were really due to cosmic rays, it would be greater at mid-latitudes than near the magnetic equator, because the relative intensities of

The solar-terrestrial Vikings. At the Danish Meteorological Institute, Eigil Friis-Christensen (behind), Henrik Svensmark (centre) and Knud Lassen (right) explained the rise in global temperatures in the twentieth century by manic behaviour in the Sun. Until the culmination, the work on climate change was all done in their spare time. The dome houses a radio dish for communicating with Denmark's Ørsted satellite, for which Friis-Christensen is project scientist.

Kirsten Fich Pedersen

cosmic rays increased towards the magnetic poles. When the opportunity came, Svensmark should look for an effect of latitude in the cloud data.

The format of the cloud climatology did not lend itself to selecting data by magnetic latitudes very easily. Before Svensmark embarked on the elaborate work, Friis-Christensen agreed that he should use ordinary geographical latitudes and see what happened when he left out the clouds of the tropical oceans.

Eureka! The variations in cloud amounts were greater by one third, increasing from 3 per cent to 4 per cent. Their more precise match to the variations in cosmic rays was not just beautiful to look at. The statistical test showed a correlation of 0.95 out of a maximum possible score of 1.00 for perfect correspondence. That figure improved to a compelling 0.97 when Svensmark compared like with like, using 12-month running averages for the cosmic rays as well as the clouds.

Nature was addressing them quite clearly, and telling the Danish physicists that it did indeed use cosmic rays to help it make clouds. The contrary possibil-

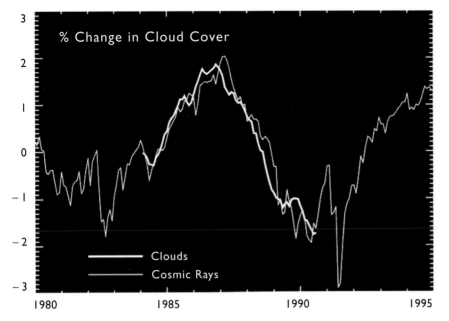

% Change in Cloud Cover

Clouds
Cosmic Rays

The missing link between Sun and climate. As solar activity diminished between 1984 and 1986, and the count of cosmic rays increased, clouds became more widespread. Satellite observations over the oceans outside the tropics showed the cloud cover increasing by 2 per cent. As the Sun became more active and cosmic rays dwindled, 1987–91, the clouds decreased by 4 per cent.

After H. Svensmark & E. Friis-Christensen, 1997; cosmic ray data from Climax, Colorado; cloud data from ISCCP

ity was that the clouds and the cosmic rays were independently obeying some other driving force. The closeness of the correlation and the effect of latitude virtually ruled that out. By January 1996, Friis-Christensen was satisfied that here was the physical mechanism required, in addition to the variations in the Sun's output of light, to explain the solar warming.

The meteorologists might quibble about the tropical clouds being left out. After all, the great cloud clusters of the tropical oceans were the chief boiler-houses driving the global weather. In investigating this question Svensmark learned that, contrary to intuition, the clouds of the tropics had relatively little influence on the global temperature. Satellite results showed that they trapped infrared rays from the warm surface to an extent that almost exactly compensated for their cooling action in blocking sunlight.

What would clinch the discovery was clearer proof of the sensitivity of the cloud-making effect to magnetic latitude. Friis-Christensen suggested a statistical technique, but when Svensmark found time to tackle the problem he preferred to work more directly with percentage changes in the cloud amounts, at different magnetic latitudes. That required quite a complex computation, to assign each 250-kilometre square in the cloud climatology grid to its magnetic latitude from the magnetic equator, which slanted almost 12 degrees south over the Andes and 12 degrees north over Indo-China.

Svensmark then computed square by square the variation in cloud cover that correlated with the cosmic ray variations over 90 months. Finally, he averaged the squares for each zone of magnetic latitude. But then he stalled. The result did not look at all good, and Friis-Christensen agreed that it should not be included in the first scientific paper, which they were urgently preparing.

The pace was punishing. Svensmark and Friis-Christensen were trying to accomplish in two months what most researchers and their supervisors might attempt in a year or more. They had to formalize the findings, consider the implications, and where possible obtain further results on cosmic rays and cloud cover. Another part of the game, as required by journal editors, was to scour the library for relevant research and ideas already published, beyond what Friis-Christensen had collected in his drawer. This search threw up interesting items that strengthened the scientific case.

A group of Russians, one of whose reported remarks had first prompted Svensmark to think about cosmic rays, came uncomfortably close to beating the Danes to their discovery. In 1995 M.I. Pudovkin of St Petersburg and his colleagues had reported that sunlight registered on the ground at stations in northern Russia increased when the Sun was active and the count of cosmic rays fell. The Russians linked this to changes in cloud cover. The thought that the Russians or others might easily follow up this local observation with global studies of cloud amounts gave added urgency to the work in Copenhagen.

'Anyone could have made this discovery in the past ten years,' Svensmark remarked. That was roughly how long the collated cloud data from the satellites had been available, to set alongside the long-standing counts of cosmic rays.

Svensmark and Friis-Christensen also found a 20-year-old suggestion that electric charges created by cosmic rays in the atmosphere could interact with sulphate dust to promote cloud formation. More recently, other scientists had confirmed that dust scavenged electric charges from the air. The two Danish physicists knew that they had blown a hole in the microphysics of cloud formation, because meteorologists did not know that cosmic rays were involved. Unable themselves to launch any airborne experiments into the clouds, they contented themselves with very general remarks on the subject.

Reckoning the effect of the variable clouds on global temperatures had to be done quite simplistically too. The only alternative was to put many scientist-years of research into cosmic rays affecting clouds of different kinds at different altitudes with different climatic consequences. That would no doubt follow, once the world's meteorologists were persuaded of the mechanism. Meanwhile Svensmark and Friis-Christensen assumed that the clouds that varied with the cosmic rays were average clouds.

And on the average, clouds cooled the planet. as shown by American satellite observations in the Earth Radiation Budget Experiment. The negative effect of clouds on temperature worked in the right direction to explain the solar warming by a more active Sun. Increased solar activity reduced the cosmic rays, and that reduced the cloud cover, which raised the temperature.

As to the size of the clouds' effect, it was 0.8 to 1.7 watt per square metre, simply for the variations seen during the 1980s, depending on which satellite radiation assessments were to be believed. An independent source, William Rossow of the International Satellite Cloud Climatology Project, gave a figure of 0.5 watt for a 1 per cent change in cloud cover, and so a 3 per cent change would give 1.5 watt. That matched the 1.5 watt officially estimated for the effect of all the carbon dioxide added to the atmosphere by human activity so far.

A cyclical variation would cause no long-term trend in climate. But there was good evidence for increased solar activity during the twentieth century, resulting in a large overall reduction in cosmic ray intensities. One could infer a significant and persistent reduction in cloud cover, causing the global warming.

The paper that Svensmark and Friis-Christensen wrote was muted on the implications for climate change. They suggested, politely, that climate modellers should put the variations in clouds due to the Sun's actions into their greenhouse calculations, to re-evaluate their assessments of 'natural' variability and the human impact. They made a passing comment that a connection between climate and changes in the Earth's main magnetic field over thousands of years could now be explained. To relate their work on clouds to the earlier discovery of the effect of the length of the solar cycle, Svensmark and Friis-Christensen pointed out that persistent cloud cover during long solar cycles might contribute to climate change.

'This, however, does not exclude that there may be additional long-term variations in the solar modulations of cosmic ray flux which also contribute to the observed effect on temperature.' That sentence described the real climatic bombshell in almost coded form. On 29 February, leap year day, Svensmark and Friis-Christensen sent the paper off to the journal *Science* in Washington DC, which had published the seminal Friis-Christensen and Lassen paper of 1991. They hoped for quick publication.

By coincidence, *Science* published in early March 1996 a round-up of recent results pointing to a solar connection with climate, by its news writer Richard Kerr. It included a graph from Judith Lean of Washington DC showing how her latest reckonings of changing solar brightness since 1600 matched quite well with the fluctuations in northern hemisphere temperatures. Her estimates of possible brightness variations had encouraged Houghton's group to circumscribe the Sun's role in climate. Now she was saying that brightness changes could account for about half the warming up till about 1970, though only a third of the subsequent warming.

Astonished oceanographers, Kerr also reported, had found that records of ocean surface temperatures, going back half a century, matched the wiggles of the Sun's brightness as measured by satellites or estimated by Lean. The variations were about a tenth of a degree C through each solar cycle. Thus quite independently of the Danish work, the solar connection was obtruding again into the scientific consciousness – and, more importantly, into the climatic observations.

The title on Kerr's article was 'A New Dawn for Sun-Climate Links?' He cautioned his readers about the mystery surrounding all claims concerning the Sun and climate. To explain why the alleged effects were so strong, some unknown amplifying mechanism was required. Just as *Science* was coming out with that issue, the paper from Svensmark and Friis-Christensen arrived in its office in Washington DC.

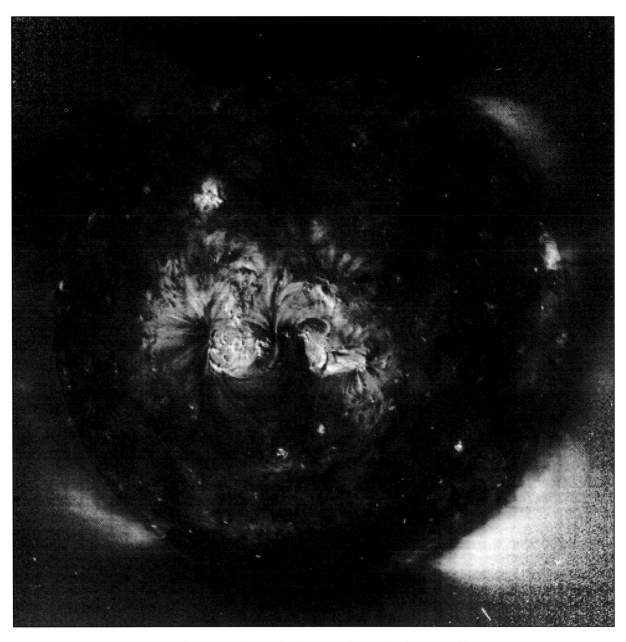

Like a plate of spaghetti. This tangle of magnetic loops tells of unimaginable stresses in the solar atmosphere. When the SOHO spacecraft imaged it, in May 1996, the Sun was supposedly very calm, at the low point in its sunspot cycle. Although half as wide as the visible face, the feature was unseen by ground-based telescopes. The details emerged in comparisons of images of gas at 1 million and 1.5 million degrees C, from SOHO's extreme ultraviolet imaging telescope.

SOHO/ESA & NASA and EIT Consortium

Chapter Ten

UNCEASING VIOLENCE

A DIFFERENT POINT OF VIEW on the Sun's behaviour came from the multinational team analysing relatively young ice from the GRIP deep ice core in Greenland. Older ice had already revealed rapid changes in temperature during the last ice age, detected by changes in the proportion of heavy oxygen in the ice. For students of historical changes of climate, the most dramatic new finding was a similar event during the past millennium.

A very cold period around 1380 AD was followed by a very warm period little more than a decade later, around 1393. The rise in mean temperature at the summit of the Greenland ice sheet was about 5 degrees C. For comparison, in the global warming of the twentieth century the difference between the coldest and warmest years was about 1.5 degrees.

The timing, speed and magnitude of the great warming of 1380–93 could not be accounted for by changes in the Sun, still less by any greenhouse effect. The Sun had been relatively active around 1350, but was quietening down when the warming occurred. Perhaps the Earth had contrived the change itself. If, for example, the Gulf Stream were choked off in 1380 and restored by 1393, that might account for temperature swing recorded in the Greenland ice. The fourteenth century event also called into question the very definition of climate, and especially the use of averages which could easily smudge out sudden warmings and chillings of great consequence to the people enduring them.

A special GRIP study of temperature fluctuations over the previous nine centuries raised other issues, about the nature and cause of the Sun's variations. The ice record showed cycles of rises and falls and re-rises in temperature over about 11.7 and 19.4 years. The GRIP team, led by Sigfus Johnsen of Reykjavik, took the view that the cycles traced back to a slow rotation of the Sun about the centre of gravity of the solar system, which was offset from the centre of the Sun.

The dominant influences, in this interpretation, were the giant planet Jupiter orbiting the Sun every 11.9 years, and Saturn aligning itself with Jupiter every 19.9 years. Since 1979, when earlier analyses of Greenland ice cores revealed a 20-year cycle of temperatures, Johnsen had pressed this planetary hypothesis of solar changes. He argued that it was more fundamental than the sunspot cycles of 11 and 22 years, which might be a by-product of the planets' effects.

In March 1996 an organization called the European Science and Environment Forum published a collection of articles on *The Global Warming Debate*. John

Emsley of Imperial College, London, was the editor. The book brought together two dozen critics of the greenhouse warming scenario. In expertise the contributors ranged from astronomers such as Sallie Baliunas and Fred Hoyle to social scientists including Roger Bate and Sonja Boehmer-Christiansen. Eigil Friis-Christensen and Knud Lassen contributed a short account on their work linking temperatures to the length of the solar cycle. It did not, of course, cover the new result on cosmic rays and clouds.

From Stockholm, Wibjörn Karlén and Johan Kuylenstierna updated for *The Global Warming Debate* the use of radiocarbon and tree growth as an indicator of solar control of the climate. They studied relics of trees growing on Scandinavian slopes above the present tree line, indicating a warmer climate. This occurred in virtually all periods in the past 10,000 years when the radiocarbon levels were low, indicating high activity by the Sun. Karlén and Kuylenstierna mentioned changes in cloud cover, influenced by the Earth's magnetic field, as a possible link between solar action and climate.

Cloud formation by solar protons figured in a contribution from St Petersburg, by Genrik Nikolsky. He recalled observing from a mountain station in the Caucasus, in October 1989, the clouding first of nearby canyons and then the entire sky, within an hour of the arrival of protons from a strong solar flare. At the same time, the American Tiros-N satellite recorded a huge decrease in water vapour over the western Pacific due to its condensation. But Nikolsky thought that ultraviolet rays from the vicinity of sunspots had more important impacts on climate.

Other supporters of the solar warming hypothesis writing in Emsley's book included the inventor of the Solar Weather Technique, Piers Corbyn, and John Butler of Armagh Observatory. As publisher, Roger Bate stressed that the European Science and Environment Forum was funded entirely by revenues from its publications, and many differing scientific views were represented. The lack of a consensus was seen as a virtue, not a weakness.

Many ordinary inhabitants of the Earth wondered what had become of the much-vaunted global warming in the early months of 1996, as prolonged wintery conditions delayed crop production in the northern mid-latitudes. While Alaska, Greenland and Siberia were unusually warm, the eastern coastal United States had more than twice the usual winter snow, and in February, many stations across the country reported the lowest temperatures ever recorded. For the United States as a whole, March 1996 was colder than any March since 1975. Central Europe was also unusually chilly, and so was Kazakhstan in central Asia.

Undistracted by mundane questions about the weather, fundamental investigations of the Sun continued. At the beginning of April 1996, Japanese physicists inaugurated their Super-Kamiokande underground observatory, as the world's largest detector for neutrinos coming from the core of the Sun. A tank of super-pure water 40 metres wide and 40 metres deep was lined with 11,000 sensitive light detectors to register faint flashes due to neutrinos hitting electrons in the water molecules.

After 30 years, and a string of experiments around the world, the count of neutrinos remained too low. Either physicists did not correctly understand how solar energy was generated in nuclear reactions, or they did not understand the neutrinos, or the Sun was varying at its core. For some physicists, the neutrino mystery remained the biggest source of doubt about human theories of the Sun.

In April 1996, a new French-Italian solar telescope on the Spanish island of Tenerife made its first trial observations of the Sun's visible surface. Called Thémis, it reinforced the two German solar telescopes already operating on Tenerife, and a Swedish instrument on nearby La Palma. With Tenerife also providing the base for two global networks of helioseismic instruments for probing the Sun's interior, in the British BISON and the French IRIS projects, the Canary Islands had become Europe's site of choice for ground-based observations of the Sun.

Earlier in the year American solar physicists had announced the first results of a new technique called helioseismic tomography. It used computers to gauge the travel time of packets of sound waves in the humming Sun, from detailed measurements of oscillations at different parts of the surface. For observations made at the Earth's South Pole, Thomas Duvall and his colleagues used the technique to probe the underside of sunspots.

They found tubes of gas flowing into the Sun beneath a sunspot, at about 2 kilometres per second, bundled together near the surface but breaking up into narrower tubes at a depth of about 600 kilometres. The downflows, which also occurred under bright regions called plages, could be traced to depths of about 2000 kilometres.

American scientists and foreign collaborators released the first results of the GONG network of six high-powered helioseismic instruments distributed around the world. GONG had started work with three stations in June 1995 and the network was complete by December 1995. Among its prime detections from the solar oscillations were two shear layers where adjacent parts of the Sun's interior rotated at different rates. These were potentially crucial for understanding the ever-changing surface magnetism and sunspots.

One shear layer confirmed by GONG was at the base of the turbulent outer region, the convection zone, about 30 per cent of the way down towards the centre of the Sun. This layer was the prime candidate for the site of the Sun's imagined dynamo for generating magnetic fields. From the GONG measurements, the outer region rotated at the same rate as the interior at around 30 degrees from the equator. The equatorial zone rotated faster, and high-latitude parts of the surface layer much more slowly, compared with the inner body of the Sun.

The other shear layer was much nearer the surface. There in the equatorial zone, an internal layer rotated about 2 per cent faster than the surface gas. This explained a puzzling discovery in 1980 that sunspots moved more rapidly across the face of the Sun than the surrounding gas did. If the sunspots and related activity were anchored to the internal layer, the mystery was cleared up.

The GONG scientists were in a hurry to publish, in the spring of 1996,

Sungazing on Tenerife. The French-Italian solar telescope Thémis has a 90-centimetre primary mirror in a vacuum tube, and active optics to correct the effects of turbulence in the air. Inaugurated in 1996 for the study of the Sun's magnetism, Thémis occupies a 27-metre tower at the Teide Observatory, alongside two German solar telescopes and instruments for helioseismology from many parts of the world. With a Swedish solar telescope on nearby La Palma, Spain's Canary Islands have become a major centre for ground-based observations of the Sun.

Angel Gómez / Instituto de Astrofísica de Canarias

ABOVE: An impression of the SOHO spacecraft.

T. Kinsberger for ESA

RIGHT: A hot horizon on the Sun. Simultaneous images from SOHO's spectrometer CDS, at four ultraviolet wavelengths, reveal gas at different temperatures. If you could visit the solar atmosphere and had ultraviolet eyes, these could be your views.

2,000,000 degrees. The high, hot atmosphere glows bright, while the Sun's visible surface and inner atmosphere appear dark. The bright spot on the right is a scene of fierce activity.

1,000,000 degrees. The horizon blazes, because gas at an intermediate altitude in the atmosphere glows at this temperature. Only a few hotspots in the foreground attain it.

100,000 degrees. In these regions the atmosphere begins heating in earnest, towards temperatures preposterously higher than the 5500 degrees of the visible surface. A cool shadow on the right masks the view beyond.

20,000 degrees. The upper atmosphere looks dark and the lower atmosphere displays a network of bright regions. The shadow of the previous image appears as rising mass of gas linked to a fainter arch on the left.

SOHO/ESA & NASA and CDS Consortium; limb rasters rotated to make the horizon horizontal.

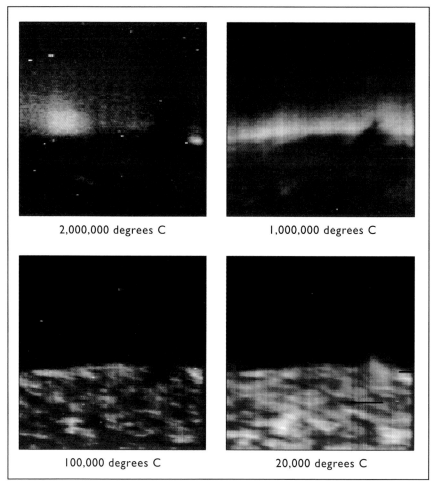

2,000,000 degrees C

1,000,000 degrees C

100,000 degrees C

20,000 degrees C

because they thought they might soon be upstaged by other helioseismic observations. Their fears were well justified, because in April the best-equipped solar spacecraft ever to fly began full-time operations.

Built in Europe and launched by a NASA rocket on 2 December 1995, SOHO was four times as big as Yohkoh, and had a much better vantage point. The Solar and Heliospheric Observatory had travelled to a special station 1,500,000 kilometres out on the sunny side of the Earth. There the Earth's gravity and the Sun's gravity were in balance, and SOHO could stay in touch with the Earth while orbiting around the Sun, untroubled by sunsets or by any but the gentlest of motions.

The accuracy of the launch and the ease of subsequent manoeuvres meant that SOHO had large reserves of fuel. The instruments were remarkably clean, thanks to care during assembly and testing. Launched at the minimum of sunspot activity, SOHO would watch profound changes in the Sun's behaviour as it approached its next maximum.

Under the deal with NASA, in which the European Space Agency was senior partner for the SOHO and Cluster missions, NASA provided the operational facility for SOHO at the Goddard Space Flight Center near Washington DC.

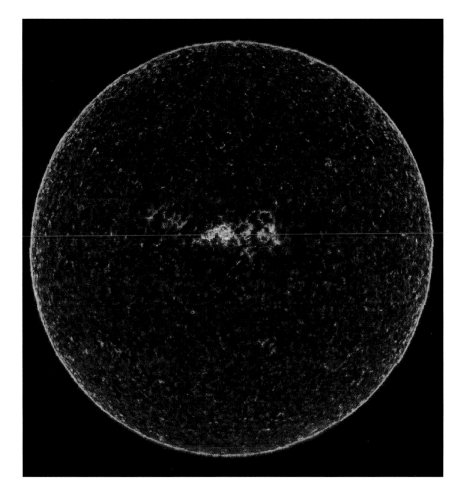

The speckled Sun. While the familiar visible Sun is evenly bright, intense specks and dark regions decorate its lower atmosphere with much greater contrast than solar physicists expected. This ultraviolet image from SOHO's spectrometer SUMER shows flames glowing at 70,000–100,000 degrees C. They make a network corresponding with a magnetic pattern on the visible surface.

SOHO/ESA & NASA and SUMER Consortium

There, excited European and US solar physicists of twelve multinational teams gathered to discuss the results pouring in from SOHO during the first half of 1996.

Although the Sun was in its quietest phase, and apparently tranquil as seen by visible light from observatories on the ground, SOHO revealed unceasing violence. Its telescopes saw giant flames shooting into the atmosphere. Operating by ultraviolet light and soft X-rays, somewhat longer in wavelength than those studied by Japan's Yohkoh satellite, SOHO's instruments could look deeper into the atmosphere. Images at different wavelengths corresponded with different temperatures in the Sun's atmosphere.

As expected, temperatures soared to over 2 million degrees C in the outer atmosphere, while the lower atmosphere and the visible surface remained comparatively cool. Progress up the temperature ladder varied greatly from place to place. In some regions, cool gas followed magnetic pathways high above the Sun's visible surface. Elsewhere, violent activity raised the temperature locally, at low altitudes. In the high-temperature images, the large, dark regions of the coronal holes remained relatively cool.

Processed images, comparing intensities at different ultraviolet wavelengths, clarified the pictures of systems of magnetic loops. Sometimes these sprawled across the solar atmosphere, half as wide as the visible Sun. The images also revealed remarkable contrasts in the outer atmosphere, which could appear dark on one side of the Sun and very active on the other. Hair-like jets seen in the images probably contributed to heating the outer atmosphere.

A spectrometer on SOHO analysed a high-velocity event, corresponding with a small streak of brightness in a scanned image, and detected relative motions of 450 kilometres per second. Richard Harrison of Chilton, England, was in charge of the CDS spectrometer. Like the other solar physicists examining detailed processes, he was always conscious of the implications of the work for human affairs.

'By taking the Sun's atmosphere to pieces we begin to understand how it influences our lives,' Harrison said. 'Surprises here on Earth don't come from the steady light and heat, which we take for granted, but from atmospheric storms that send shock waves through the solar system. By making temperature and density maps of the Sun's atmosphere, we expect to find out how these storms develop.'

Another spectrometer revealed a vast number of bright regions created by magnetic field lines looping through the atmosphere. The brightness could change by a factor of ten in a distance of a few thousand kilometres, or in a few seconds of time. And the instrument revealed that the thick streaks called polar plumes, which climbed far into space from the relatively cool atmosphere near the poles, were anchored in bright regions near the Sun's visible surface.

The atmosphere was relatively cool near the poles, and magnetic lines ran freely into space. Here was the source of the fast solar wind, with twice the speed of the wind from magnetically constrained regions near the Sun's equator. And in the polar plumes SOHO's ultraviolet coronagraph caught oxygen atoms in the very process of acceleration into the windstream.

They went from less than 100 kilometres per second at 250,000 kilometres above the solar surface, to about 225 kilometres per second a million kilometres farther out. The result meshed nicely with a theory from Lindau, Germany, predicting that heavy atoms would be better able to absorb energy from magnetic waves in the Sun's atmosphere. The scientists were on the track of the natural electromagnetic accelerator that drove the solar wind.

SOHO looked outwards as well as inwards, and a big picture came from a solar-wind mapper. It charted a hole burnt by the solar wind, in the breeze of gas arriving from the stars. This instrument avoided looking at the Sun, because it would be dazzled, but it surveyed the sky all around.

The mapper saw an ultraviolet glow from hydrogen atoms coming on the interstellar breeze and lit by the Sun. Charged particles of the solar wind broke the incoming atoms, so that they no longer glowed. From the shape of the resulting hole, the scientists concluded that the solar wind from high-latitude regions of Sun was less strong than from its equator, at least during that quiet phase of solar activity. The wind was also weaker over the Sun's north pole than over the south pole, as suggested by the results from Ulysses.

The Earth was visible to the mapper, because a cloud of hydrogen gas called the geocorona enveloped it and glowed in the ultraviolet. The geocorona would have hampered observations of the heliosphere glow by a satellite close to the Earth. SOHO, far out in space, saw the geocorona from the outside, and would be able to monitor effects of increasing solar activity on the Earth's outer atmosphere.

Particle detectors in SOHO, as in Ulysses, saw cosmic rays arriving from the Milky Way, and varying in intensity as the Sun's activity changed. The instrument also detected the fake cosmic rays of lesser energy made by atoms charged by the solar wind and accelerated through millions of volts by shock waves in the heliosphere. So they brought news to SOHO from distant parts of the empire of the Sun, perhaps 5 or 10 billion kilometres away.

Few highly energetic particles came to SOHO from the quiet Sun itself, but a source of a fast solar wind rotating with the Sun created shock waves that delivered accelerated particles to SOHO on a 26-day cycle, like a garden spray. The same 'corotating interaction region' cut down the count of cosmic rays coming from the Milky Way, by the mechanisms studied by Ulysses in its voyage over the Sun's poles. As the Sun became more active, SOHO's scientists would be able to trace energetic particles to their source in violent events on the Sun. It would be a matter of comparing the particle results with images and analyses of the atmosphere.

The non-stop solar wind yielded other secrets to an instrument in SOHO that analysed its chemical composition more thoroughly than ever before. It detected a catalogue of ingredients, ranging from sodium to nickel, not previously registered in the wind. By comparing the abundances of the elements, scientists could deduce the temperatures in the Sun's atmosphere where the solar wind originated.

SOHO also measured comprehensively and precisely the proportions of atoms of the same chemical elements with different masses – the isotopes. These proportions gave new clues to the elements' creation in dying stars, to the physics of the Sun, and to the history of the solar system, including the Earth itself.

As expected, the most remarkable early results came from SOHO's oscillations imager, SOI-MDI. Developed by Californian scientists and engineers, it divided the face of the Sun into a million points and measured small changes in the wavelength of visible light. From these the team could directly measure motions, brightness and magnetic fields at the Sun's surface, and infer the motions, temperature, density and composition of the solar interior.

Stresses caused by magnetic fields provoked the activity in the Sun's atmosphere, in the network of bright specks and dark regions seen by SOHO's ultraviolet instruments. The network corresponded with magnetic regions on the visible surface, as if the atmosphere read a message written in invisible ink on the surface below. As a guide to that relationship, the oscillations imager produced the best maps of the Sun's magnetism ever available, showing the spotty patterns of magnetic field lines running in and out of the Sun.

By measuring the magnetism once every minute, the oscillations imager

The fountains of the Sun. Warm gas wells up to the visible surface and spreads outwards sideways, making features called supergranules some 30,000 kilometres wide. SOHO's oscillations imager MDI displays the supergranules by distinguishing horizontal flows towards or away from the instrument – seen most plainly in slanted views away from the centre.
SOHO/ESA & NASA and SOI-MDI Consortium

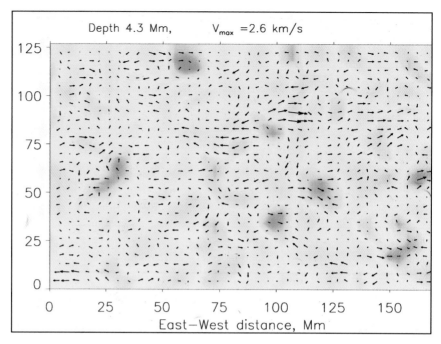

Depth 4.3 Mm,   V$_{max}$ =2.6 km/s

Flows just below the Sun's surface. At a depth of 4300 kilometres, the directions and lengths of the arrows depict horizontal motions of up to 2.6 kilometres per second. The red and blue tints denote relatively warm and cool gas. The area covered is 170,000 kilometres wide. Subtle measurements by the MDI instrument in the SOHO spacecraft probe the Sun's interior at much shallower depths than was possible before.

SOHO/ESA & NASA and SOI-MDI Consortium

made movies. The most obvious effect in observations over a few hours was a general shift due to the Sun's rotation. But changes were also apparent in the magnetic patterns, on a short timescale. The main aim was to relate the changes in the surface magnetism to activity beneath the surface, the chief goal of the oscillations imager. It detected motions by shifts in the wavelength of light, to record the hum of the Sun.

The gas in the Sun's bright oscillating surface rose and fell in waves 100 kilometres high. They moved up towards SOHO and then receded, with the typical period of five minutes. Computers identified many different modes of sound waves reverberating through the Sun, and used them to probe the interior better than ever before. The oscillations imager mapped currents of gas flowing horizontally just below the Sun's surface.

'What pleases us is that shallow flows can be observed,' said Philip Scherrer of Stanford, California, principal investigator for SOI-MDI. 'Ground-based instruments have detected motions deep inside the Sun. With SOHO we can do that too, but now we also provide the missing link to motions at the visible surface.'

To observe the top few thousand kilometres, where much of the outward solar activity originated, required delicate work which only SOI-MDI in SOHO could manage. It had to detect waves dipping only a short distance into the Sun and then resurfacing. The new computational method of helioseismic tomography detected differences in sound speed depending on whether the sound travelled with the flow of gas or against it.

The gas moved at up to a kilometre per second, faster than a supersonic jet plane. The motions concentrated the magnetic regions detected at the surface. At 800 kilometres depth, the gas flowed in much the same directions as at the visible surface. But 1500 kilometres down, the flows reversed. The probers had

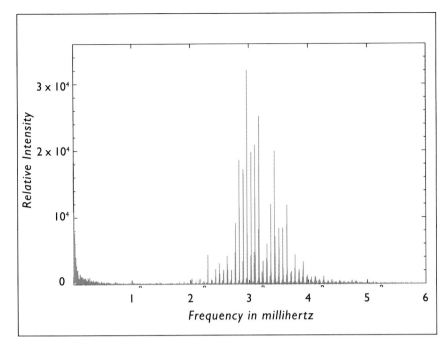

The solar musical scale. A very early impression from the GOLF instrument showed individual frequencies of the Sun's hum coming to the SOHO spacecraft very clearly, with far less background noise than expected. The peaks around 3 millihertz are solar oscillations of about 5.5 minutes' duration.

SOHO/ESA & NASA and GOLF Consortium

already reached the bottom of the outermost turnover of gas in the boiling convection zone of the Sun. Many solar physicists had expected two or three times that depth, for the convection regions 30,000 kilometres wide that linked ascending and descending flows. Instead, they were shallow and pancake-like.

The purposes of the oscillations imager were not modest. By making movies of the Sun's interior, Scherrer and his colleagues expected to relate the motions to their measurements of surface magnetism. They would search for the dynamo beneath the surface that supposedly generated the Sun's magnetic field and ruled its surface activity. The programme was like a prospectus dealing with the profound human ignorance about the light in the sky, that persisted four centuries after Galileo.

'We may begin to solve the mystery of why dark sunspots occur,' Scherrer said, 'and why they become most numerous every 11 years or so.'

The Sun's hum came to SOHO more sweetly and tunefully than anyone expected. Detecting it from the ground was like listening to music with a jet engine running nearby. Much random noise accompanied the oscillations. The experts had blamed turbulence on the Sun, but as soon as SOHO started work the scientists realized that the turbulence had been in the Earth's atmosphere, which the spacecraft had left far behind it.

The critics who had questioned the value of putting the helioseismic instruments into space were confounded. SOHO was so good that helioseismic instruments on the ground would be put in the shade, at least for as long as SOHO operated. The GONG team had been prudent to rush its early findings into print.

The cleanness of the Sun's oscillations, Nature's bonus to the experimenters, was a discovery in its own right. The Sun's surface was better behaved than anyone imagined possible. The technical benefit was enormous. Out in space, in its peaceful orbit where the Sun never set, SOHO achieved unprecedented hi-fi recordings of the oscillations.

A European oscillations instrument in SOHO, called GOLF, also detected motions of the surface, but was devoted to vibrations of the whole Sun. These were especially suitable for probing deep into the interior, right down to the nuclear reactor at the core. It registered the same kind of musical scale that ground-based instruments had seen, but now more quickly and accurately. GOLF detected shifts in the frequencies and strength of the oscillations, over intervals of days, which might be related to surface activity. Nevertheless, prolonged recordings would be needed before the space results on whole-Sun oscillations first matched, and then surpassed, the results from the global networks on the ground.

SOHO's intensity monitor, VIRGO, detected the oscillations not by motions, but by small rhythmic changes in brightness, recorded earlier with the European instrument in the Soviet Phobos spacecraft. They occurred as the sound waves squeezed and eased the light-emitting gas at the surface of the Sun. The whole Sun's brightness waxed and waned every few minutes in obedience to the oscillations. The strobing was too slight to see without instruments, being only about one ten-thousandth of the Sun's average brightness. But again, analyses showed the notes of the hum coming through clearly and remarkably free of noise.

VIRGO was a set of instruments, including one which divided the Sun up into a number of segments, and others that measured the intensities of the whole Sun in light of different colours, minute by minute. Intensities were a matter of climatic as well as helioseismic interest, especially for Claus Fröhlich of Davos, Switzerland, leader of the VIRGO team.

Fröhlich had long suspected that variations in the Sun's output of radiant energy were understated. The meteorologists said they were of minor importance for climate change, and assigned only about a quarter of a watt per square metre for their contribution to the global warming. When VIRGO observed changes in brightness in different segments of the Sun, as a sunspot moved across its face, the variations were continuous. The sensitive measurements achieved with SOHO suggested that averages used to define the Sun's output might not represent the effective radiation over a period.

'This introduces an uncertainty of up to half a watt,' Fröhlich said, 'which is quite impressive.'

Thanks to the bonus of good behaviour in the Sun, scientists concerned with all of the helioseismic instruments in SOHO searched with renewed hope for other kinds of oscillations, besides the sound waves. Gravity waves might occur, with periods of about one hour. They would be like the great internal waves that ocean scientists found in the deep sea, between layers of water of different density, which mimicked the rise and fall under gravity of the swell at the surface of the sea.

Gravity waves could give the Sun a new way of working. Unlike sound waves, they could transfer sustantial amounts of energy. They could even link changes in the Sun's nuclear core to events at the surface, and so help to explain the variability of the Sun. There was friendly rivalry between the experimental teams with helioseismic instruments in SOHO to see who, if any one, would discover the gravity waves.

Would-be forecasters of the solar weather, concerned about its effects on the Earth a few days later, hoped that SOHO would provide them with an early-warning system. Scientists studying Yohkoh images had found hints that voids appeared in the very hot atmosphere of the Sun as it was preparing to erupt. SOHO gave a more detailed picture of events before the giant outbursts called mass ejections.

In the quiet Sun, such occurrences were comparatively rare, but SOHO's visible-light coronagraph recorded two mass ejections early in the mission. Observations repeated over many hours made spectacular movies showing the billions of tonnes of gas bursting out of the Sun's atmosphere and into the solar system at 550 kilometres per second. The same composite instrument was able also to observe the atmosphere quite close to the solar surface.

'I believe that for the first time we can see the Sun preparing itself for a mass ejection,' said Guenter Brueckner of Washington DC, the leader of the coronagraph team. 'In the days preceding such an event, multiple magnetic loops appear in our images of the inner corona. They tell us that the Sun is reorganizing its magnetic field.'

The speckled pattern of magnetism seen by SOHO's oscillation imager would change dramatically in the years to come, when the Sun was due to swap its north and south magnetic poles, and sunspots and mass ejections would become much more numerous. Among the key ultraviolet instruments that would watch the seething atmosphere change its behaviour, the extreme ultraviolet telescope, EIT, routinely recorded the whole Sun in four ultraviolet colours.

'EIT is beginning a career similar to the meteorological satellites that monitor the weather on the Earth every day,' said its principal investigator, Jean-Pierre Delaboudinière of Orsay, France. 'Just as those have revolutionized meteorology, so our observations give us vivid new impressions of the Sun's weather. We shall see more precisely than ever before the changes in solar weather with the magnetic seasons, which also affect conditions at the Earth.'

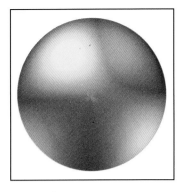

Hoping for gravity waves. An unusual impression of the Sun, from the badge of one of SOHO's experiments, visualizes internal oscillations of an undiscovered kind. Unlike the sound waves already studied by helioseismologists, gravity waves could cause important variations in the behaviour of the Sun.

VIRGO Consortium

Two agents of climate change. On 1 May 1996 the Sun gave vent to a mass ejection while Comet Hyakutake was flying very close to it. The SOHO spacecraft imaged the comet (top of picture) at the same time as the mass ejection burst out. The visible Sun is hidden by the mask screening the LASCO coronagraph. Mass ejections help to disperse cosmic rays before they reach the Earth, making the world a little warmer. Comets on the other hand occasionally collide with the Earth, causing environmental and climatic disasters like the one that wiped out the dinosaurs.

SOHO/ESA & NASA and LASCO Consortium

Chapter Eleven

THE STRENGTH OF THE SHIELD

W HEN THE DANISH discovery about cosmic rays and clouds became generally known, the effects of the varying Sun would be apparent to any quizzical eye, in the global temperatures as assessed year by year for the Intergovernmental Panel on Climate Change. The cloud effect was of the right magnitude to be significant in climate, and was apparently visible in the natural fluctuations of recent decades. But the variation within a sunspot cycle would by itself cause no global warming. In a succession of identical sunspot cycles the cloudiness would go up and down, but on average would stay the same. The changes in cloudiness from year to year, and even between the peaks and troughs of the sunspot cycle, would be undramatic in their effects because the heat reservoir of the oceans would cushion them.

Another factor came into play, in an overall change in the solar wind. It greatly increased the variability of cosmic rays received in the air from century to century, and therefore the possible changes in cloud cover. Here were the 'additional long-term variations' mentioned almost cryptically in the paper that Henrik Svensmark and Eigil Friis-Christensen had sent to *Science*. And here Friis-Christensen's climate studies converged with his main professional work concerning the Earth's magnetism, including the intended research with the satellite Ørsted.

To gauge the vigour of a magnetic storm on the Earth, scientists assessed the variations reported by a number of widely scattered magnetometer stations. The maximum change in the strength of the local magnetic field in a period of three hours gave an index for each station. Comparing the effects at different latitudes, and on both the sunlit and dark sides of the planet, gave a global index.

One record of past events went right back to 1868. It drew on magnetic measurements from only two stations, but these were on opposite sides of the Earth, at Greenwich in England and Melbourne in Australia. If two were all you could have, it would be hard to pick a better pair. From the old data, modern experts derived a measure of magnetic storminess spanning nearly 130 years. They called it the *aa* index. The record showed a remarkable pattern. Between the late nineteenth century and the late twentieth century the averaged *aa* index climbed in much the same way as the Earth's temperature climbed. There was even a setback at mid-century.

Friis-Christensen had long known that the *aa* graph of magnetic variability

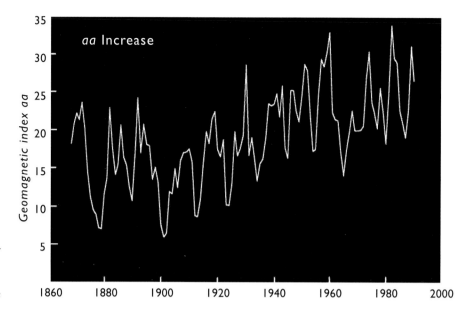

aa Increase

Geomagnetic index *aa*

A stronger shield from the solar wind. The *aa* index records the variable intensity of magnetic disturbances on the Earth due to some changing quality in solar wind – perhaps its speed. During the past century the rising *aa* index has roughly matched the warming of the Earth, apparently because of the solar wind's effects on cosmic rays.

After K. Lassen and E. Friis-Christensen

matched the graph of rising global temperature changes, in nearly the same fashion as the accelerating sunspot cycles. But the *aa* index directly measured variations in electric currents in the Earth's outer atmosphere, caused by the gusty solar wind interacting with the Earth's magnetic shield. It was far-fetched to suggest that magnetic variability could itself warm the Earth. Instead, indirectly and over long periods, the *aa* index must measure a changing quality in the solar wind – perhaps an increase in its average speed – arising from an intrinsic change in the Sun itself.

The practical significance of the *aa* graph for climate became transparent with the discovery of the link between cosmic rays and clouds. The *aa* index defined, from decade to decade, the solar wind's effectiveness in shielding the Earth. When the average *aa* index was high, the Sun provided at the Earth a persistent extra shield that was worth, in electrical terms, more than a billion volts with which to repel the cosmic rays.

American scientists had suggested that the *aa* shield disappeared entirely when the Sun was extremely quiet, as in the Maunder Minimum of 1645–1715 during the Little Ice Age. Without it, the average count of cosmic rays reaching the atmosphere would be far greater than in the twentieth century. A limit set by available water vapour in the atmosphere probably curbed the extra cloud-making, but for Isaac Newton, Peter the Great and their contemporaries, it must have been a dismal time to be alive.

Rivalling the supposed greenhouse warming promised to be quite easy. The enhanced greenhouse effect was set by its proponents at 2.4 watts per square metre, for greenhouse gases of all kinds added by human activity since the eighteenth century. A rough guess of 10 per cent more cloud, around 1700, would suggest a change since then of 5 watts to warm the Earth. You could be more conservative with your clouds and their effects and still have numbers of the right order for a strong solar warming.

The large numbers for cosmic ray changes associated with the changes in the *aa* shield were not conjectural. On the contrary, scientists used the weakening or disappearance of the *aa* shield just as a theory to explain the observations. These showed very high rates of manufacture of radioactive materials in the air around 1700. The best indicator was radioberyllium at different levels in the ice cores drilled in Greenland and Antarctica.

Scientists in Switzerland and France had found that, for ice dating from the 1890s, the count of radioberyllium atoms per gram of ice was twice as high as around 1980. Deeper in the polar ice, at around 1700 and the Maunder Minimum, the count was higher still. Greenland and Antarctica gave similar results. Even allowing for local changes in snowfall, the radioberyllium testified to a very large increase in the cosmic rays that made it.

Such changes had long been known from the radiocarbon wiggles detected and analysed in the old trees. But radioberyllium gave a clearer picture because it settled out of the atmosphere within a year or two, and stayed out. Radiocarbon on the other hand became involved in living things and in carbon dioxide exchanges with the oceans, which were themselves highly sensitive to climate. Old radiocarbon recycled into the atmosphere diluted the additions due to high intensities of cosmic rays.

Combined with a delay of many years in the uptake into the trees, which smudged the short-term variations, the dilution of the radiocarbon made the changes in cosmic rays look much less dramatic than they really were. That did not matter when the radiocarbon wiggles were just a token of changes in the Sun's behaviour which supposedly acted on the Earth's climate by quite different mechanisms. The discovery that cosmic rays could directly increase cloud cover made the doubling revealed by the radioberyllium a matter of over-riding importance, together with the changes in the solar wind which made it possible.

By the late nineteenth century, the *aa* shield was in place again but not as strong as a hundred years later, according to the *aa* index. Half of the global warming since 1700 took place in the twentieth century, mostly before 1950. The historical record of rising temperatures accorded very much better with the *aa* index than with rising carbon dioxide.

One task for Ørsted had always been to investigate the *aa* shield. The Danish satellite would help Friis-Christensen and his fellow physicists to grasp the *aa* index better from a scientific point of view. Apart from its changes over decades and centuries, the *aa* index also varied over days and weeks. It gave a special perspective on the Earth's interaction with the solar wind, and on short-term and long-term changes in the Sun.

No one knew why the *aa* index seemed to depend on the speed of the sunspot cycles. But the emphatic way in which the graphs of sunspot speed and of the *aa* index both guided the global temperature graph left no doubt about their relevance to climate change. The discovery about cosmic rays and clouds gave the *aa* index a new and highly practical meaning. Its changes were now a matter just as important for understanding and monitoring climate change governed by the Sun, as the changing carbon dioxide levels in the air had been for the greenhouse warming.

Proposals for magnetic missions in space might shoot to the top of the observational agenda, when the discovery registered with the scientific community. Ensuring an adequate monitoring of magnetic changes, in the ever-varying interactions with the solar wind, would require a succession of special satellites beyond Ørsted and its Argentine companion carrying the Danish magnetometer. The Magnetometry Mission with two satellites, proposed by Friis-Christensen and his British, French and German colleagues for a launch early in the new century, was the best next step.

The European Space Agency's way of getting excellent missions was to let space scientists of its member states propose any projects they liked and then compete like matadors to decide which one should be chosen. Most of the beautiful ideas elaborated with great expense of spirit left the arena wounded. This blood sport was highly effective in the science programme, and was adopted for selecting research satellites for the Earth observation programme. So the Magnetometry Mission was up against enticing schemes for measuring the Earth's gravity more accurately, for example, or observing the interactions between living plants and their environments.

The first bullfight was due at a meeting of European Earth observation scientists at Granada in Spain in May 1996. In the light of the arguments, nine proposals would be whittled down to a select few earmarked for further scientific and engineering studies. Descriptions of the proposed missions were printed and circulated in April. At the last minute Friis-Christensen added anonymously, to the description of the scientific motives for the mission, a key paragraph quite different from the reasons normally given for wanting to fly magnetometers in space.

'A controversial topic in atmospheric science,' Friis-Christensen wrote, 'is the possible connection between the geomagnetic field on the one hand and climate and weather on the other. … A potential source of climate variations is the varying cosmic ray flux that in the atmosphere creates ionization changes which affect microphysical processes ….'

This idea had not appeared in the explanations of the Danish Ørsted satellite published only three years earlier. But Friis-Christensen went no further in explaining the connection with cloud cover. Even so, he was queried about it later as a possible early disclosure of the discovery to astute readers.

'I put in the cosmic rays because they were, or would become, an important part of the case for the Magnetometry Mission,' Friis-Christensen said. 'But I hoped I had disguised our thoughts a little.'

He had two reasons for reticence. One was the fear that someone else might repeat the discovery and publish it formally ahead of Svensmark and Friis-Christensen. He owed it to his young colleague, and to himself as co-author, to avoid that at all costs. The other reason concerned the conventions of scientific behaviour. Although these were often violated, in major or minor ways, the general view was that ideas should not be mooted publicly before they were formally published in a respected journal. Apart from any other consideration, journal editors did not like it.

A wide penumbra of preprints, circulated among co-professionals well in advance of publication, softened this convention. By the 1990s preprints were often available on the Internet. There was a distinction between a paper labelled as 'submitted', meaning merely that the authors had paid the postage to send it to a journal, and the 'accepted' tag when the journal had decided to publish, after submitting the paper to expert referees. Only when 'accepted' did the paper become fully respectable, and the date of its acceptance was always specified, in case of arguments about priority if other people came up with the same idea.

Svensmark and Friis-Christensen did not circulate any preprint of their manuscript submitted to *Science*. Friis-Christensen hoped that the journal might accept it in time for him to speak about the discovery in Granada, in connection with the bid for the Magnetometry Mission, and meanwhile he remained discreet. Well not entirely. In mid-May a visiting journalist who had followed the solar warming story for several years wanted an update. Friis-Christensen said nothing about the mechanism of the solar warming but conveyed the force of the conclusions.

'I firmly believe,' he told the journalist off the record, 'that the whole effect of the global warming till now is due to the Sun.' That remark, by the way, was the origin of this book.

Science turned down the paper. The tone of the rejection implied that the journal could not fault the science. Rather, the referees seemed to be uneasy about its publication. There were also comments that further evidence would be required. This provoked a new round of feverish activity in Copenhagen.

One referee asked specifically for better evidence of the effect of magnetic latitude on cloud-cover variations. Svensmark's earlier attempt at providing this had ended in failure, after elaborate calculations of the cloud data square by square. He went back to the problem and found an error in his computations.

When he put that right, the result looked much better. The outcome was a neat U-shaped graph that bottomed with a 2 per cent effect of cosmic rays on cloud cover near the magnetic equator. The effect increased to 3 three per cent at around 25 degrees magnetic latitude, and to 4.5 per cent at 40 degrees.

'For physicists, that's the most important curve,' Friis-Christensen said appreciatively when he saw the result of Svensmark's labours.

Svensmark also decided, in the light of the referees' reports, to look for effects at much shorter timescales. If the connection between cosmic rays and clouds was intimately microphysical, there should be, besides the variations of averages over months and years, effects discernible from day to day, as reported by Pudovkin in Russia.

The painstaking collations of the International Satellite Cloud Climatology Project lagged several years behind events. In early 1996, Svensmark had access to new cloud data for 1990–92. A change in the analytical procedures used at the project's headquarters in New York meant that he could not simply extend the time series for 1984–90 with which he had been working. On the other hand, the cloud data for 1990–92 were available at 3-hour intervals, so offering a chance to see how the Sun's variations affected the day-to-day weather of the world.

Svensmark had already located the 3-hourly information, ISCCP-D1, on the Internet, but the amounts of data were reckoned in gigabytes and too great to handle conveniently. He therefore started with the cosmic rays, looking for large short-term variations due to major outbursts of activity on the Sun. The biggest event was in June 1991, when the count of cosmic rays dropped to the lowest level recorded in four decades of routine observations. Rapid changes in the counts occurred from day to day, in data available from a cosmic ray station in Tokyo.

Selecting the June 1991 cloud data from ISCCP-D1, Svensmark looked to see whether effects of the cosmic rays were evident in the daily cloud cover seen by the geostationary satellites. The result was emphatic. The average cloud cover fell by 2 per cent for about a week, coinciding with the solar action. The clouds gradually increased again during the following few days as the Sun quietened and the cosmic rays increased again.

The event, a Forbush decrease, was associated with a quickfire succession of major solar flares. In this respect, Svensmark had fulfilled the request of Jean-Claude Pecker of Paris, to find a one-to-one relation between flares and meteorological changes. But an outburst of energetic particles from the Sun itself had no discernible effect on clouds. Everything seemed to depend on the variations in the cosmic rays coming from the Galaxy, modulated by disturbances in the solar wind.

A similar though smaller drop in the count of cosmic rays occurred in March 1991. Again Svensmark gathered in the cloud data and again the solar event was visible in the clouds. The *Science* paper had to be kept brief, so Svensmark and Friis-Christensen added to it only the June 1991 event, as a single example of a short-term effect of cosmic rays on clouds. They also included the successful result on the effect of magnetic latitude on the longer-term cloud variations.

When Friis-Christensen had despatched the revised version to *Science*, with a covering letter reasoning with the editor, he had to go off to the Earth observation meeting in Granada and keep mum. It was an exasperating experience. Supporters of some other projects scored points by explaining in detail how they would help to elucidate the greenhouse warming.

It was little consolation that a proposal by British, German, Belgian and French meteorological researchers, for a mission called Grace, cast doubt on the assumptions of the Intergovernmental Panel on Climate Change and wanted much better observations of clouds in particular. The idea that the magnetometers in space were also relevant to the climate attracted scorn on the grounds that everyone knew the Sun had very little to do with it. Unable to utter the key word 'clouds', Friis-Christensen knew he was short-selling the Magnetometer Mission.

The solar-terrestrial space fleet was almost complete. SOHO and Wind were busy far out on the sunward side of the Earth, and Japan's Geotail was continuing operations on the dark side. In the previous summer, the Russians had launched its Interball mission with the first of two pairs of satellites, also probing the tail. In February 1996, NASA had put Polar into a high orbit over the Earth's poles. The main contribution still awaited was the set of four satellites of the Cluster mission, which would enhance the value of the other spacecraft by giving the first 3-D views of the sneaky behaviour of electrified gas and magnetic fields in the vicinity of the Earth's magnetic windscreen.

Everyone clapped when Ariane 501 lifted off from Europe's spaceport at Kourou in French Guiana. For 37 seconds it looked grand. It was the first of the new Ariane 5 launchers conceived to give Europe serious weight-lifting capacity for future space operations, and was quite different in design from the previous generations of Arianes.

Oops. At a height of 3500 metres, the rocket's progress ended in a sideways tilt. Aerodynamic stresses broke the Ariane 5 and explosives incorporated for safety's sake completed the job. The shower of smoking debris looked like a fireworks display.

The event was so bizarre that the fault had to be in the guiding computer's software, not the rocket's hardware. Engineers expected that about one in ten

There goes Cluster. Self-destruction of Europe's brand-new Ariane 5 launcher on 4 June 1996 resulted from a steering error by an onboard computer. Among the wreckage raining into the swamp at Kourou in French Guiana were the four identical satellites of the Cluster mission. Their loss set back the efforts by solar-terrestrial physicists to make sense of the solar wind's influence on the Earth.

N. Lecore / Gamma for ESA / CNES

space launches would fail, so although the loss of the rocket was an embarrassment, it was not a special cause for grief. They would sort out the software and try again.

Those in tears at Kourou, on 4 June 1996, were the scientists of the Cluster mission. Ariane 501 carried their four satellites prepared after 10 years of effort. A thousand scientists in Europe and the United States had workstations ready to receive Cluster's results for at least two years. But the computer screens stayed blank and youngsters worried about losing their jobs. The broken satellites lay in a tropical swamp.

Eigil Friis-Christensen attended the launch as a representative of the Danish government. He would soon be caught up in urgent discussions of the European Space Agency's solar system working group about how to replace Cluster with a possible new mission. All the same, it was a black day for solar-terrestrial physics and the inter-agency solar space fleet lost four unrivalled satellites.

In the sky-blue satchel issued by the agency to mark the Ariane-Cluster launch, Friis-Christensen carried the manuscript of the scientific paper that would blast official climatology apart as comprehensively as Ariane 501. The software guiding the human species in climatic matters would prove to be defective, and reputations of eminent scientists would lie wrecked in the swamp where science and politics mix.

The day after the Ariane explosion the Intergovernmental Panel on Climate Change published its latest findings, as *Climate Change 1995*. The three volumes, the fruit of huge efforts by all concerned, were out only just in time for study before the big climate conference in Geneva the following month. Although the conclusions had been widely leaked in advance, they still caused a minor uproar in London.

The World Energy Council took exception to the strong hint in the scientific report by John Houghton's group, about 'a discernible human influence' on the climate. Speaking for the council, Michael Jefferson denied that global patterns were yet apparent. John Emsley commented in similar terms for his European Science and Environment Forum, which consisted of fifty-four independent scientists in Europe and the United States sceptical about the greenhouse warming. Emsley said that the conclusion about a human influence was not supported by the scientific chapters of the report.

The scientific journal *Nature* quoted Houghton's robust defence of his group's work as 'a unique, very solid and authoritative piece of work, written by the world's best scientists'. There was no question of forcing a consensus, he said, and politics had nothing to do with the scientific message provided for policymakers.

'We do recognize that the message gets distorted when politics comes into play,' Houghton said. 'That is inevitable. But it is not the scientists' fault.'

Reactions were noisier in Washington DC. Textual analysis by the Global Climate Coalition, a fossil-fuel lobby group, revealed that Ben Santer's chapter on detection of climate change had been altered since its presentation at the Madrid meeting, when it was officially accepted. So far from the summary for policymakers being based on the original scientific text, the Santer chapter was amended so that it would more clearly support the summary. Houghton retorted that the Global Climate Coalition's scurrilous allegations had absolutely no basis in fact. Santer, on the other hand, explained that changes were necessary to improve the report's scientific clarity.

Everything then became very nasty indeed, and scientists learned that climate politics was a dangerous game. The Republican chairman of the US House of Representative's subcommittee on energy and environment, Dana Rohrabacher, wanted to outlaw all federal support for research on climate change. He started a witch-hunt against Ben Santer himself, demanding a full explanation of the funding of his research by the US Department of Energy. Even scientists who disliked Santer's artwork trembled at the thought of a censorship of research by the world's Rohrabachers.

On his return to Copenhagen from the Ariane-Cluster disaster at Kourou, Friis-Christensen learned that *Science* had rejected the revised version of the paper on cosmic rays and clouds. The reasons included a suggestion that the work should be continued for a full solar cycle, before coming to any conclusion. The added information provided in the authors' revisions would in any case make the paper too long for the three-page limit adopted by *Science*, and the editor recommended publishing a more extensive report in another journal.

Svensmark and Friis-Christensen had made the additions to meet earlier criticisms. The central point of the paper required neither a lot of space nor an extended period of observations. To show that cosmic rays made clouds required only that the cosmic rays should vary, for whatever reason, and that the clouds should follow suit. It would be absurd to delay publication of the discovery for a number of years until the cloud climatologists had caught up with the mid-1990s situation.

Nevertheless the final rejection by *Science* left the Danes with a problem of scientific etiquette. Friis-Christensen had been invited to speak about solar effects on climate at a gathering of space scientists in July in Birmingham, England. The invitation arose from the earlier work with Knud Lassen on the length of the solar cycles, but to withold from their colleagues in solar-terrestrial physics a discovery of unusual importance for their subject would be silly and discourteous. Continuing anxiety about someone else announcing the discovery first was another consideration.

Conferences were a grey area in scientific publication, alongside the shuffling of preprints. You could say anything you liked at a conference, or stick up a poster. But the status of your remarks remained related, by the rules of the game, to how far along the line you were towards formal publication. It would be better if the Svensmark and Friis-Christensen preprint circulated at the time of the Birmingham meeting could be labelled 'accepted'. With that aim, Friis-Christensen spoke with the editor of the *Journal of Atmospheric and Terrestrial*

Physics, which had published his last paper with Knud Lassen, asking to be put on a fast track for refereeing. The editor said he would see what he could do.

The new paper underwent further evolution. The authors were still not happy about the U-shaped graph showing the effects on clouds at different magnetic latitudes, so they replaced it with another showing that the correlation between cloud variations and cosmic rays was much higher at high latitudes than near the magnetic equator. The remark about effects of prolonged cloudiness during slow sunspot cycles raised a needless issue about irregularities in the cycles, so they omitted it. They also left out the short-term event of 1991, preferring to plan another paper based on a more thorough review of the daily cosmic ray and cloud data. But Svensmark developed a new graph showing cosmic rays from 1980 to 1996 and cloud amounts from the main satellite data sets. There were good correspondences for southern oceanic clouds from the US Air Force satellite and Nimbus 7, as well as the ISCCP C2 and D2 data from the International Cloud Climatology Project.

With Svensmark's consent, Friis-Christensen decided that he would disclose the discovery at Birmingham come what may. In the event the journal was unable to react in time, so the preprint still carried the label 'submitted' and critics would say the work had not been approved by the authors' peers. It was a tricky situation to be in. If there had been any doubt in Friis-Christensen's mind about the force of the findings he would have held them back.

The Royal Astronomical Society of London was to run the press office for the COSPAR meeting, and it had already identified Friis-Christensen's invited talk as a topic of special interest. He received a request for a press release to be made available in Birmingham. In theory any journalist could be present at the talk, and there was no point in excluding from the written document the main news that Friis-Christensen would be imparting. So he prepared a press release for COSPAR that summarized the findings, embargoed until the day of his talk. The decision to disclose was then irreversible.

From the heart of the greenhouse camp, just before the Geneva conference, the politically beleaguered Ben Santer and his colleagues published in the journal *Nature* a new report on 'A search for human influences on the thermal structure of the atmosphere'. It added a further seven computer-generated daubs representing changes high in the atmosphere computed to result from human activity. Besides the options of carbon dioxide and sulphate, the cooling effect of depleting the ozone layer now provided an extra way of tweaking the charts to make them look more like the observed changes. There was no attempt to find out what the changes in the upper air might be, in a similar computation for a solar warming.

The pictures were still poor, compared with the chart of actual changes observed in the upper air. That did not matter. The authors used a statistical table filling most of a page to prove them beautiful. This they did by showing that, in some cases anyway, the pictures could not have been generated by mere natural variability in the atmosphere. The explanations were hard to follow, but

THE STRENGTH OF THE SHIELD

an attentive reader might discover that the variability used for comparison was not really natural.

Never mind, the journal *Nature* recruited another lead author from Houghton's group to comment on the new Santer paper. Neville Nicholls, from Australia, discussed shortcomings in the work, but happily concluded that Santer's results provided 'the clearest evidence yet that humans may have affected global climate'. *Nature* headlined his commentary, 'An incriminating fingerprint.'

The source of the slow solar wind. A feature called a helmet streamer stretching millions of kilometres into space, from the Sun out of view on the right. Ultraviolet emissions distinguish hydrogen atoms (ABOVE) and charged oxygen atoms (RIGHT). Differences between these images from SOHO's ultraviolet coronagraph UVCS give clues to the mechanism that accelerates charged particles into the solar wind.

SOHO/ESA & NASA and UVCS Consortium

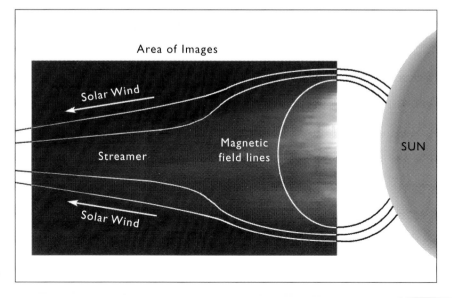

Overpowering the Sun's magnetic field. An interpretation of the helmet streamer seen in the ultraviolet images shows the solar wind above and below the helmet. It drags out the lines of the magnetic field like bubble-gum. At the helmet's tip, the field lines almost meet. They continue like that, opposing each other across a narrow sheet, out into the realm of the planets.

After J. Kohl

Chapter Twelve

COUP DE GRÂCE

WHEN THE PARTIES to the Climate Convention, signed in Rio four years earlier, met in Geneva in July 1996 they were supposed to strengthen the treaty with more precise commitments to curb their carbon dioxide emissions. Despite all the campaigning about the greenhouse warming, global rates of emission from fossil fuels increased by 12 per cent between 1990 and 1995. Few industrialized countries were going to fulfil a hope expressed in Rio, that emissions from fossil fuels might be cut back to 1990 levels by the year 2000. The big exceptions were the disrupted economies of Eastern Europe and the former Soviet Union, where emissions were down by 25 to 30 per cent.

This information, supplied by the World Energy Council, also showed the delegates assembling in Geneva that the largest regional increases were in the developing countries of Asia and the Middle East, at 30 and 35 per cent respectively. The developing countries had made no commitment at Rio, and many of them still regarded any suggestion that they should curb emissions as condemning them to continued poverty.

'It's like telling a poor trader who saved for 20 years to buy a van, to carry on making deliveries using his donkey cart,' commented Abdul Bar al Gain of Saudi Arabia.

The Alliance of Small Island States, on the other hand, had been assured they would soon be washed away by a rising sea. They wanted a binding protocol on all countries to reduce greenhouse gas emissions by 20 per cent by the year 2005. The Climate Action Network, an alliance of Greenpeace, the World Wide Fund for Nature, the Natural Resources Defense Council and other environmental groups, was also active at the meeting, calling for drastic cuts in the emissions.

Among the nations ranged against the curbers were the Third World countries that relied on oil exports for their livelihoods. Lobbyists from the Global Climate Coalition represented industrial interests in the West. The first week of the meeting was declarative and unproductive because everyone knew that decisions would be made only when ministers showed up.

A thousand kilometres away from the Palais des Nations, on the leafy campus of Birmingham University in England, the big international meeting on space science, COSPAR 96, began on 15 July. Many of the reports concerned the multinational fleet of spacecraft devoted to solar and solar-terrestrial physics. The missing Cluster satellites were the ghosts at the banquet, but a torrent of information coming from spacecraft with novel powers made dogmatic opinions, about what the Sun might or might not do on our planet, singularly rash and untimely that summer.

Results from SOHO, the flagship of the space fleet, were the subject of the inaugural lecture by Martin Huber, head of the European Space Agency's space science department. A string of detailed presentations by European and American scientists involved in the mission confirmed the successes of the twelve individual telescopes, spectrometers and particle detectors in SOHO. Its revolution in solar science would be more complete when all the actions of the Sun were pieced together in joint observations and broad concepts exploring the Sun all the way from its nuclear core to the Earth's vicinity and beyond.

'SOHO takes solar science by storm,' said Roger Bonnet, the European Space Agency's director of science who had never doubted the climate connection. 'By the end of the mission we shall be able to comment with much more confidence on important but puzzling aspects of solar behaviour that affect our lives on the Earth, whether in short-lived magnetic storms or long-lasting changes of climate.'

That day Eigil Friis-Christensen, as requested, put copies of a two-page press notice on the table in the COSPAR press room in Birmingham. Headlined 'The missing link in solar-climate relationship', it was marked for release three days later, when he would give his talk. As a result, the discovery of the link between cosmic rays and clouds became a subject of gossip among space scientists at a civic reception in Birmingham that evening.

The intellectual temperature was rising at the Conference of the Parties to the Climate Change Convention in Geneva. Patrick Michaels of Charlottesville, Virginia, one of the reviewers of the scientific report whose criticisms had been disputed, gave a press conference to put his point of view about the failure of the climate models to predict the changes of the twentieth century in a way that matched the observations.

'You must not take any one scientist's evidence,' John Houghton said, when questioned about Michaels' comments.

'It is the best science on climate the world has to offer,' Bert Bolin said, lifting the three volumes of his panel's report like a barbell. 'I stake my reputation and honour that it is so.'

Deadlock faced the government representatives in Geneva. As a developing country heavily dependent on coal, China had joined with eleven oil-producing states in rejecting the conclusions of Bolin's Intergovernmental Panel on Climate Change. The United States, by far the largest fossil-fuel user in the world, was dithering. France, Russia and Japan were among a string of other countries unhappy about the proposal for formal curbs on emissions of greenhouse gases, based on the Bolin panel's findings.

The culminating ministerial segment began on 17 July. The job of the ministers, visiting for two days, was to try to help finalize a decision by quick political footwork. Voices became strident, and none more so than that of the British environment minister John Gummer.

'Alarm bells ought to be ringing in every capital throughout the world,' Gummer said.

Declaring that climate change would be at least as disastrous for mankind as the Second World War, he called for a string of measures including a ban on exports to developing countries of technologies deemed to be dirty. Applause was loudest when Gummer lambasted the Australians for thinking their coal exports to Japan more important than the future of their own children.

Merylyn Hedger of the World Wide Fund for Nature spoke for those who applauded the British minister. 'The fossil fuel lobby is totally blown out of the water!'

'There can be no question but that the findings meet the highest standards of scientific integrity,' said Timothy Wirth, the US under-secretary for global affairs, in judging the work of Bolin's panel. With these remarks the US delegation had suddenly rounded on the 'naysayers and special interests' who were trying to obfuscate climate change. It also accepted that there ought to be cuts in greenhouse gas emissions.

'We believe the circumstances warrant the adoption of a realistic but binding target,' Wirth said.

Thus the Americans rescued the Geneva conference from abject failure. They sidelined the Chinese and the Arabs and opened the way to an agreement to discuss future action, at least among the industrialized countries. Some reporters called the change in the American position a U-turn. It was more like a political soft-shoe shuffle to save the Clinton administration from opprobrium without committing it to much more than further talks.

The US delegation made it clear that drastic cuts by 2005 were not realistic. If the greenhouse warming were as dire as the Bolin panellists said, the submersible island states and drought-prone grainlands gained not so much as a milligram's relief in the emissions of carbon dioxide, as a result of any decision at Geneva in the summer of 1996.

The Sun looked down from a cloud-free sky to give Geneva a pleasant summer's day, thanks to an anticyclone centred over Birmingham. There, the COSPAR press office sent the Danes' press release along with others to the Reuters news agency. And when journalists enquired about interesting news from the conference, the press officers made an even-handed mention of the solar warming story along with other tidbits. Science editors of some leading newspapers brushed the solar warming aside, because everyone knew the greenhouse was to blame.

Nick Nuttall from *The Times* of London interviewed Friis-Christensen and Svensmark. He filed a story that started with dying stars as the source of the cosmic rays influencing the climate on the Earth. Nuttall quoted Friis-Christensen as saying that cosmic rays ionized the atmosphere, increasing the formation of water droplets.

The press release about the missing link in the solar-climate relationship was embargoed until 18 July 1996, and at midnight by London clocks the main BBC radio news captured the irony of timing. It led with the news of the US government falling into line in Geneva, and followed it immediately with a brief account of work by 'a Danish team of scientists'. While saying it was controversial, the reporter David Whitehouse commented that 'it could undermine much of our thinking about global warming'.

In the morning newspapers then coming off the presses, *The Times* carried its report from Birmingham on page 7, under the headline 'Exploding stars "may cause global warming"'. Exactly matching it in column-centimetres was another report by the same journalist, Nick Nuttall, on the discovery of shrimps and a bristled worm found fossilized by a volcanic event 400 million BC.

A rival among the London broadsheets, *The Guardian*, ran a story from the Birmingham meeting about the sulphur dioxide geysers of Jupiter's moon Io, as observed by NASA's Galileo spacecraft. Any attention to the solar warming would have confused *The Guardian*'s readers. Earlier in the week an editorial in the newspaper had assured its readers that the greenhouse warming was a fact, and that the flow in the Indus River would diminish by 43 per cent by the year 2000. As for the opposition from fossil-fuel producers to restrictions on greenhouse gases, that was like the tobacco industry's tactics about cancer and cigarette smoking.

The media in Copenhagen were less inhibited and it was, after all, a Danish story. The report on the results of Svensmark and Friis-Christensen by Annette Hagerup and Jens Kjaergaard made a splash on the front page of the leading daily *Berlingske Tidende*. But as the Sun rose over Europe that morning, pictures of the flaming debris of a Boeing 747, scattered on the sea off Long Island, refocused the attention of the world's news editors .

After an early breakfast, about a hundred space scientists were present in a mechanical engineering lecture hall at Birmingham University, to hear Eigil Friis-Christensen's presentation on changes in the Earth's climate. He was preceded by Janet Luhmann of Berkeley, California, with another invited talk about the coupling of the solar wind to the Earth's magnetosphere. She spoke of twistings of the magnetic field lines that were difficult for the human brain to grasp, and urged her fellow solar-terrestrial physicists to be more precise in stating what kind of response accompanied what kind of change in the solar wind.

Friis-Christensen had 20 minutes in a tightly controlled programme. He spoke quietly but clearly, and began by referring to the Intergovernmental Panel on Climate Change and the greenhouse scenario. During the last half-year, he said, a mechanism for a solar effect on climate had been discovered. He acknowledged the role of Henrik Svensmark who was present in the audience.

In a sketch of the background, which corresponded to the talk that Friis-Christensen had originally been invited to give, he noted that the changes in solar output of light, as measured by satellites at about 0.1 per cent, were barely enough to explain climate change. But real effects occurred, linked to solar activity. Karin Labitzke and Harry van Loon had matched increases in atmospheric temperatures over four solar cycles to increases in radio emissions from the Sun, which were an indicator of solar activity. Climatologists dismissed the result as a coincidence.

A different manifestation of solar energy came from variations in the *aa* index of magnetic activity, Friis-Christensen noted. It climbed as the temperature climbed, during the twentieth century. So did the shortening of the solar cycle lengths, as reported earlier by Friis-Christensen and Lassen. Again that was called a coincidence. Friis-Christensen reminded his audience of how Mick Kelly and Tom Wigley had achieved the best fit to twentieth century temperatures with solar forcing alone, and no greenhouse contribution, but they had judged the result 'unrealistic'.

On the other hand, Michael Schlesinger and Navin Ramankutty of the University of Illinois had responded more positively to the discovery of the link between the solar cycle length and the climate. Taking account of the Sun's past influence, they said, at least halved the temperature increase expected from a doubling of carbon dioxide. 'Including solar forcing reduces climate sensitivity by at least 50 per cent,' was the way Friis-Christensen expressed the Schlesinger-Ramankutty conclusion.

In coming to his main news, Friis-Christensen noted with regret the death in the previous week of Edward Ney, who had written about a possible link between cosmic rays and cloud cover in 1959. But the chairman was watching the clock and Friis-Christensen had to rush through his key viewgraphs. One displayed the match between cloud cover and cosmic ray counts from 1984 to 1990, including the peak in cosmic rays and cloudiness at the end of 1986. Another was for 15 days in mid-June 1991, where the cloud cover diminished in response to the sharp drop in cosmic rays due to a solar outburst.

Finally, Friis-Christensen showed how the magnetic latitude affected the strength of the response of clouds to cosmic ray variations. He said that the graph confirmed the causal relationship. Then he ran out of time and stopped, with some viewgraphs remaining undisplayed. In a few minutes allotted to reactions and questions, members of the audience were friendly and in some cases enthusiastic, but these were solar-terrestrial physicists. Asked what meteorologists thought of his work, Friis-Christensen paused and replied, 'I had better not say.'

'We could go on talking about this all morning,' said the chairman briskly. He was himself due to present a report at another session. Cutting the discussion short, he called on a Japanese scientist to speak about ion pressures observed by the Geotail satellite. Events in Birmingham that day felt like an anticlimax, but from a global standpoint Friis-Christensen's announcement of the cloud results drew a line under five years of scientific history.

The Danish newspaper *Information*, following up the big story in *Berlingske Tidende* with its own, highly critical report, contacted Bert Bolin in Geneva for his opinion on the Friis-Christensen and Svensmark result. He told the reporter that Friis-Christensen's work had been found to be of no significant importance for climate.

'I find the move from this pair scientifically extremely naive and irresponsible,' Bolin said. This was strong language for a professor of meteorology in Stockholm to use about a professor of physics in Copenhagen.

Ben Santer of Livermore was also asked for an opinion. He was scathing about the presentation at Birmingham of material that had not been critically reviewed by the scientific community.

'I am particularly sceptical about scientists who believe they have a hotline to God,' Santer said.

The row continued in the Danish press, with most newspapers remaining sympathetic to Svensmark and Friis-Christensen. Even Svensmark's wife was being quizzed by the newspapers. Some relief came when, two days after the Birmingham announcement, the Danish cyclist Bjarne Riis won the Tour de France.

Because it was high summer and most of the greenhouse people were on vacation, the explosion was on a slow fuse. Outside Denmark, Claus Fröhlich in Switzerland fed the story to *Der Spiegel* in Germany.

By September, Bert Bolin had read Svensmark and Friis-Christensen's preprint, and his comments were very different in tone from the unguarded remark quoted by *Information* some weeks earlier. Bolin's first considered opinion appeared in an article on the Danish discovery in the Swedish magazine *Ny Teknik*, written by Staffen Dahllöf.

'It is pleasing to see such a sane and sincere scientific investigation,' Bolin told Dahllöf. 'It differs quite a lot from other questionings of the greenhouse effect. Naturally I was surprised by the big changes they report, in the clouds … I can't see that their findings are given a satisfactory explanation. They do not conclude anything about the effects of human activity. But there is no doubt that this is serious science.'

The greenhouse warming theory, at least in its official scary form, was already in its death throes when Svensmark and Friis-Christensen delivered their coup de grâce. Even if there had been no solar warming theory to replace it, month by month the evidence mounted against any accelerating warming as required by the rise in carbon dioxide and other greenhouse gases. The theory had survived just long enough to carry the diplomats and ministers through the 1996 Geneva conference.

The scientific report in *Global Change 1995* had been published only in May. It caused growing consternation when outside experts found time to read it carefully. Despite all the efforts of the authors, many contradictions remained within the text. And readers were in for some shocks if they took the trouble to follow up the references to work brushed aside in the report. The most glaring case was the discovery that clouds absorbed sunlight and acted as heaters in the sky. The computer models used by the Intergovernmental Panel on Climate Change were simply wrong.

Referring back to the questionnaire posed early in this book, one could by the summer of 1996 complete it as follows.

About the Sun

Does the Sun control changes in the Earth's climate, over decades and centuries?
Yes. Svensmark and Friis-Christensen's result on recent cloud cover gives an explanation of why Lassen and Friis-Christensen's empirical indicator of solar vigour, the length of the solar cycle, matches climate changes back to 1500.

Is the physics of the solar warming persuasive?
Yes, much more so than it seemed in 1989. The manic behaviour of the Sun in the twentieth century has had physical consequences on the Earth.

Are variations in solar brightness sufficient to explain the global warming of the twentieth century?
No, but they help.

Is there another mechanism that is sufficient?
Yes, reductions in cloud cover due to a stronger solar wind that reduces the cosmic rays reaching the Earth.

Can the solar spacecraft discover this mechanism?
No – Earth-observing spacecraft did the job. But observations by Yohkoh, Ulysses, SOHO, Wind, and the rest provide the framework of new knowledge needed for a complete re-appraisal of solar-terrestrial relationships, including new approaches to weather forecasting.

What is the solar prognosis for climate in the twenty-first century?
Probably a cooling.

About the greenhouse warming

Are greenhouse gases warming the Earth?
Not sufficiently for the effect to be detectable. With the physics of the solar warming in place, there is little scope left in the observed temperature changes in the twentieth century for any contribution from the greenhouse warming.

Is the physics of the greenhouse warming persuasive?
No, much less so than it seemed in 1989.

Is the meteorology of clouds understood well enough for assessing human impacts on climate?
Probably not. The rate of startling discoveries, including sunlight absorption by clouds as well as cosmic ray effects, suggests that meteorologists have to rebuild their science comprehensively.

Are the predictions of the computer models of climate credible?
No. They all have to be done again, taking account of the discoveries about

clouds and soil dust, and the solar effects which are now too remarkable to ignore.

Can the Earth-observing spacecraft prove the greenhouse warming?
Rather, they disprove it. The microwave soundings indicate a more-or-less level global temperature in the lower atmosphere over the period 1979–94, despite an increase of 6 per cent in carbon dioxide levels.

What is the greenhouse prognosis for climate in the twenty-first century?
Officially, a global warming by 2 degrees C, by 2100. An unofficial interpretation of the solar and greenhouse data taken together indicates that any enhanced greenhouse effect is small compared with the solar effects. For practical purposes the combined, countervailing effects of greenhouse gases and man-made dust might be ignored, in much the same way as the Intergovernmental Panel on Global Change chose to belittle the Sun. But in the transformed scientific landscape, greater open-mindedness is desirable about all aspects of the Earth system and global change.

The implications for meteorology and climatology were formidable. On average, roughly two-thirds of the Earth was covered by cloud at any one time. A 3 per cent change was therefore equivalent to adding or subtracting cloud cover from 2 per cent of the Earth's surface, an area the size of Canada or of Europe right up to the Ural mountains. And all done on a seeming whim of the Sun.

Here was a major process of which the weathermen had no inkling. The cosmic rays varied by 20 per cent through the sunspot cycle, affecting 3 per cent of the clouds. The unvarying 80 per cent of cosmic rays were presumably also provoking cloud formation at the same rate. Altogether, cosmic rays were then responsible for about one seventh of all the world's cloud cover. It was as if, without cosmic rays, every Sunday would be cloudless.

The bid to explain the solar warming by letting the Sun bat the clouds away ran into one notable snag. The Intergovernmental Panel on Climate Change reported mainly increases in observed cloud cover during the twentieth century, while the story about cosmic rays required that they should have diminished. The long-term data on clouds were often questionable, because of contradictory results in some cases and changes of reporting methods in others. Even so, a general reduction in differences between day and night temperatures, in Australia, Europe, India and North America, implied an increase in cloudiness.

There would be places to go to for other investigations of the cloud history, besides the formal meteorological records – to astronomical observatories, for example, for data on observations spoiled by cloudiness. Cloud data from weather satellites, the most reliable source, might be pushed back to the 1960s. But the Danish team had an effective strength of one and a half people, and thousands would be needed for all the research provoked by the solar warming.

It opened a new frontier of science even wider than the greenhouse warming had created, because the Sun and the solar wind were now involved as well as all the intricacies of the Earth system. In the end, solar effects on climate

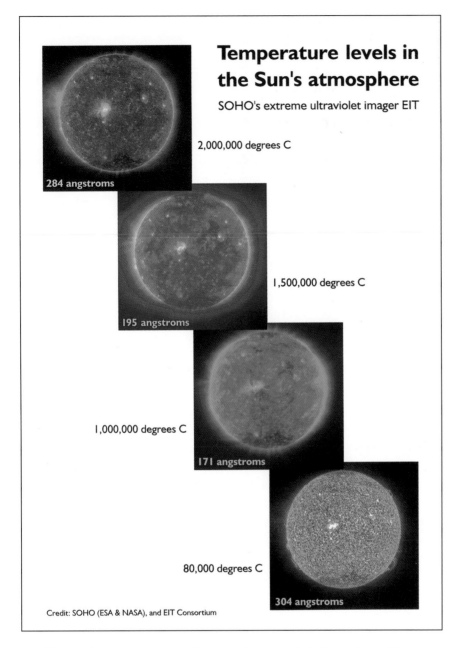

Temperature levels in the Sun's atmosphere

SOHO's extreme ultraviolet imager EIT

2,000,000 degrees C

284 angstroms

1,500,000 degrees C

195 angstroms

1,000,000 degrees C

171 angstroms

80,000 degrees C

304 angstroms

Credit: SOHO (ESA & NASA), and EIT Consortium

A ladder of temperature through the Sun's atmosphere. The extreme ultraviolet imager on the SOHO spacecraft monitors the Sun's behaviour every day at four ultraviolet wavelengths, emitted by charged atoms at different temperatures. Roughly speaking, the hotter regions are higher in the atmosphere, but heights vary from place to place. As the flickering activity penetrates from one level to another, it heats the atmosphere and propels the solar wind into space. Regular monitoring of the Sun is needed for understanding changes on the Earth.

would require many teams of researchers, and dedicated satellites and supercomputers, to follow up all the issues and implications. A new scientific industry would spring up in Sunspot Valley.

For a start it would give a big boost to solar and solar-terrestrial research in general. The known but questionably estimated variations in the Sun's output of light were definitely to be added to its climatic influences on clouds. The possible effects of the dumping of solar particles into the auroral zones by the active Sun were still up for grabs. But it seemed likely that the link from cosmic rays to clouds would remain the biggest factor influencing the climate, and the *aa* shield of the solar wind was its main controller.

An urgent task would be to relate magnetic observations of *aa* fluctuations

Advance warning of a solar outburst. Multiple loops in the magnetic field were seen by SOHO's coronagraph LASCO on 31 January 1996, in a view of the atmosphere close to the Sun. On 3 February, the magnetic mayhem flung a mass ejection into the solar system.

SOHO/ESA & NASA and LASCO Consortium

over short timescales to observations of the Sun and the solar wind by the multinational fleet of solar spacecraft. Then physicists might define the qualities in the solar wind that created the *aa* shield, and could abolish it if the Sun's mood changed. They would need to trace any special effects in the solar wind back to the Sun and into its magnetically warped interior where the changes originated.

Attention to the influences on cosmic rays, as studied by Ulysses and other spacecraft, would have to continue through successive solar cycles. Reversals of the Sun's magnetic poles in each solar cycle altered the behaviour of cosmic rays. Around the sunspot minimum of the mid-1980s, the main period covered by Svensmark's research on clouds, the Sun's magnetic poles and the Earth's pointed in opposite directions. The most important cosmic rays, positively charged, entered the solar system via the stretched-out magnetic field surrounding the Sun's equator. They reached the outer planets first. In that configuration, activity by the Sun and the *aa* shield were more effective in repelling the cosmic rays than they were in the mid-1990s. By then the Sun's magnetic poles had flipped over, and the positive cosmic rays approached the Sun's poles, spilling out towards the planets from the sunward side. A full analysis, taking account of the Sun's magnetic reversals, might well confirm a 22-year cycle in solar effects on the weather.

The entire subject of palaeoclimatology, which examined climates of the past, was open to re-scrutiny in the light of solar processes and their effects on clouds. All those failed attempts to link weather and climate to the 11-year sunspot cycle and other cycles would be worth evaluating afresh, to find new linkages. And on the shortest timescales, even the daily weather forecasters would need to take the counts of cosmic rays into account in setting up their computer models.

For meteorologists a priority would be to look afresh at cloud physics, and Henrik Svensmark picked on that aspect for his own early attention. The impression from the solar event of 1991 was that the cosmic rays took about a day to breed their contributions to the clouds. Still working intensively, Svensmark began to grapple with the theoretical microphysics of charged atoms and electrons, strewn by the cosmic rays, interacting with dust particles, water droplets and ice crystals. In pursuing more observational data, for short-term cosmic ray decreases, he began to form impressions of clouds clearing, and then new clouds forming.

Meanwhile, the author of this book was anxious to satisfy himself that he should believe what the Danish physicists were saying. He first confirmed that warm and cool years during the twentieth century seemed to occur when the radioberyllium in the polar ice indicated, respectively, low and high cosmic rays. But when he began making rough graphs of his own, relating the record of global temperatures to the cosmic rays, he had 24 hours of panic when he thought that he had rediscovered a major greenhouse warming in some years with temperatures too high to match the cosmic rays. He checked the data, sharpened his pencil and plotted the graphs more carefully.

For the years 1954–94, global land air temperatures published by the Intergovernmental Panel on Climate Change could be compared with the direct record of cosmic rays, routinely measured by John Simpson and his Chicago colleagues. This period also included one of the century's two main phases of substantial warming. A match emerged in the author's graph between fluctuations in temperature and variations in the cosmic rays. Usually the data fitted to within 0.2 degree C. But about one year in three was crazy, being warmer than the cosmic rays implied that it should be, by 0.2 to 0.6 degree.

One of the discrepant years was 1973. In that year, the author had visited the Galapagos islands with a BBC producer, in preparing a TV programme on molecular evolution. He remembered stepping gingerly over many fluffy white corpses of booby chicks, which had starved because of the abnormal weather and water temperatures of El Niño that year. The warming of the Pacific Ocean in an El Niño event could affect the global mean temperature. When he checked the other discrepant years and found that in almost every case there was an El Niño event, he was satisfied that the cosmic ray story was right.

Reassuring shortfalls in temperature were also present, in the aftermath of volcanic eruptions. There were four major events in the period 1954–1994: Bezymianny in Kamchatka in 1956, Agung in Bali in 1963, El Chichón in Mexico in 1982, and Pinatubo in the Philippines in 1991. After Bezymianny and El Chichón, global temperatures were 0.2 to 0.4 degree C below the solar expectations. In the other cases, Agung and Pinatubo occurred simultaneously with a rapid increase in the cosmic rays, and again, high temperatures in adjacent years were due to El Niño.

Thus the Danish discovery made possible a detailed assessment of year-by-year and decade-by-decade changes, never attemptable before. An impressive example was the succession of years 1979–84. The global temperature was in

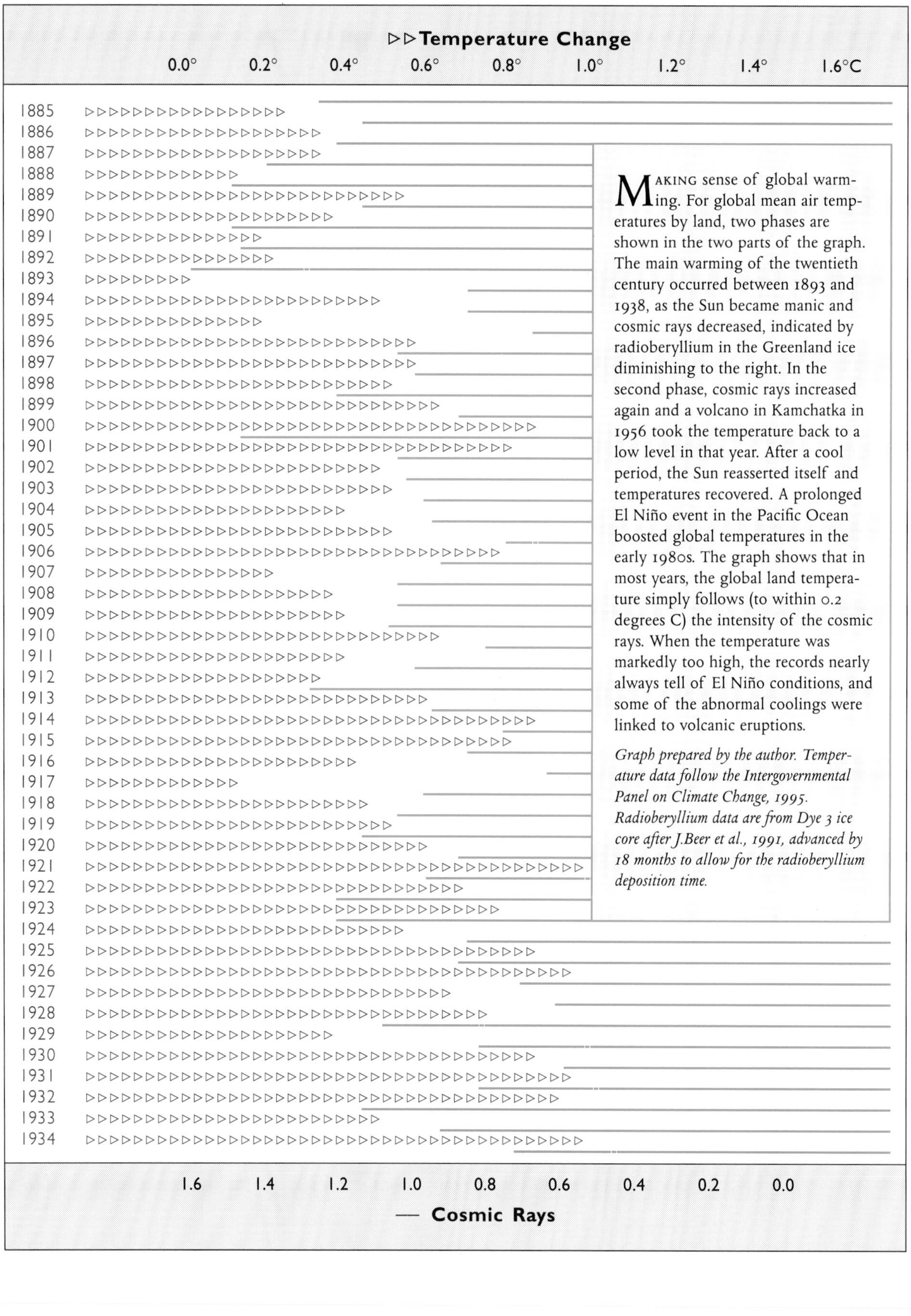

| 0.0° | 0.2° | 0.4° | 0.6° | 0.8° | 1.0° | 1.2° | 1.4° | 1.6°C |

1885
1886
1887
1888
1889
1890
1891
1892
1893
1894
1895
1896
1897
1898
1899
1900
1901
1902
1903
1904
1905
1906
1907
1908
1909
1910
1911
1912
1913
1914
1915
1916
1917
1918
1919
1920
1921
1922
1923
1924
1925
1926
1927
1928
1929
1930
1931
1932
1933
1934

M AKING sense of global warming. For global mean air temperatures by land, two phases are shown in the two parts of the graph. The main warming of the twentieth century occurred between 1893 and 1938, as the Sun became manic and cosmic rays decreased, indicated by radioberyllium in the Greenland ice diminishing to the right. In the second phase, cosmic rays increased again and a volcano in Kamchatka in 1956 took the temperature back to a low level in that year. After a cool period, the Sun reasserted itself and temperatures recovered. A prolonged El Niño event in the Pacific Ocean boosted global temperatures in the early 1980s. The graph shows that in most years, the global land temperature simply follows (to within 0.2 degrees C) the intensity of the cosmic rays. When the temperature was markedly too high, the records nearly always tell of El Niño conditions, and some of the abnormal coolings were linked to volcanic eruptions.

Graph prepared by the author. Temperature data follow the Intergovernmental Panel on Climate Change, 1995. Radioberyllium data are from Dye 3 ice core after J.Beer et al., 1991, advanced by 18 months to allow for the radioberyllium deposition time.

| 1.6 | 1.4 | 1.2 | 1.0 | 0.8 | 0.6 | 0.4 | 0.2 | 0.0 |

— **Cosmic Rays**

▷▷ **Temperature Change**

0.0°	0.2°	0.4°	0.6°	0.8°	1.0°	1.2°	1.4°	1.6°C

1935 ▷▷▷▷▷▷▷▷▷▷▷▷▷▷▷▷▷▷▷▷▷▷▷▷▷▷▷▷▷▷▷▷▷▷
1936 ▷▷▷▷▷▷▷▷▷▷▷▷▷▷▷▷▷▷▷▷▷▷▷▷▷▷▷▷▷▷▷▷
1937 ▷▷▷▷▷▷▷▷▷▷▷▷▷▷▷▷▷▷▷▷▷▷▷▷▷▷▷▷▷▷▷
1938 ▷▷▷
1939 ▷▷▷▷▷▷▷▷▷▷▷▷▷▷▷▷▷▷▷▷▷▷▷▷▷▷▷▷▷▷▷▷▷▷▷▷▷▷▷
1940 ▷▷▷▷▷▷▷▷▷▷▷▷▷▷▷▷▷▷▷▷▷▷▷▷▷▷▷▷▷▷▷▷▷▷▷▷
1941 ▷▷▷▷▷▷▷▷▷▷▷▷▷▷▷▷▷▷▷▷▷▷▷▷▷▷▷▷▷▷▷▷▷▷▷
1942 ▷▷▷▷▷▷▷▷▷▷▷▷▷▷▷▷▷▷▷▷▷▷▷▷▷▷▷▷▷▷▷▷▷▷▷
1943 ▷▷▷▷▷▷▷▷▷▷▷▷▷▷▷▷▷▷▷▷▷▷▷▷▷▷▷▷▷▷▷▷▷▷▷▷▷▷
1944 ▷▷▷
1945 ▷▷▷▷▷▷▷▷▷▷▷▷▷▷▷▷▷▷▷▷▷▷▷▷▷▷▷▷▷▷▷▷
1946 ▷▷▷▷▷▷▷▷▷▷▷▷▷▷▷▷▷▷▷▷▷▷▷▷▷▷▷▷▷▷▷▷▷▷▷
1947 ▷▷▷▷▷▷▷▷▷▷▷▷▷▷▷▷▷▷▷▷▷▷▷▷▷▷▷▷▷▷▷▷▷▷
1948 ▷▷▷▷▷▷▷▷▷▷▷▷▷▷▷▷▷▷▷▷▷▷▷▷▷▷▷▷▷▷▷▷▷▷▷▷▷▷
1949 ▷▷▷▷▷▷▷▷▷▷▷▷▷▷▷▷▷▷▷▷▷▷▷▷▷▷▷▷▷▷▷▷▷▷▷▷▷
1950 ▷▷▷▷▷▷▷▷▷▷▷▷▷▷▷▷▷▷▷▷▷▷
1951 ▷▷▷▷▷▷▷▷▷▷▷▷▷▷▷▷▷▷▷▷▷▷▷▷▷▷▷▷▷▷▷▷
1952 ▷▷▷▷▷▷▷▷▷▷▷▷▷▷▷▷▷▷▷▷▷▷▷▷▷▷▷▷▷▷▷▷▷
1953 ▷▷▷▷▷▷▷▷▷▷▷▷▷▷▷▷▷▷▷▷▷▷▷▷▷▷▷▷▷▷▷▷▷▷▷▷▷▷▷
1954 ▷▷▷▷▷▷▷▷▷▷▷▷▷▷▷▷▷▷▷▷▷▷▷▷▷▷▷▷▷▷
1955 ▷▷▷▷▷▷▷▷▷▷▷▷▷▷▷▷▷▷▷▷▷▷▷▷▷▷▷▷▷▷
1956 ▷▷▷▷▷▷▷▷▷▷▷▷▷▷▷▷▷▷
1957 ▷▷▷▷▷▷▷▷▷▷▷▷▷▷▷▷▷▷▷▷▷▷▷▷▷▷▷▷▷▷▷▷▷
1958 ▷▷▷▷▷▷▷▷▷▷▷▷▷▷▷▷▷▷▷▷▷▷▷▷▷▷▷▷▷▷▷▷▷▷▷▷▷
1959 ▷▷▷▷▷▷▷▷▷▷▷▷▷▷▷▷▷▷▷▷▷▷▷▷▷▷▷▷▷▷▷▷▷▷▷▷
1960 ▷▷▷▷▷▷▷▷▷▷▷▷▷▷▷▷▷▷▷▷▷▷▷▷▷▷▷▷▷▷▷▷▷
1961 ▷▷▷▷▷▷▷▷▷▷▷▷▷▷▷▷▷▷▷▷▷▷▷▷▷▷▷▷▷▷▷▷▷▷▷▷▷
1962 ▷▷▷▷▷▷▷▷▷▷▷▷▷▷▷▷▷▷▷▷▷▷▷▷▷▷▷▷▷▷▷▷▷▷▷▷
1963 ▷▷▷▷▷▷▷▷▷▷▷▷▷▷▷▷▷▷▷▷▷▷▷▷▷▷▷▷▷▷▷▷▷▷▷▷▷▷▷
1964 ▷▷▷▷▷▷▷▷▷▷▷▷▷▷▷▷▷▷▷▷▷▷▷▷▷▷▷
1965 ▷▷▷▷▷▷▷▷▷▷▷▷▷▷▷▷▷▷▷▷▷▷▷▷▷▷▷▷
1966 ▷▷▷▷▷▷▷▷▷▷▷▷▷▷▷▷▷▷▷▷▷▷▷▷▷▷▷▷
1967 ▷▷▷▷▷▷▷▷▷▷▷▷▷▷▷▷▷▷▷▷▷▷▷▷▷▷▷▷▷▷
1968 ▷▷▷▷▷▷▷▷▷▷▷▷▷▷▷▷▷▷▷▷▷▷▷▷▷▷▷▷▷
1969 ▷▷▷▷▷▷▷▷▷▷▷▷▷▷▷▷▷▷▷▷▷▷▷▷
1970 ▷▷▷▷▷▷▷▷▷▷▷▷▷▷▷▷▷▷▷▷▷▷▷▷▷▷▷▷▷▷▷▷
1971 ▷▷▷▷▷▷▷▷▷▷▷▷▷▷▷▷▷▷▷▷▷▷▷▷▷▷▷▷▷▷
1972 ▷▷▷▷▷▷▷▷▷▷▷▷▷▷▷▷▷▷▷▷▷▷▷▷
1973 ▷▷▷▷▷▷▷▷▷▷▷▷▷▷▷▷▷▷▷▷▷▷▷▷▷▷▷▷▷▷▷▷▷▷▷▷
1974 ▷▷▷▷▷▷▷▷▷▷▷▷▷▷▷▷▷▷▷▷▷▷▷▷
1975 ▷▷▷▷▷▷▷▷▷▷▷▷▷▷▷▷▷▷▷▷▷▷▷▷▷▷▷▷▷▷▷▷▷▷
1976 ▷▷▷▷▷▷▷▷▷▷▷▷▷▷▷▷▷▷▷▷
1977 ▷▷▷▷▷▷▷▷▷▷▷▷▷▷▷▷▷▷▷▷▷▷▷▷▷▷▷▷▷▷▷▷▷▷
1978 ▷▷▷▷▷▷▷▷▷▷▷▷▷▷▷▷▷▷▷▷▷▷▷▷▷▷▷▷▷▷
1979 ▷▷▷▷▷▷▷▷▷▷▷▷▷▷▷▷▷▷▷▷▷▷▷▷▷▷▷▷▷▷▷
1980 ▷▷▷▷▷▷▷▷▷▷▷▷▷▷▷▷▷▷▷▷▷▷▷▷▷▷▷▷▷▷▷▷▷
1981 ▷▷▷
1982 ▷▷▷▷▷▷▷▷▷▷▷▷▷▷▷▷▷▷▷▷▷▷▷▷▷▷▷▷▷▷▷▷
1983 ▷▷

1.6	1.4	1.2	1.0	0.8	0.6	0.4	0.2	0.0

— **Cosmic Rays**

▷▷ Temperature Change

| | 0.0° | 0.2° | 0.4° | 0.6° | 0.8° | 1.0° | 1.2° | 1.4° | 1.6°C |

1953
1954
1955
1956
1957
1958
1959
1960
1961
1962
1963
1964
1965
1966
1967
1968
1969
1970
1971
1972
1973
1974
1975
1976
1977
1978
1979
1980
1981
1982
1983
1984
1985
1986
1987
1988
1989
1990
1991
1992
1993
1994

| +2.0 | +1.0 | 0.0 | -1.0 | -2.0 | -3.0 |

• • • Cosmic Rays

The recent warming. A direct count of cosmic rays is available since 1953. As their intensity diminished, retreating to the right in this graph, so the global mean air temperature, by land, rose with it. In most years the temperature simply rose or fell in accordance with the cosmic rays. Dips in 1956 and 1982 were due to volcanoes. El Niño warming events in the Pacific Ocean caused temporary heat waves, for example in 1973, 1983 and 1987–88. Since 1989 an El Niño series of unprecedented length explains the abnormal warmth of recent years, when added to the effect of intense solar activity and low cosmic rays, 1989–1991.

Graph prepared by the author. Temperature data follow the Intergovernmental Panel on Climate Change, 1995.
Cosmic ray data are from Climax, Colorado, and the University of Chicago.

step with decreasing cosmic rays, in 1979–80. In 1981–83 a particularly strong El Niño event occurred, raising global temperatures – except in 1982, when the El Chichón eruption exerted its cooling effect. With those diversions over, the global temperature reverted in 1984 to a relatively low reading specified by a rising count of the cosmic rays as the sunspot numbers dwindled towards their mid-1980s minimum.

This preliminary check, done merely for the personal reassurance of the author, showed that climatology had become an exact science. The cases where global mean temperatures by land departed by more than 0.2 degree C from the expectations from cosmic rays focused attention on El Niño as the principal extra variant. The high temperatures of the early 1990s were due to a combination of an exceptionally low cosmic ray count and the century's most protracted succession of El Niños.

The same thing had happened in the early 1940s (*see* graph on previous pages). The radioberyllium record, a proxy for cosmic ray measurements, showed counts insufficiently low to explain fully the temperature peak at that time. The Sun was much more vigorous in reducing the cosmic rays than it had been in 1890, which explained a general warming of 0.6 degree in the early decades of the century. Top-ups of the global temperature by 0.2 to 0.4 degree C evidently resulted from a long El Niño, 1939–43.

A full accounting for each year's temperature and the general trends would have to take account of all the factors. Besides its influence on the cosmic rays, affecting the clouds, the Sun also varied in brightness. According to the calculations of Peter Foukal of Cambridge, Massachusetts, and Judith Lean of Washington DC, the Sun was particularly bright around the sunspot maximum of 1980–82. This may have helped with the temperature blip of 1981. And a gradual warming of the oceans was a likely result of the increasing frequency of warm years since 1900. That would contribute to the global warming, in opposition to the cooling effect of increasing levels of man-made dust.

As for the enhanced greenhouse effect, the year-by-year record left no room for 0.4 degree C warming in the period 1960–90. That was the figure required by the Intergovernmental Panel on Climate Change in its medium estimate when it took account of the cooling effects of dust. This related to land and sea temperatures taken together, which fluctuated much less than the land temperatures shown in the graphs here. On a generous interpretation of the data, between a small shortfall of temperature in 1959 (compared with the expectations from the cosmic rays) and a small excess in 1990, one might imagine a rising trend of 0.2 degree over 30 years.

This increase, if real, had to be shared with the intensification of solar brightness, to which the panel itself assigned about 0.1 degree C for 1960–90. Allowance also had to be made for the long-term effect of the gradually warming oceans. So the greenhouse warming over the 30-year period was 0 to 0.1 degree. If it was there at all, it fell very far short of the 0.6 degree expected from the greenhouse gases alone, in the calculations for the Intergovernmental Panel on Climate Change of the kind that inspired the Rio Climate Convention.

'Is the Sun still burning?' Almost out of reach of cosmic rays, under 1200 metres of rock at Gran Sasso in Italy, the multinational GALLEX experiment detects ghostly particles called neutrinos coming from the Sun's core. A few of the neutrinos interact with gallium chloride held in solution in the large tank, making atoms of germanium. As there are not as many neutrinos as expected, some theorists wonder if the Sun can vary its rate of nuclear burning. Fundamental uncertainties about the Sun's behaviour bode ill for predictions of its influences on climate.

T. Kirsten, MPI, Heidelberg

As for the computer modellers of climate, they would no doubt follow the suggestion of Svensmark and Friis-Christensen and put the cloudiness due to cosmic rays into their models, to see what that did to 'natural' variability. There would be big zonal effects due to the action of the Earth's magnetism cutting the cosmic rays in the tropics and admitting more at high latitudes.

The climate modellers would be curious also to know what became of their greenhouse effect. They would have three broad possibilities to consider. One was that the effects of pollution and sulphate particles had cancelled it out, as Friis-Christensen and Lassen had long suggested, and as at least one computer model had hinted could happen. If that were the case, there might be mileage still in the mainstream greenhouse story. Sulphate emissions and other forms of air pollution were the subject of curbs – for example to reduce acid rain. When those were effective, the greenhouse warming might escape from under the sulphate cooling and the climatic holocaust, you might argue, was merely postponed for some decades.

As a second possibility the greenhouse warming might be so limited by natural feedback processes that its net effect was only a small fraction of a degree. Richard Lindzen of Cambridge, Massachusetts, had reasoned from the outset that reactions of water vapour, presumed by the computer modellers to amplify the effect of carbon dioxide, might in reality work the other way, and curb the warming.

The last of the obvious options for explaining the absence of a greenhouse warming was the most radical. So far from the rise in carbon dioxide causing the global warming, the global warming might have caused the rise in carbon dioxide. That this idea was not nonsensical appeared in the way the carbon dioxide went down and up again in the last ice age, when the only man-made combustion was in meagre wood fires. An Australian drilling in Antarctica showed a rapid drop in carbon dioxide by 10 parts per million in the late sixteenth century, during the Little Ice Age.

The hesitation in the rise in carbon dioxide in the air, in the cooling that followed the Mount Pinatubo eruption, was a contemporary hint of a natural effect on carbon dioxide. Even then, the enhanced greenhouse effect of increasing carbon dioxide would not be defunct, because it could be Nature's way of intensifying a solar warming.

All climate forecasting for the Earth had to go on hold, because it required first a climate forecast for the Sun. That was beyond reach as far as any comprehension of the mechanisms went. A cautious opinion was simply that the Sun was unusually active in the late twentieth century, batting the cosmic rays away more vigorously than for several previous centuries, but the *aa* shield was not growing any stronger. A betting man would expect the Sun to go quieter, bringing extra clouds and a cooling of the Earth.

One betting man had already implied much the same thing, before the Danish announcement of the effect of cosmic rays on clouds. Piers Corbyn of Weather Action still kept secret the Solar Weather Technique by which he gambled against the UK Meteorological Office's long-term forecasts. But he ex-

pressed his scorn for the greenhouse warming in John Emsley's book, *The Global Warming Debate*, published early in 1996.

'It appears now that the natural (we suggest solar powered) warming processes are coming to an end,' Corbyn wrote. 'Hence the greenhouse predictions should run into increasingly dramatic failure.'

After the Danish announcement about cosmic rays affecting cloud cover, Corbyn was asked for his opinion. He had already adopted Friis-Christensen and Lassen's early finding on the length of the solar cycle, as a valuable guide to the level of solar activity, and he welcomed the new result as an addition to knowledge about physical mechanisms. It accorded with Brian Tinsley's ideas about electric currents in the air, published in 1994, which had also stressed the importance of cosmic rays. But for Corbyn any direct effect of cosmic rays on cloud formation was only one of a variety of ways in which the Sun affected the weather and climate.

'There's a lot more to it than that,' he said. 'We see roughly cyclical effects of solar action not directly linked to intensities of cosmic rays from the Galaxy, but involving solar protons, ultraviolet rays, the ozone layer, Sun-Earth magnetic orientations, and even the slant of the orbit of the Moon, which interrupts the solar wind.'

Some support for the idea that a Little Ice Age might be at least deferred for a few decades came from the indications, in the radioberyllium peaks, of four

'Hunters in the Snow.' In 1565, when Pieter Brueghel the Elder painted this picture, the Earth's climate was see-sawing in the Little Ice Age. Contemporary rates of formation of radioberyllium and radiocarbon indicate a shortlived increase in cosmic rays at the time, during a general trend in the sixteenth century towards warmer conditions.

Kunsthistorische Museum, Vienna / The Bridgeman Art Library

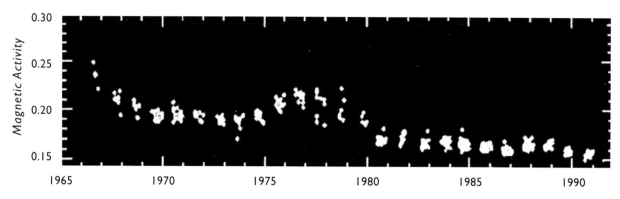

0.30

0.25

0.20

0.15

Magnetic Activity

1965   1970   1975   1980   1985   1990

Sudden quietening of a star. Magnetic activity in a sun-like star in the Pisces constellation, 54 Piscium, went through a cycle closely resembling the 11-year sunspot cycle. Then the magnetic activity switched off. Astronomers suspect that the same thing happened to the Sun in the Maunder Minimum of the late seventeenth century, when the world turned cold.

After S. Baliunas & R. Jastrow, 1993

minima of solar activity around AD 1320, 1440, 1690 and 1890. Reckoning simple-mindedly from an average interval of about 140 years, the next such event might occur around 2030. A student of solar cycles, Charles Sonett of Tucson, Arizona, predicted that solar activity would peak around 2030 and that solar warming would continue until the mid-twenty-first century.

The Mount Wilson study of sun-like stars gave a general warning of the recurrence of cold spells. Watching ten sun-like stars for 25 years was like watching one for 250 years. In that combined data set, Mount Wilson recorded 35 years of minimal magnetic activity, in 54 Piscium and the altogether lazy Tau Ceti. From the astronomical evidence, a Little Ice Age could strike suddenly at any time.

In 1980, 54 Piscium switched off its magnetic activity, with no obvious change in rhythm up to that point. Before the Maunder Minimum plunged the Earth into the trough of the Little Ice Age in the mid-seventeenth century, the last solar cycle was about 10 years in length, by Knud Lassen's reckoning, similar to the cycles of the late twentieth century.

Changes on the Earth, now extended to the Sun, would remain a matter for vigilance at the ground observing stations and by satellites. Nature was never the kindly mother of Gaian fancy, and the climate would have deadly shocks in store. For scare stories one could look to the abrupt changes of climate revealed in the Greenland ice cores.

There were scenarios for more or less sudden chills due to rearrangements of the ice and the ocean currents. Ice surging off Antarctica could flood the coastal zones more suddenly and disastrously than the sea-level rise advertised by the Intergovernmental Panel on Climate Change. On dates unspecifiable giant meteorites would fall, throwing dust into the air to bring darkness at noon. Homemade giant eruptions would cause volcanic winters, and geophysicists looked nervously at the heaving island of Iwojima off Japan, which could be the Earth's next big bang.

Apart from variations in the Sun itself, the Earth's attitude and orbit had gradually changed since the end of the last ice age, putting the Sun lower and farther in the North Atlantic summer sky where ice ages were born. Severe glaciation had been the normal condition of the planet for millions of years, and still was. The warm intervals like the last 10,000 years were unusual. Conceivably Al Gore's tasteless remark about the summer of 1988 being 'the

Kristallnacht of the warming holocaust' would need amending to say, 'Remember 1988, it won't be that good again for 120,000 years.'

The political moral was simple, though unattractive to frugal governments. As Joseph taught the Pharaoh long ago, the Earth is a dangerous place to live, so granaries should be kept full.

Cloud watcher. Successive Meteosat spacecraft contributed to the cloud climatology record used to discover the action of cosmic rays. Developed by the European Space Agency to observe the European and African segment of the globe, the first Meteosat flew in 1977. The sixth is seen here during pre-launch inspection at Cannes, France.

ESA

Retrospect

WHAT WENT WRONG?

T HE THREAT of a greenhouse catastrophe was lifted from the lives of
ordinary citizens everywhere. They could rejoice that the Warming War
ended much more quickly than the Cold War. Real estate prices in Alaska
and Siberia might fall, hotels accustomed to multinational hordes of greenhouse officials and consultants might have to consider other promotions. But
there would be no more excuse for the rich to say that the poor should stay
poor for the sake of the planet. The Arab could trade his donkey for a van
without the sky turning incandescent.

Ordinary folk might charitably dismiss the greenhouse business as just another example of the neurotic capacity of human beings to worry about the
wrong things. They would still have excellent reasons for economizing with
the use of fossil fuels, and planting more trees than they felled. And they could
expect to benefit from faster growth of plants due to enhanced carbon dioxide,
without a severe climate penalty.

The environmental movement had made the greenhouse warming the cen-
tre-piece of its efforts. It would have to heal itself. While environmentalists
could still take satisfaction from progress with international agreements to protect the ozone layer, and to maintain biodiversity by protecting endangered
species, they had to see the dangers of unbridled busybodying. Horror stories
lacking a secure scientific foundation could harm their cause. They might learn
from their own slogan about thinking globally but acting locally, where nameable human beings and other species suffered from nameable strangers who
fouled their habitats.

Journalists too would have to examine their consciences, after misleading
their readers for several years about the greenhouse warming. They would have
to re-learn elementary principles about the nature of scientific evidence and
opinion. Journalists especially had to consider how they had allowed official
climatologists and environmental pressure groups to manipulate them. Scientists would have to negotiate with governments to rescue from the greenhouse
wreckage their many excellent programmes of research into global change,
and redirect them to a humbler desire to learn from Nature. Amid the impending realignment of a huge sector of research, there would be an urgent need to
repair the image of science itself in the taxpayer's eye.

The greenhouse story would become a textbook case for historians, phi-
losophers and political scientists. People would wonder where science went

wrong. But the premise was false, because cutting-edge physics never erred. On the contrary it performed its usual magic of sorting out fact from fiction with commendable speed, thanks to a few people in Copenhagen working in their spare time with personal computers.

The aberration was confined to a small but resolute minority who claimed to speak for all relevant science. They managed for a few years to command the attention of governments. The supercomputers were their ouija boards, and environmentalists and the media their willing barkers. An unlucky tail of biologists, geographers, social scientists and others believed the computers and redirected their careers towards such second-order science fiction as the spread of malaria in the greenhouse world.

Why did it happen? Every generation of scientists throws up individuals who like to hobnob with ministers or glorify their specialist knowledge by preaching policy. They oblige their peers of every generation to learn afresh, the hard way, that science and politics do not mix except in nasty emulsions that can send geneticists to the gulag or blow up the world.

Cutting-edge research was always anarchistic and iconoclastic. At the moments when Nature chose to whisper its messages, science was deaf to politics and prejudice. That was its irresistible strength. In the four short centuries since Galileo sketched his sunspots, Nature's murmurs guided the human species from cosmic angels to the Big Bang, and from the abacus to the microchip.

So unless Nature itself confirmed the opinions of the greenhouse brigade, which admittedly seemed a strong possibility to begin with, they could not expect to reign for long. Querying what they said was a much larger though unorganized constituency. It ranged from archaeologists who knew about radiocarbon and palaeoclimates, to solar physicists who stressed the many mysteries about the Sun that remained unsolved. Most powerful in resources and a capacity for discovery were the space scientists.

At a personal level the fight of the Danish physicists was very like David against Goliath. In this case Goliath never had a chance, because the slingshot were spacecraft. Those bundles of high technology, schooled to look after themselves in the harsh environment of space, compared in cost with the big computers of the climate modellers. The difference was that the computers were blind and the spacecraft had sensors far better than any human eyes or noses.

You could not go on sending them out to examine the Earth, the Sun, the solar system and the universe, for four decades, without plenty of gratifying surprises. When Henrik Svensmark summoned up on the Internet the data of the International Satellite Cloud Climatology Project he was tapping into a small part of the body of knowledge created with unsung effort by space scientists and engineers of many countries. The story in a nutshell was that clever little robots in space rescued the human species from a blunder magnified by the supercomputers.

If physics remained in excellent shape, the same could not be said for science applied in public affairs. The greenhouse warming hypothesis was sustained, in the face of much contrary evidence, by scientists of many nationalities who persisted in approving the reports of the Intergovernmental Panel on Climate Change. The panel, for its part, was entrained with the politics of the Climate Convention which was being created and developed in parallel with its work. Any radical change in the scientific assessment would have been politically embarrassing.

In an ordinary discourse, no one would blame the greenhouse enthusiasts for being wrong. Even Newton and Einstein made grand mistakes. Science depended on the eager pursuit of hypotheses to see where they might lead. The trouble in this case was that ordinary discourse gave way to an arrogation of authority quite inappropriate to science.

Most questionable was the role of British scientists and the UK Meteorological Office at Bracknell, where, to use John Houghton's own word, the scientific assessment was orchestrated. He obtained special funding to undertake this role because the British government was keen that he should. Pushing the greenhouse warming was vital for the nation's foreign policy.

The mobilization of science to serve national purposes had an honourable tradition in the United Kingdom. During the Second World War academic scientists responded to the nation's needs with energy and inventiveness. They came up with code-breaking computers, microwave radar, penicillin, nuclear weapons concepts, and countless lesser contributions to eventual victory.

In peacetime, too, many excellent programmes of government-funded research served the nation's needs for defence, technological innovation, the health service, agriculture and environmental protection. The greenhouse project did not fit those normal peacetime categories. Science in support of foreign policy was usually confined to such things as ciphers or research connected with overseas aid. In the late 1980s atmospheric issues were adopted, to allow the United Kingdom to maintain 'a seat at the table' in environmental diplomacy. Previous science programming went into reverse.

The Natural Environment Research Council had been starved of resources. In the early 1980s the funding of British science in general was in perpetual crisis and researchers were told they must compete in the market place. Resentful Oxford scientists had mutinied against a proposal to give the Prime Minister an honorary degree. With the launch of the greenhouse initiative, direct funding of climate research was accompanied by a restored budget for the Natural Environment Research Council. The government created a pool of money for global environmental research by other agencies too. British scientists were as grateful as a beaten puppy receiving a friendly pat. Now there was money to be had, if only out of other researchers' budgets, provided you played the greenhouse game.

There followed a Monty Python re-run of the mobilization of British scientists in the Second World War. Fifty years on, the aim was again to save the world, but now in the diplomatic struggle with the coal and oil producers. Once more the Americans had to be dragged into the conflict, this time against the better judgement of George Bush. And if policy said that the pin-striped warriors in the front line needed scary statistics about the greenhouse warming, British science would supply them, painted green and range tested on the playing fields of Bracknell.

The last and most important question to ask, about the United Kingdom's special role in greenhouse diplomacy and its supporting science, was why the British government was so keen on it. What explained the greening of Prime Minister Margaret Thatcher? When she sketched her new policies to the Royal Society in September 1988, some listeners may have imagined that she had suddenly changed from the world's sharpest politician into just another concerned grandmother. That would have been a scurrilous misjudgement.

The speech to the Royal Society was a step in a project that she had pursued for two years, and which was already well advanced. In the political background, Europe was making endless trouble about British pollution of fresh water, the beaches, the sea and the air. On the other hand, the idea that nations should resolve to curb their carbon dioxide emissions suited the United Kingdom exceptionally well, given the impending demise of the nation's coal industry and the Prime Minister's support for nuclear power.

She set out to wrest the initiative in environmental matters from the European Commission, by making the greenhouse warming a global issue, with the British not just at the table but in the chair. The French and Dutch governments wanted to evolve a common European policy on greenhouse gases but the British environment minister vetoed that. Instead, the United Nations and its specialized agencies found the British becoming hyperactive on unaccustomed subjects, and giving very practical support in creating the global apparatus of the Intergovernmental Panel on Climate Change.

In her memoirs Baroness Thatcher explained a more partisan consideration in her policy. The environmental lobby used the concern about global warming to attack capitalism, growth and industry. She wanted authority in the environmental debate 'to ensure a sense of proportion'. Leading the defence against green socialism would be science.

Sonja Boehmer-Christiansen, a science policy researcher in Brighton, England, analysed the British role in the intergovernmental exercise much more thoroughly than is attempted here. By a pleasing irony her own work was funded as one of the many spin-offs of British global change research. In a talk at an international relations conference in 1994, her conclusion minced no words.

'Britain achieved its goal of a seat at the table by creating the famous scientific consensus of the Intergovernmental Panel on Climate Change,' Boehmer-Christiansen said. The trick was done, she thought, by 'a negotiated agreement between scientific institutions largely competing with each other for scarce resources'.

About the politics of the greenhouse warming, there were plenty of subsidiary questions. Why, for example, did the Yanks let the Brits get away with it, despite many protests from distinguished meteorological researchers in the United States? But amid the ruins of policy and reputation, it was British science, renowned since Newton's time as a fountain of discovery, that would have to look to its credentials and re-appraise its relationship to the nation state. O! what a fall was there, my countrymen.

The need to protect the ivory tower of academic research was perhaps the over-riding lesson of the whole affair. Often attacked by those who thought all publicly funded science should have predictable utility, the ivory tower was the most productive building in the city of science, in respect of highly original discoveries. It was also the most likely source of politically uncontaminated results, playing a role analogous to intelligence in the military sphere, which was entrusted to those responsible for the operations only at great hazard.

Experts as soothsayers had a tradition going back to astrologers and inspectors of entrails, but their role in modern society would have to be circumscribed. Expert advisors expressed only their personal opinions and could never speak for science as a whole. As discovery advanced by replacing widely held opinions with new ones, it was entirely normal for the majority to be out of date, not least the honoured greybeards. Scientists and politicians everywhere would have to learn afresh that consensus in science was a meaningless concept. When Nazi scientists showed their solidarity against the Jewish doctrine of relativity, in a book called *A Hundred Against Einstein*, the hairy fellow growled that one would be enough. He meant that adverse evidence from Nature produced by a solitary researcher could destroy theories that no amount of ranting could touch.

The sincerity and intellectual conviction of John Houghton and his group at Bracknell were not in question. Their motive was to save the world and their belief in the greenhouse warming was genuine. Such virtues carried no weight in science, where discoveries could be made by people of any political persuasion or moral intent. As for personal certitude, the immunologist Peter Medawar put the point succinctly.

'I cannot give any scientist of any age better advice than this,' Medawar wrote. 'The intensity of the conviction that a hypothesis is true has no bearing on whether it is true or not.'

Corresponding advice to politicians and research administrators was never to demand urgent results from scientists, in any situation of severe ignorance. That was like trying to bend the universe to a Lilliputian will. If Nature was being coy and scientists said they needed more time for research, they meant it. No amount of badgering would produce a sensible result until the work was done. Premature information was, for policy purposes, as untrustworthy as a paper aeroplane.

Concerning the fragile Earth system, the good news was that science had since the 1960s made quite rapid progress overall in understanding climate change and many other aspects of global change, natural and man-made. Sensible climate forecasts were still a long way off and might never be possible. So whatever rumours the politicians might hear about the Sun's changing moods, they had better not rush off and sign a treaty to increase their emissions of greenhouse gases in a bid to ward off the cold.

As for the Danish heroes of this little saga, the years of loneliness amid the storms of the greenhouse ocean were over. By Desmond Bernal's declension, squirming opponents would say the work was not original and then that they, the opponents, had always suspected that cosmic rays made clouds. Gullible folk might even believe them, but who cared? The solar-terrestrial Vikings had reached the ultima Thule exclusive to those who changed the course of human knowledge. There, the only verdict that mattered any longer was posterity's.

REFERENCES

These are given by the page number plus a key word or phrase.
Abbreviated tags are used for publications of the Intergovernmental Panel on Climate Change.

CC'90. J.T. Houghton, G.J. Jenkins & J.J. Ephraums (eds) *Climate Change: The IPCC Scientific Assessment,* Cambridge University Press, Cambridge, UK, 1990

CC'92. J.T. Houghton, B.A. Callander & S.K. Varney (eds) *Climate Change 1992: The Supplementary Report to the IPCC Scientific Assessment,* Cambridge University Press, Cambridge, UK, 1992

CC'94. J.T. Houghton, L.G. Meira Filho, J. Bruce, Hoesung Lee, B.A. Callander, E. Haites, N. Harris & K. Maskell (eds) *Climate Change 1994: Radiative Forcing of Climate Change and an Evaluation of the IPCC IS92 Emission Scenarios,* Cambridge University Press, Cambridge, UK, 1994

CC'95. J.T. Houghton, L.G. Meira Filho, B.A. Callander, N. Harris, A. Kattenberg & K. Maskell (eds) *Climate Change 1995: The Science of Climate Change,* Cambridge University Press, Cambridge, UK, 1996

9   Ørsted and electromagnetism: M. Pihl, 'The first spark of electrotechnics,' offprint, Danish Foreign Ministry

10   Galileo on sunspots: *Istoria e Dimostrazione delle Macchie Solari,* 1613; cited e.g. in J.J. Fahie, *Galileo, His Life and Work,* Murray, London, 1903

11   Cassini on a dearth of sunspots: quoted in R.W. Noyes, *The Sun, Our Star,* Harvard University Press, Cambridge, Massachusetts, 1982

11   Herschel on sunspots and weather: *Philosophical Transactions of the Royal Society,* vol. 91, pp. 265–83, 1801

11   Herschel on infrared rays: *Philosophical Transactions of the Royal Society,* vol. 90, pp. 255–83, 1800

12   Thomson (Kelvin) and the longevity of the Sun: J. Burchfield, *Lord Kelvin and the Age of the Earth,* Macmillan, London, 1975

15   Biermann on the solar wind: L. Biermann, *Zeitschrift für Astrophysik,* vol. 29, pp. 274 ff., 1951

15   Parker on the solar wind: e.g. E.N. Parker, *Interplanetary Dynamical Processes, Interscience,* New York, 1963

17   Light meters in space: reviewed by C. Fröhlich et al. in C.P. Sonett et al. (eds) *The Sun in Time,* University of Arizona, Tucson, 1991, pp. 11–29

18   Graph of solar light variation: after R.C. Willson & H.S. Hudson, *Nature,* vol. 351, p. 42, 1991

20   Forbush on cosmic-ray variations: e.g. S.E. Forbush, *Journal of Geophysical Research,* vol. 59, pp. 525 ff., 1954

21–2   Solar-terrestrial events, March 1989: data and commentaries from texts of lectures by J.H. Allen, US National Geophysical Data Center, Boulder, Colorado

26   Two meteorologists not afraid: K. Labitzke & H. van Loon, e.g. *Journal of Atmospheric and Terrestrial Physics,* vol. 50, pp. 197–206, 1988

29   'Warmer in 1988': J. Hansen, quoted in John Gribbin, *Hothouse Earth,* Bantam Books, New York, 1989

29–30 A sceptical meteorologist (and the next six paragraphs): R.S. Lindzen, 'Global Warming: The Origin and Nature of Alleged Scientific Consensus,' offprint, MIT, 1992: hysteria, p. 4; A. Gore quote, p. 5; loss of a grant, p. 4; behaviour of Science p. 4; NRC report, p. 6; 1989 petition, p. 5; C. Schneider quote, p. 5; R. Redford quote, p. 5

30   'I had been relying': M. Thatcher, *The Downing Street Years,* Harper Collins, London, 1993 pp. 638–41; quote from p. 640

31   The British Prime Minister ensured: S.A. Boehmer-Christiansen, 'Britain and the Intergovernmental Panel on Climate Change: Promoting Global Research or Managing National Politics?' text of paper presented at the British International Studies Association, York, December 1994

31   'A clear understanding': J.T. Houghton, *Global Warming: The Complete Briefing,* Lion Books, Oxford, 1994, p. 126

32   'Not only does knowledge': B. Bolin, 'Greenhouse Gases and Global Change', in N. Calder (ed.) *Scientific Europe,* Foundation Scientific Europe, Maastricht, 1990, p. 160

34   The Maunder Minimum: J.A. Eddy, *Science*, vol. 192, pp. 1189–202, 1976

36   Scientific climatology took a stride forward: N. Calder, *Nature*, vol. 252, pp. 216–18, 1974; J.D. Hays et al., *Science*, vol. 194, pp. 1121–132, 1976

37   Graph of ice ages: after N.J. Shackleton & N.D. Opdyke, *Quaternary Research*, vol. 3, pp.39–55, 1983, tuned by J. Imbrie and J.Z. Imbrie; N. Calder, *Nature*, vol. 252, pp. 216–18, 1974

38   Fourier, Arrhenius and greenhouse history: *see* e.g. J.T. Houghton, *Global Warming: The Complete Briefing*, Lion Books, Oxford, 1994, pp. 21–2

39   Graph of carbon dioxide: after CC'90 p. 9, fig. 1.4, and C.D. Keeling et al., *AGU Geophysical Monographs*, vol. 55, pp. 165–236, 1989

41   A former president of the US NAS: F. Seitz (ed.) *Scientific Perspectives on* the *Greenhouse Problem*, George C. Marshall Institute, Washington DC, 1989

43   Vegetation from space: N. Calder, *Spaceship Earth*, Viking, London, 1991, pp. 95–128

43   Calculations by an American expert: P.M. Fearnside, 1982

44.   Microwave sounding units, results: e.g. N. Nicholls et al. in CC'95, esp. pp. 147–8

44   Solar-terrestrial events, August & October 1989: data and commentaries from texts of lectures by J.H. Allen, US National Geophysical Data Center, Boulder, Colorado

47   'I had been led to expect': J.T. Houghton, *Global Warming: The* Complete *Briefing*, Lion Books, Oxford, 1994, pp. 7–8.

47   'We have a full repairing lease': M. Thatcher quoted in J.T. Houghton, *Global Warming: The Complete Briefing*, Lion Books, Oxford, 1994, p. 134

47–8   *Climate Change*, 1990: *see* full reference to CC'90 above

48   Graph of greenhouse warming: after CC'90 p. xxii, fig. 8

48   'An authoritative statement': CC'90, p. v

49   'I worry': H. Tennekes, *Weather*, vol. 45, p. 67–8, 1990

49   'An ingenious novel': Voltaire, *Lettres Philosophiques*, 1734

49   Monsoon maps: from CC'90, p. 145

50   'The unequivocal detection': CC'90, p. xxix

50   Water vapour: R.S. Lindzen, 'Global Warming: The Origin and Nature of Alleged Scientific Consensus,' offprint from MIT, 1992, p. 2

51   Earth Radiation Budget Experiment: V. Ramanathan et al., *Science*, vol. 243, pp. 57–63, 1989

52   Thermostat Hypothesis: V. Ramanathan & W. Collins, *Nature*, vol. 351, pp. 27–32, 1991

52   'Although clouds produce net cooling': U. Cubasch & R.D.Cess, 'Processes and Modelling,' in CC'90, p. 79

52   GRIP project: S.J. Johnsen, conversation 1996

54-6   Solar cycle length: E. Friis-Christensen & K. Lassen, *Science*, vol. 254, pp. 698–700, 1991

54   A graph of the temperature rise: CC'90, p. 206, fig. 7.6(a) after P.D. Jones, *Journal of Climatology*, vol. 1, pp. 654–60, 1988

55   Graph of solar warming: after E. Friis-Christensen & K. Lassen, *Science*, vol. 254, pp. 698–700, 1991

55   He had been struck: G.C. Reid, *Nature*, vol. 329, pp. 142–3, 1987

56   Snow melt correlation: N. Nicholls et al. in CC'95 p. 157

56   An unorthodox meteorologist: P. Corbyn interviewed in *The Guardian*, London, 27 June 1996; conversation 1996

59   Ulysses mission: special issue, *Astronomy and Astrophysics Supplement Series* vol. 92, No. 2, pp. 207–440, 1992

59   'How would you expect': R. Marsden, conversation 1994

60   'Imagine you are sitting': J.A. Simpson, conversations 1994, 1996

60–4   Radiocarbon fluctuations: H.E. Seuss in *Radiocarbon Dating and the Methods of Low Level Counting*, IAEA, Vienna, 1967; C. Renfrew, *Before Civilization*, Cape, London, 1973; C.P. Sonett, *Meteoritics*, vol. 20, pp. 383–94, 1985; G.W. Pearson et al., *Radiocarbon*, vol. 25(2) pp. 911–34, 1986; P.E. Damon & C.P. Sonett, in C.P. Sonett et al. (eds) *The Sun in Time*, University of Arizona, Tucson, 1991, pp. 360-88

62   Graph of radiocarbon wiggles: after J. Klein et al. *Radiocarbon*, vol. 22, pp. 950–61, 1980; adapted from P.E. Damon & C.P. Sonett, in C.P. Sonett et al. (eds) *The Sun in Time*, University of Arizona, Tucson, 1991, pp. 360–388

64   Science paper: E. Friis-Christensen & K. Lassen, *Science,* vol. 254, pp. 698–700, 1991

64–5   'The problem today': J. Leggett, *Air Scare,* Heinemann Educational Books, Oxford, 1991, p. 15

66   'We don't yet know': D. Gough, conversation 1992

67   Phobos experiment: C. Fröhlich et al. in G. Berthomieu & M. Cribier (eds) *Inside the Sun,* Kluwer, Dordrecht, 1990, pp. 279–88

67   Gough was claiming to see inside the Sun: D. Gough, offprint of talk at National Academy of Science, 1991

69   'We can link changes': C. Fröhlich, conversation 1994

70   'Cluster will eliminate': R. Schmidt, conversation 1994

71   'One of the difficulties': R.M. Bonnet, *Les Horizons chimériques,* Dunod, Paris, 1992, p. 255

71–2   Solar-terrestrial events, June 1991: data and commentaries from texts of lectures by J.H. Allen, US National Geophysical Data Center, Boulder, Colorado

72   Graph of post-Pinatubo temperatures: after CC'95, Technical Summary, p. 33

72   Post-Pinatubo temperatures: W.L. Gates et al. in CC'95, esp. pp. 257–58

73   Post-Pinatubo carbon dioxide: D. Schimel et al. in CC'95, esp. pp. 80–2

75–8   Yohkoh: Z. Svestka & Y. Uchida, *The Yohkoh (Solar-A) Mission,* Kluwer, Dordrecht, 1991; L. Culhane, R. Bentley and A. Phillips, conversations 1992–96

78–9   *Science* paper: E. Friis-Christensen & K. Lassen, *Science,* vol. 254, pp. 698–700, 1991

79–82   Updated report: CC'92, *see* full reference above

80   An eminent crystallographer: J.D. Bernal, conversation 1958

80   Kelly and Wigley tried mixing: P.M. Kelly & T.M.L. Wigley, *Nature,* vol. 360, pp. 328–30, 1992

81   According to the Swiss space scientist: C. Fröhlich, *Journal of Geophysical Research,* vol. 92, pp. 796–800, 1987

81–2   IPCC comments on Friis-Christensen & Lassen: CC'92, esp. p. 14, p. 19, pp. 64–5 and pp. 162–3

82   Houghton's conclusion about the Sun: J.T. Houghton, *Global Warming: The Complete Briefing,* Lion Books, Oxford, 1994, p. 87

82   Caveat about referees: CC'92, p. 183

82–3   Ulysses past Jupiter: various authors, *Science,* vol. 257, esp. pp. 1496–557, 1992; R.G. Marsden, conversation 1994

83–4   Revelle co-authored a paper (and the following four paragraphs): R.S. Lindzen, 'Global Warming: The Origin and Nature of Alleged Scientific Consensus,' offprint, MIT 1992: Revelle and White cited, p. 6; Lindzen's alleged retraction, pp. 6–7; 'The pressure was frequently effective,' pp. 5–6; 'The remarkable centrality,' p. 7

85   'It has often been commented': J.T. Houghton, *Global Warming: The Complete Briefing,* Lion Books, Oxford, 1994, pp. 132–3

85   GRIP: S.J. Johnsen, conversation 1996

86   Geotail: A. Nishida speaking at COSPAR 96, Birmingham 1996

89–90   Hurricane Andrew data from C. Flavin & O. Tunali, *Climate of Hope,* Worldwatch Paper 130, Worldwatch Institute, Washington DC, 1996

90   Houghton on Andrew and other hurricanes: J.T. Houghton, *Global Warming: The Complete Briefing,* Lion Books, Oxford, 1994, pp. 11–13 and pp. 86–7

91   A special study of tropical cyclones: L. Bengtsson et al., *Tellus,* vol. 47A, pp. 175–96, 1995

91   Observations of the real world: N. Nicholls et al. in CC'95, esp. pp. 169–70.

91   Solar activity Nov. 1992: concerning Yohkoh, A. Phillips, conversation 1996; concerning Ulysses, E. Smith, conversation 1996

92   The good ship Vickers (and the following eight paragraphs): V. Ramanathan et al., *Science,* vol. 267, pp. 499–502, 1995; *also* V. Ramanathan, conversation 1996

93   In Tasmania, Colorado, Wisconsin and Alaska: R.D. Cess et al., *Science,* vol. 267, pp. 496–8, 1995

94   'Now does seem to be time': Teya Ryan, quoted by R.S. Lindzen, 'Global Warming: The Origin and Nature of Alleged Scientific Consensus,' offprint from MIT, 1992, p. 10, note 6

94   'The greenhouse warming may be fiction!': treatment for proposed TV series about the Sun, Henk van Mierlo Productions, The Hague, N. Calder scriptwriter

95   The institute's brochure for the public: *Weather, Climate and Oceans,* Danish Meteorological Institute, Copenhagen, undated

96   A by-product of that event: W. Karlén et al., *The Earth's Climate - Natural Variations and Human Influence,* Elforsk AB, Stockholm, 1993; 'The model calculations' p. 38–9

96   A baby satellite: brochure, 'A Danish microsatellite with a high scientific profile', Copenhagen, undated

97   Example concerning China: S. Hameed & G. Gong, *Geophysical Research Letters,* vol. 21, pp. 2693–96, 1994; Danish response in K. Lassen & E. Friis-Christensen, *Journal of Atmospheric and Terrestrial Physics,* vol. 57, pp. 838–45, 1995

98   One of the lead authors: J.M. Melillo et al., *Nature,* vol. 363, pp. 234–40, 1993

99   Graph of Chinese springtime: after K. Lassen & E. Friis-Christensen, *Journal of Atmospheric and Terrestrial Physics,* vol. 57, pp. 838–45, 1995

99   'It's just a preliminary analysis': D. Kicklighter, conversation 1993

99–100 Some American astronomers did their best: S.Baliunas & R. Jastrow, preprint for *Energy,* 1993

100 'This result suggests': Baliunas & Jastrow p. 10

105 At Armagh Observatory: C.J. Butler & D.J. Johnston, *Journal of Atmospheric and Terrestrial Physics,* vol. 58, pp. 1657–72, 1996

108 'We have to look for one-to-one relations': J-C Pecker at Royal Society/British Academy meeting on the Sun and climate, 1989

108 The lower atmosphere in the polar regions: C.J.E. Schuurmans, 'Influence of solar flare particles on the general circulation of the atmosphere,' *Nature,* 1965

108–9 A scientific paper written more than 30 years earlier: E.P. Ney, *Nature,* vol. 183, p. 451, 1959

109 'Ulysses tells us': R. Marsden, conversation 1994

110 Ulysses solar wind graph: after *International Heliospheric Study Newsletter* No. 10, June 1996

110 'Our instrument senses': J. Geiss, conversation 1994

110 'Now the spacecraft': A. Balogh, conversation 1994

111 The new paper: K. Lassen & E. Friis-Christensen, *Journal of Atmospheric and Terrestrial Physics,* vol. 57, pp. 838–45, 1995

111–12 To nag Friis-Christensen: B.A. Tinsley, *EOS,* vol. 75(32), pp. 369 and 374, 1994

112 'Concern about the Earth's changing climate': the same text used in video indexes on Ulysses (1994), SOHO (1995) and Cluster (1995): European Space Agency, Paris: produced by Derek Nelson, script by N. Calder

112–14 Ulysses south polar pass: workshop at ESA/ESTEC, Noordwijk, Netherlands, September 1994

114 'It is as if there is a man in the Sun': A. Balogh, conversation 1994

114 'We went to the south pole': A. Balogh, conversation 1994

115 A dozen prime sites around the world: listed in CC'95, pp. 298–9

115 Robert Charlson had pointed out: R.J. Charlson et al., *Science,* vol. 255, pp. 423–30, 1992

115–16 The French team found: H. Le Treut et al., 1995, cited by A. Kattenberg et al. in CC'95, p. 293

116 'I am convinced': H. Le Treut, conversation 1996

116–17 An unusually long run of El Niño: D. Phillips (ed.) *The Global Climate System Review,* 5th Edition for 1991–3, World Meteorological Organization No. 819, Geneva, 1995, esp. pp. 9–20

119 At Elsinore: W. Shakespeare. *Hamlet,* Act III, scene ii

119 Clouds must not be construed: U. Cubasch & R.D. Cess, in CC'90, p. 79

119 'The determination of cloud-dependent': R. Dickinson et al. in CC'95, p. 197

119 *Climate Change* 1995: *see* full reference under CC'95, above

119 The reports about clouds: V. Ramanathan et al., *Science,* vol. 267, pp. 499–502, 1995; R.D. Cess et al., *Science,* vol. 267, pp. 496–8, 1995

119 Less than two months later: P. Pilewskie and F. Valero, *Science,* vol. 267, pp. 1626–9, 1995

120 'This is such a basic thing': V. Ramaswamy of GFDL, quoted by R.A. Kerr, *Science,* vol. 267, p. 454, 1995

120 'The evidence is weak for the claim': R.E. Dickinson et al. in CC'95, p. 208

121 Hurricanes crossing the US coast: N. Nicholls et al. in CC'95, pp. 169–70

121 'We detect significant surface cooling trends': J.D. Kahl et al., *Nature,* vol. 361, pp. 335–7, 1993

121 'No general warming has been observed in the Arctic': N. Nicholls et al. in CC'95, p. 146

122 *Climate Change* 1995 revised the best estimate: CC'95, Summary for Policymakers, pp. 5–6

122 Plus 2 degrees achievable: CC'90, Policymakers Summary, p. xxii, fig. 9

122 An interim report called *Climate Change* 1994: CC'94, *see* full reference above

123 Maps of greenhouse warming: from CC'95, p. 307

123 'Since the primary area of uncertainty': B.D. Santer et al. in CC'95, p. 423

125 The research was striking enough: P. D. Ditlevsen et al., *Nature,* vol. 379, pp. 810–12, 1996

126–7 Ulysses north polar pass: reviewed by speakers at COSPAR 96, Birmingham, July 1996

129–30 An opportunity for Corbyn: P. Corbyn, poster presentation at European Conference on Applications of Meteorology, Toulouse, September 1995, distributed by Weather Action Faxcall

130 A BBC producer: Chris Wells, 'Sunshine with Scattered Showers', BBC1, 4 July 1996

132 'The resources have to come from somewhere': D. Pearce quoted by E. Masood, *Nature,* vol. 378, p. 429, 1995

137 A meteorological posse: V. Ramanathan, F.P.J. Valero & R.D. Cess, GEWEX (Global Energy and Water Cycle Experiment) Newsletter, February 1996

137 A broad cooling cloud of mineral dust: X. Li et al., *Nature,* vol. 380, pp. 416–19

137–42 Everything depended on Chapter 8: B.D. Santer et al., Chapter 8, 'Detection of Climate Change and Attribution of Causes' in CC'95, pp. 407–43

137–8 An unfriendly intervention: P.J. Michaels et al., *Journal of the Franklin Institute,* vol. 331A, pp. 123–33, 1994

138 'The ones which describe the climate system most realistically': CC'90 Introduction, p. xxxviii

138 'There are a number of serious problems': B.D. Santer et al. in CC'95, p. 427

139 Maps of greenhouse warming: from CC'95, pp. 38 and 27

141 Charts of high-altitude warming: from CC'95, p. 428

141 'The best and most scientifically accurate wording': J.T. Houghton, *Nature,* vol. 382, p. 665, 1996

141 'Our ability to quantify': CC'95, Summary for Policymakers, p. 5

142 'That observations suggest': B. Bolin et al. in CC'95, Preface, p. xi

142 'It's Official': headline in *Science,* vol. 270, p. 1565, 1995

142 'We come to the difficult question': B.D. Santer et al. in CC'95, p. 439

147 Graph of cover and cosmic rays: after H. Svensmark & E. Friis-Christensen, *Journal of Atmospheric and Terrestrial Physics,* in press

148 A group of Russians: M.I. Pudovkin et al., *Journal of Atmospheric and Terrestrial Physics,* vol. 57, pp. 1349–55, 1995

148 A 20-year old suggestion: R. Dickinson, *Bulletin of the American Meteorological Society,* vol. 56(12), pp. 1240–8, 1975

148 More recently other scientists: A.K. Barlow & J. Latham, *Quarterly Journal of the Royal Meteorological Society,* vol. 109, pp. 763–70, 1983

148 The size of the clouds' effect: Svensmark & Friis-Christensen cite G. Ohring & P.F. Clapp, *Journal of Atmospheric Science,* vol. 37, pp. 447–54, 1980; V. Ramanathan et al., *Science,* vol. 243, pp. 57–63, 1989; and P. Ardanuy et al., *Journal of Geophysical Research,* vol. 9, pp. 1–2, 1991

149 A round-up of recent results: R.A. Kerr, *Science,* vol. 271 pp. 1360–1, 1996

151 GRIP results: S.J. Johnsen, conversation 1996

151 Earlier analyses of Greenland ice cores: W.B. Hibler & S.J. Johnsen, *Nature,* vol. 280, pp. 481–3, 1979

152 The book brought together two dozen critics: J. Emsley (ed.) *The Global Warming Debate,* The European Science and Environment Forum, London, 1996

152 Many ordinary inhabitants: *Climate System Monitoring Monthly Bulletins,* January-April 1996, World Climate Research Programme, Geneva, 1996

153 A new technique called helioseismic tomography: T.L. Duvall et al., *Nature,* vol. 379, pp. 235–7, 1996

153 The first results of the GONG network: various authors, *Science,* vol. 272, pp. 1281–309, 1996

154–61 SOHO: conversations, 1994-6, with project manager F. Felici, project scientists V. Domingo, A. Poland and B. Fleck, and principal investigators J-L Bertaux, P. Bochsler, G.E. Brueckner, J-P Delaboudinière, C. Fröhlich, A.H. Gabriel, R. Harrison, D. Hovestadt, J.L. Kohl, H. Kunow, P. Scherrer, J.J. Torsti and K. Wilhelm; *also* ESA press conference on SOHO results, Paris, May 1996

163   One record of past events: K. O'Brien et al. in C.P. Sonett et al. (eds) *The Sun in Time,* University of Arizona, Tucson, 1991, pp. 317–59

164   Graph of *aa* increase: after K. Lassen & E. Friis-Christensen, *Scientific Report,* 93–100, Danish Meteorological Institute, 1993

164   American scientists had suggested: J. Feynman & N.U. Crooker, *Nature,* vol. 275, p. 626, 1978; M. Stuiver & P.D. Quay, *Science,* vol. 207, pp. 11–18, 1980

165   Scientists in Switzerland and France: J. Beer et al. in C.P. Sonett et al. (eds) *The Sun in Time,* University of Arizona, Tucson, 1991, pp. 343–59; G.M. Raisbeck, conversation 1996

166   'A controversial topic': *Magnetometry Mission,* ESA, Noordwijk, SP-1196 (5), 1996, p. 26

168   A mission called Grace: *Earth Radiation Mission,* ESA, Noordwijk, SP-1196 (3), 1996

170   Remarks by M. Jefferson, J. Emsley and J.T. Houghton quoted by E. Masood, *Nature,* vol. 381, p. 455, 1996

170–1 Textual analysis by the Global Climate Coalition, and comments by B.D. Santer and J.T. Houghton quoted by E. Masood, *Nature,* vol. 381, p. 546, 1996; explanations by J.T. Houghton, *Nature,* vol. 382, p. 665, 1996

171   The Republican chairman: D. Rohrabacher's moves were reported by C. Macilwain, *Nature,* vol. 382, p. 195, 1996

172   The new paper: H. Svensmark & E. Friis-Christensen, *Journal of Atmospheric and Solar-Terrestrial Physics,* in press

172   From the heart of the greenhouse camp: B. Santer et al., *Nature,* vol. 382, pp. 39–46, 1996

173   Never mind, the journal *Nature*: N. Nicholls, *Nature,* vol. 382, pp. 27–8, 1996

174   Diagram of streamer: based on sketch from J. Kohl, personal communication, 1996

175   Information, supplied by the World Energy Council: E. Masood, *Nature,* vol. 382, p. 103, 1996

175   'It's like telling a poor trader': Abdul Bar al Gain, quoted in *Nature,* 1995

175   The Alliance of Small Island States, and other groupings: noted in C. Flavin & O. Tunali, *Climate of Hope,* Worldwatch Paper 130, Worldwatch Institute, Washington DC, 1996

176   'SOHO takes solar science by storm': R.M. Bonnet quoted in ESA Information Note, July 1996

176   'You must not take': J.T. Houghton quoted by P. Brown, *The Guardian,* London, 17 July 1996

176   'It is the best science': B. Bolin quoted by P. Brown, *The Guardian,* London, 17 July 1996

177   'Alarm bells ought to be ringing' and other remarks: J. Gummer quoted by P. Brown, *The Guardian,* London, 18 July 1996

177   'The fossil fuel lobby': M. Hedger quoted by P. Brown, *The Guardian,* London, 18 July 1996

177   'There can be no question': T. Wirth quoted by P. Brown, *The Guardian,* London, 18 July 1996

177   'We believe the circumstances': T. Wirth quoted by P. Capella, *The Times,* London, 18 July 1996

178   Earlier in the week: editorial, 'Taming the Climate', in *The Guardian,* 15 July 1996. 'Current projections show the average flow of the Indus river in Pakistan falling by 43 per cent and the Niger in Africa by 31 per cent by 2000.' This appears to be a misreading of 2100.

179   Increases in atmospheric temperatures: e.g. K. Labitzke & H. van Loon, *Journal of Climatology,* vol. 5, pp. 290 ff., 1992; *see also* J.D. Haigh, *Science,* vol. 272, pp. 981–4 and references therein

179   Friis-Christensen reminded his audience: P. M. Kelly & T. M. L. Wigley, *Nature,* vol. 360, pp. 328–30, 1992

179   On the other hand: M. Schlesinger & N. Ramankutty, *Nature,* vol. 360, pp. 330–3, 1992

180   'I find the move': B. Bolin quoted in *Information,* Copenhagen, 19 July 1996

180   'I am particularly sceptical': B.D. Santer quoted in *Information,* Copenhagen, 19 July 1996

180   'It is pleasing to see': B. Bolin quoted by S. Dahllöf, *Ny Teknik,* Stockholm, 5 September 1996

182   Increases in observed cloud cover: N. Nicholls et al. in CC'95, pp. 162–3 and 169

189   According to the calculations: P. Foukal & J. Lean, *Science,* vol. 247, pp. 56–558, 1990

189   The 0.6 degrees expected: CC'90, p. xx, fig. 6

190   Lindzen had reasoned: R.S. Lindzen, 'Global Warming: The Origin and Nature of Alleged Scientific Consensus,' offprint from MIT, 1992, p. 2

190   An Australian drilling in Antarctica: P. Jones, *Nature,* vol. 381, 376–9, 1996

191   'It appears now': P. Corbyn in J. Emsley (ed.) *The Global Warming Debate,* The European Science and Environment Forum, London, 1996, p. 75

191 'There's a lot more to it': P. Corbyn, conversation 1996

192 A student of solar cycles: e.g. P. Damon & C.P. Sonett in C.P. Sonett et al. (eds) *The Sun in Time,* University of Arizona, Tucson, 1991, esp. pp. 384–6

197 The scientific assessment was orchestrated: J.T. Houghton, *Global Warming: The Complete Briefing,* Lion Books, Oxford, 1994, pp. 132–3

197 In the later 1980s atmospheric issues: S.A. Boehmer-Christiansen, in various publications, is the source for much of what follows, especially the text of her paper 'Britain and the Intergovernmental Panel on Climate Change: Promoting Global Research or Managing National Politics?' presented at the British International Studies Association, York, December 1994

198 A more partisan consideration: M. Thatcher, *The Downing Street Years,* Harper Collins, London, 1993, pp. 639–41

198 'Britain achieved its goal': S.A. Boehmer-Christiansen *as before,* British International Studies Association, York, December 1994

199 'I cannot give any scientist': P.B. Medawar, *Advice to a Young Scientist,* Harper & Row, New York, 1979, p. 39

FURTHER READING

About the Sun and the solar wind, and their terrestrial effects:
Robert W. Noyes, *The Sun, Our Star*, Harvard University Press, Cambridge,
  Massachusetts, 1982
Herbert Friedman, *Sun and Earth*, Scientific American Books, New York, 1986

A more recent but more technical book about the Sun:
Kenneth J.H. Phillips, *Guide to the Sun*, Cambridge University Press, Cambridge, UK, 1992

About Ulysses, SOHO, and the ill-fated Cluster:
Nigel Calder, *Beyond this World: Scientific Missions of the European Space Agency*,
  BR-112, ESA, Paris, 1995

About climate change in general:
H.H. Lamb, *Weather, Climate and Human Affairs*, Routledge, London, 1988

About the greenhouse warming scenario:
John Houghton, *Global Warming: The Complete Briefing*, Lion Books, Oxford, 1994

Criticisms of the greenhouse warming scenario:
John Emsley (ed.) *The Global Warming Debate*, European Science and Environment Forum,
  73 McCarthy Court, Banbury Street, London SW11 3ET, 1996

INDEX